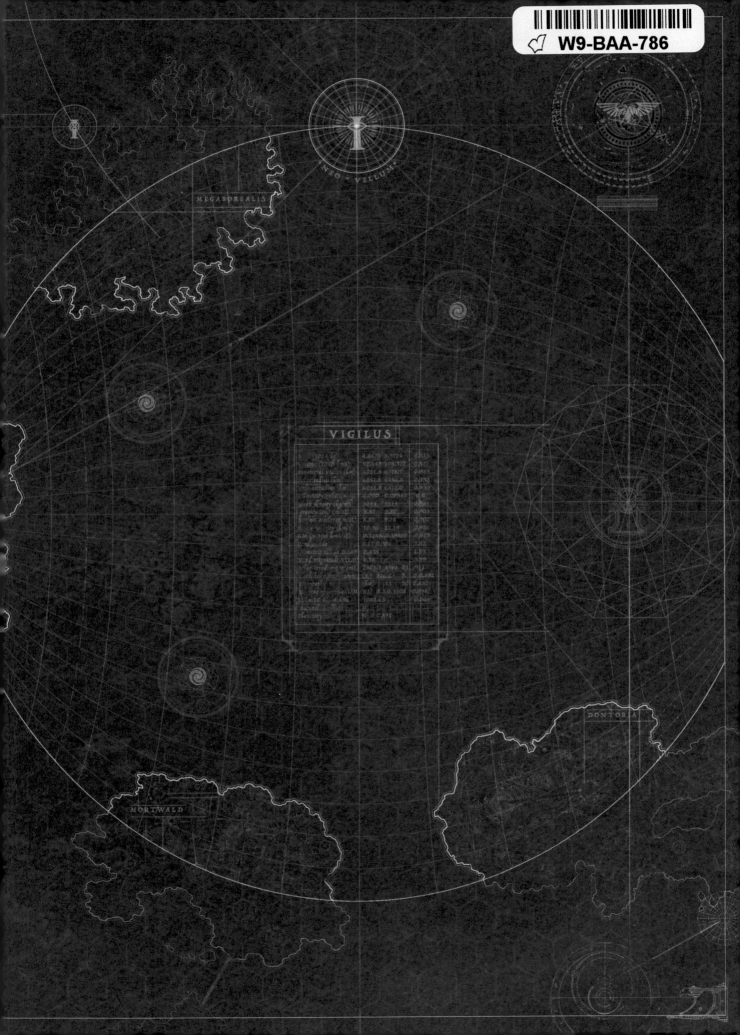

MEGABOREALIS

NEO · VELLUM

VIGILUS

DONTORIA

MORTWALD

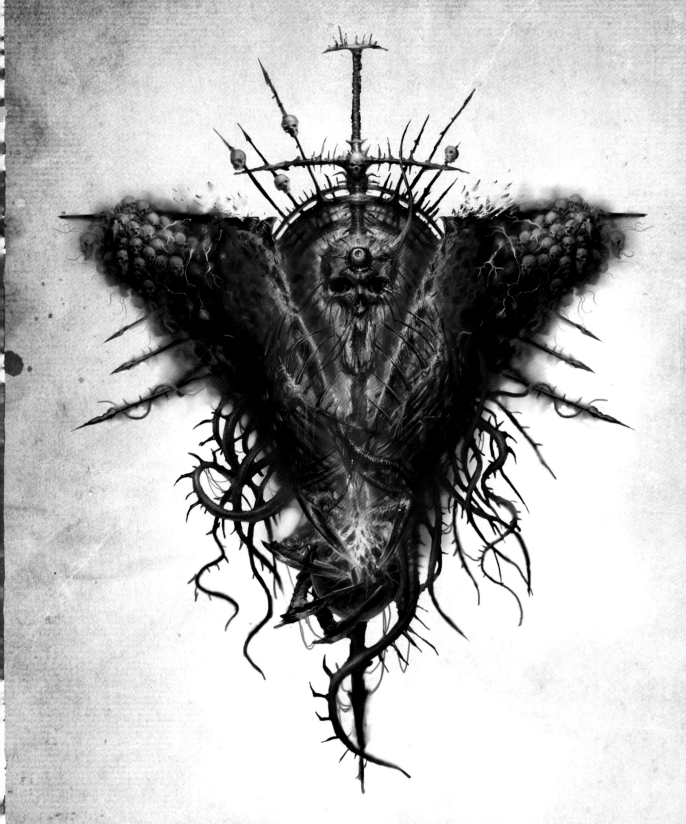

VIGILUS ABLAZE

WAR OF NIGHTMARES

CONTENTS

PRODUCED BY GAMES WORKSHOP IN NOTTINGHAM

With thanks to the Mournival and the Infinity Circuit for their additional playtesting services

Games Workshop Ltd, Willow Rd, Lenton, Nottingham, NG7 2WS

games-workshop.com

GLOBAL DESTRUCTION

The bitter tale of invasion, desperation and heroism that unfolded during the War of Beasts was only the beginning. There was an even greater threat to Vigilus, the Nachmund Gauntlet and the Imperium Nihilus as a whole – that of the Warmaster Abaddon, and the dread legions of Chaos that marched at his command.

The Cicatrix Maledictum forever changed the Imperium of Man, and as it tore open across the length of the galaxy, a thousand new wars began. In the Segmentum Obscurus, the populous but arid planet Vigilus became a point of crucial strategic importance. That world lay at the northern end of the Nachmund Gauntlet, one of the few stable corridors across the Great Rift. Through its haunted reaches, spacecraft could cross from the heartlands of the Imperium Sanctus to the desperate and anarchic Imperium Nihilus and back again with at least some chance of arriving at their destination intact.

Yet as the Great Rift opened it disgorged an invasion fleet of Orks that fell upon Vigilus like an avalanche. The sudden influx of greenskins triggered an insurrection of Genestealer Cultists that had long dwelt beneath the planet's surface. Even before the Noctis Aeterna cut Vigilus off from the Astronomican, its every continent was riven by war. The name of the Vigilus System was soon on the lips of the High Lords of Terra themselves. The Lord Commander of the Imperium, the Primarch Roboute Guilliman, swore that the planet would endure, and sent the Chapter Master of the Ultramarines, Marneus Calgar, to ensure his word was true. Yet the most awful danger to the planet only revealed itself when warriors of the Black Legion were sighted amongst the planet's spires. They were the harbingers of Abaddon the Despoiler himself, who approached the beleaguered planet at the head of a crusading force mighty enough to conquer the entire system if necessary. Here, on this most vital linchpin, the forces of the Imperium were to be tested as never before.

IN THIS BOOK

This book is the second of a two-part series set in the Vigilus System. It contains an overview of the war for Vigilus thus far, from the initial Ork invasion and the subsequent Genestealer Cult uprising, to the diabolical campaign of an even more terrifying foe – the Warmaster of Chaos, Abaddon the Despoiler.

Inside you will find:
- The history of the War of Nightmares on Vigilus.
- Rules for playing an epic campaign set on Vigilus, or another planet in the Imperium Nihilus.
- Battlezone and war zone rules that represent the perilous environs of this planet.
- Datasheets, Detachments, special rules and Stratagems for the Chaos forces that took part in this great struggle.

A WORLD OF ARIDITY AND STRIFE

Vigilus was a world hostile to human life, though long ago the Imperium colonised it nonetheless. It had no oceans or seas, its only major bodies of water being immense fortified reservoirs that were jealously defended by those who possessed them. The planet was riven by earthquakes, in part due to the mining operations undertaken by the Adeptus Mechanicus controlling the industrial realm known as Megaborealis – these were so extensive they brought the planet to the brink of civil war more than once, and still the Tech-Priests would not say what it was they sought with such desperate intensity. Because of this, the planet's settlements were built wide as well as tall, the sky-scraping, mountainous hive cities joined by thousands of miles of industrial manufactorums and Sectors Mechanicus. Each hivesprawl, as they were known, supplied something vital to its fellows and imported critical resources in its turn. These artificial continents were once protected by the planet's principal export, the Bastion-class force field, a crackling perimeter defence that was as much psy-tech as it was conventional barrier. In the early stages of the War of Beasts, when the Orks landed their colossal ships in the planet's wastes, these barriers kept them at bay. Yet when the warp storms of the Noctis Aeterna disrupted the psy-barriers, the greenskins gleefully invaded the hivesprawls, in turn spurring the Genestealer Cultists to rise from within. The Imperial counter-attacks did serious damage to the Ork scrap cities in the wastelands and purged many a nest of xenos cultists with fire, even rooting out the dreaded infections of Chaos in places. Ultimately, however, the Imperium reacted too late to save the hivesprawls from being seized in a hundred theatres of war. The Vigilus Senate was forced to concede swathes of the planet to its conquerors and instead concentrate on fighting a rearguard action in order to have any chance of saving the planet.

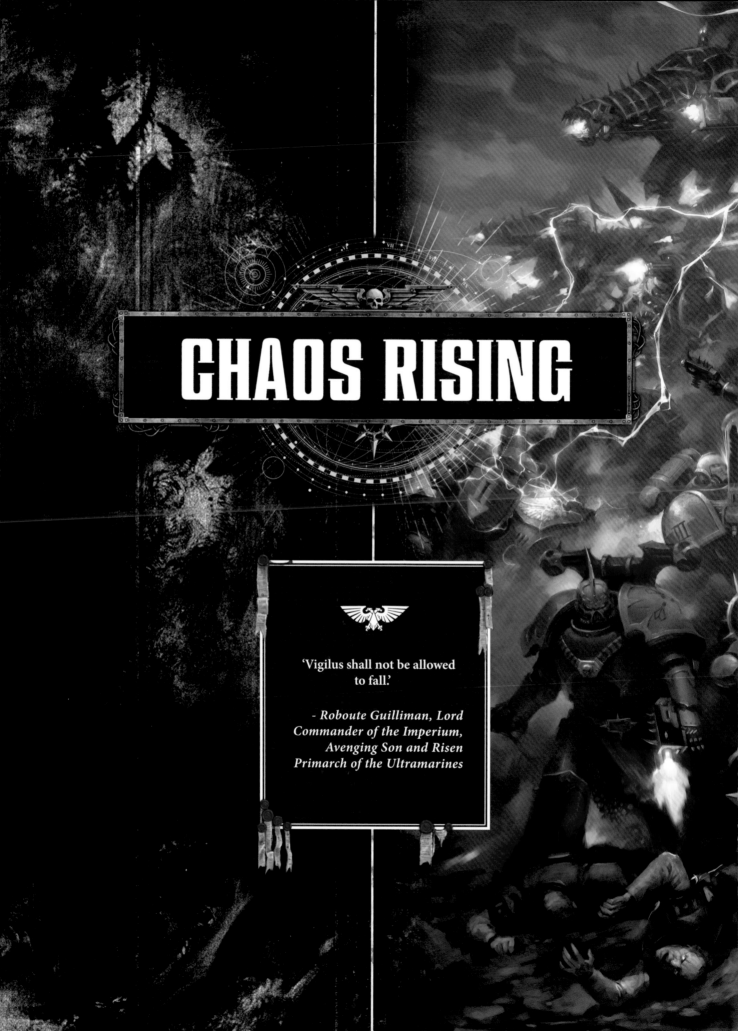

CHAOS RISING

'Vigilus shall not be allowed to fall.'

- Roboute Guilliman, Lord Commander of the Imperium, Avenging Son and Risen Primarch of the Ultramarines

DOOM FROM THE SKIES

The defenders of Vigilus had fought long to hold back the xenos invaders. With the Ork assault blunted and the Genestealer Cult largely contained, they had begun to think they had endured the worst. Only when the skies lit with the engine flares of a vast Chaos fleet did they realise the magnitude of their error.

The doom of Vigilus was closing in from a dozen directions at once. From the wilderness came the greenskin hordes, whooping and hollering whenever the Imperium launched an assault on their scrap cities – as not for nothing is it said that to counter-attack the Orks in strength is to kick a daggerwasp's nest. Too stubborn to give up despite the decisive strikes of the Adeptus Astartes, the greenskins charged headlong into the cities wherever they could force a hole in the defences, or hurried for sites on the horizon where smoke trailed and explosions boomed. Though close to half of the Ork invaders that had originally invaded Vigilus had been slain in violence or fire, many more had sprung from the aftermath.

The leader of the Ork war effort, a hulking brute known as Krooldakka the Speedlord Supreme, kept on the move throughout the War of Beasts, knowing that he was a primary target, but that the Imperials did not have the resources to hunt him down while the hivesprawls were under attack. His hit-and-run assaults took their toll on everything from trench lines to armoured mega-convoys. After the Siege of Mortwald, many Imperial Knights swore a vow of duty to claim his head, but at the onset of the Chaos invasion none had claimed success.

From below each hivesprawl came a seemingly endless infestation of Genestealer Cultists from the Cult of the Pauper Princes, boiling up from their hidden warrens to claim city streets, dockyards and water purification plants. In scores of hab-zones and city plazas they were put down by the local Astra Militarum forces and their Space Marine allies, but there always seemed to be more. The false continent of Dirkden was abandoned to the insurrectionists, with Purestrain Genestealers running openly in the streets.

War raged for the reservoirs of Oteck Hivesprawl, known as the Hollows, while the space elevator that supplied Megaborealis with water mined from frozen asteroids was seized by the higher echelons of the cult. Though less aggressive than the Orks, the cult fought with such cunning and careful forethought they even overcame the

Skitarii and Adepta Sororitas kill teams sent to root them out.

These two xenos races were portrayed as savage and brutish by the Imperial propaganda machine, but in truth both showed a hidden cunning that stymied Imperial efforts to rid Vigilus of their presence. Claims that victory in the War of Beasts was close at hand rang out every new dawn, but some began to detect a note of desperation under the strident calls to action.

These bestial foes were not the only scourge upon the citizens of Vigilus. The Drukhari raided from the glacier mines of the frozen south, while their Aeldari cousins sought vengeance against the upper echelons of Hyperian society. From within the ranks of the common people, the seeds of Chaos worship grew to infect healthy minds, and plague spread fast across Dontoria. Even the stars themselves seemed to bleed as the Cicatrix Maledictum yawned in the night sky, a livid

purple wound that appeared ready to swallow the planet entire.

The worst of all threats became clear only when it was almost too late to stop it – that being the approach of the Heretic Astartes. Via the report of a single survivor from a Space Marine strike force sent to the neighbouring planet of Nemendghast, word had reached Marneus Calgar that the armies of Abaddon the Despoiler were inbound, poised to tear Vigilus apart once and for all. With the Imperial prohibition forbidding the citizens from looking at the night sky in case the Cicatrix Maledictum drove them insane, the vanguard of the Chaos Space Marines found it easy enough to covertly seize the upper reaches of the hive-spires that pushed through the smog clouds. Led by Haarken Worldclaimer, known to his Raptor hosts as the Herald of the Apocalypse, this secret invasion had already conquered the high spires of Vigilus' cities by the time the senate heard of it.

On the same day that these tidings were brought to Calgar, Haarken Worldclaimer gave voice to a singular message, his words relayed from a thousand Raptor masks and hijacked vox gargoyles. The planet belonged to Abaddon, and the Warmaster would soon be there to claim it. Marneus Calgar listened well to the herald's threats, for every word was a spike of spite driven into his heart. The Lord Macragge had been acting as a strategic nexus for the Vigilus Senate at the time, but as he listened, his expression hardened to that of a pugilist more than ready to fight.

BATTLE IN THE VOID

It was Haarken Worldclaimer's gloating call that kicked the planet into a new phase of war. The Vigilus Senate vowed to intervene before the situation turned critical, and the motion was passed for a naval expedition to head the incoming doom off before it could reach the planet itself. Soon a new theatre of war opened in the void.

All eyes looked to Calgar as he gave a series of curt commands that saw his aerial assets redeployed – not to strafe ground targets, but to begin a new war above the clouds. Shaken by the news that the legendary Warmaster of Chaos was inbound, but resolving to prove equal to the task, Marneus issued a summons that saw the deadliest ships in the Imperial fleet gather above the sky-docks of Saint's Haven. His intent was to stymie the bulk of the Chaos invasion before it hit home, or to die in the attempt.

The Herald of the Apocalypse repeated his claim over and over, using his doleful message as a weapon to slash at the remaining hope and sanity of the Vigilus citizenry. Marneus Calgar

swiftly put into place an array of contingencies, tasking his pilots and close assault squads with the immediate engagement of any Chaos Space Marine or Daemon Engine that dared broadcast the fell message. It was not difficult to find them for, having hidden for weeks, the Black Legion were no longer prioritising stealth, but instead the infliction of fear. They too ached for the kill, to feel their blades puncture the ceramite battle plate of their hated foes and sink into the flesh beneath. It was a wish that was soon granted.

As his airborne warriors engaged the enemy in the pollution-choked skies of Hyperia Hivesprawl, Calgar and his honour guard made to leave the planet, leaving its defence

in the capable hands of Pedro Kantor of the Crimson Fists. The Lord Macragge took a shuttle to his flagship, the *Laurels of Victory*, cut through Arch-Commodore Hentzmann's ceremonial greetings as quickly as he could without causing offence, and cast off towards the coordinates given by the Librarian Maltis, the sole survivor from the Nemendghast strike force. Out the Ultramarines fleet sailed, past the spinning wreckage of the Imperial cordon smashed to pieces by the Ork assault, past Neo-vellum and Omis-Prion and into the bleak and unwelcoming void towards Nemendghast.

After less than a week's travel, the auspex horizon was haunted by disturbing anomalies, chief amongst

them an ancient vessel with a dark and bloody history. Calgar's gravest suspicions were all but confirmed. Breaking the three seals of his craft's Sanctum Perjorum and consulting its forbidden data by the light of a blessed candle, Calgar checked the energy signature his steersmen had given him with the most ancient data at his disposal. Sure enough, the craft at the head of the invasion fleet was none other than the *Vengeful Spirit*, the flagship of the Arch-traitor and orchestrator of the Heresy, Primarch Horus himself. Its evil silhouette was distinguishable against the roiling tides of the Great Rift, and it filled those who had heard of it with intense foreboding.

Calgar ordered his fleet to form a double cordon, creating a layered broadside defence to intercept the Black Legion armada. The Imperial ships possessed no arcane tricks, no secret weapons from the prehistory of the Imperium or the depths of the Eye of Terror. What they had instead was a colossal amount of firepower, and the Lord

Macragge intended to use it to the full. Together with Hentzmann, he devised a dozen firing solutions and contingencies, launching hundreds of torpedoes into the void to ensure that should any ships from the Chaos fleet break away from the Imperial crosshairs, they would be met with a firestorm that would cripple them in short order.

Minutes slid by, then hours. The Chaos vessels hove in closer and closer, not changing their

heading so much as one degree. This was a statement in itself, the implication being that the Imperial fleet represented no jeopardy at all. Although they were still out of strike range, Abaddon and his lieutenants drove on at full speed as if the entire might arrayed ahead of them was nothing more than a tissue of cobwebs.

Calgar's frown of consternation deepened to a scowl. He knew Abaddon would not be so blasé, so foolish, as to charge directly into a firebase without dispersing at all. But he knew not what manner of duplicity was hidden behind the posturing of the infamous Warmaster, that genius of the Black Crusades, whose name was spoken only in whispers.

He realised the answer a moment too late when a shimmering blur appeared upon the bridge of the *Laurels of Victory*. It expanded into a blinding portal of white light, and the hellish denizens of the warp screamed out, hungry for blood.

THE BRIDGE ASSAILED

The bridge of the *Laurels of Victory* burst into hectic action as the warp portal yawned open, disgorging pale-skinned hellspawn. Leaping forth from a tide of writhing, crab-clawed androgynes came a four-armed monstrosity that headed straight for Calgar.

The Ultramarines, many of whom had faced Daemons before, laid down a storm of bolter fire that shredded the foremost invading creatures. These were not the slow and methodical plague-spawn that had defiled Ultramar, but a fast and dexterous breed that danced through the firestorm and endured grievous wounds with shrieks of ecstatic glee.

The four-armed giant bore down on Calgar as his Gauntlets of Ultramar spat mass-reactive shells into its pierced and jewel-strung torso. Lethro Ados and Nemus Adranus of his Victrix Honour Guard stood between their lord and his assailant, but their blows were met by the creature's shimmering shield, and they were knocked aside. The Daemon's great spear darted in. Calgar caught it behind the tip, holding

it an inch from his heart, but he could not stop it, for the polearm was slick with nameless fluids. The creature leaned into the blow, and the spear slid through Calgar's grip to impale him through the heart. Quick as a snake, the creature lashed out a claw and tore out Calgar's throat.

The bridge erupted into bedlam as the warriors of the Victrix Guard redoubled their attack. One by one the Daemons were fought back by the veterans of Macragge until the battle became a stalemate. When the ship's Navigator, Senioris, revealed his mystical warp eye by removing his ornate bandanna, the backlash of aetheric forces racked the bridge. The four-armed Greater Daemon that led the host fell back into the warp with a despairing wail and, as the Navigator advanced, the portal closed. Yet the damage had been done. As vox reports came from across the fleet relating similar events on all its principal warships, the dreadful truth became clear. The battle against Abaddon's fleet had been lost before it had even begun.

A DARK NEW DAWN

The Ultramarines fleet returned to the war-torn planet of Vigilus to find it in an even more desperate state than when they left. Pillars of smoke rose high from every hive and population centre – and still the worst was yet to come, for the true architects of the latest string of disasters were drawing perilously near.

The Daemon assault on the *Laurels of Victory*'s bridge had left anarchy and destruction in its wake. A dozen similar strikes had ensured the inter-ship clarion array rang with agonised screams and panicked orders, interspersed with the static of the void. The lead ships of the Ultramarines fleet were reeling, dealt a crippling blow from afar by Abaddon's hellish allies. Blood swilled across the command decks of a dozen strike cruisers, and strobing images of daemonic killers plagued every ship within a hundred thousand miles.

Arch-Commodore Hentzmann, upon seeing Marneus Calgar with his throat torn out and a gaping wound in his chest, saw only one path left open to him. With the surety of a man used to the burden of command, he made his decision quickly. If they were to turn back now they could live again to fight another day – and ensure the Lord Macragge was brought back from the brink of death. The Victrix Guard, their primary duty to protect their master, nodded curtly in reinforcement of the decision.

With the remonstrations of the Ultramarines officers still yearning for a fight ringing in his ears, Arch-Commodore Hentzmann ordered a fighting retreat. One by one his fellow captains followed suit, for the *Laurels of Victory* led the fleet in spirit as well as in rank. Within the hour the entire Imperial blockade was falling back, lances and bombardment cannons blazing as they made for their muster point in the orbit of Vigilus.

Abaddon's arrogance had proved well founded, for though his fleet took significant damage, it was far from broken, and its return fire ravaged many an Imperial craft in exchange. With the daemonic minions of his dark patrons at his beck and call, the Warmaster of Chaos had crippled the Imperial defence with a single stroke. His passage to Vigilus was all but unbarred.

Even as Hentzmann fought valiantly to buy his fleet time to recover, Marneus Calgar was hurried to the prime apothecarium of the *Laurels* by his Victrix Guard. There he was treated by a conclave of elite Apothecaries. His second heart had kicked in as soon as his primary heart had been sliced in two by the Daemon's spear, saving him from an untimely death, and his Belisarian Furnace had triggered a rush of stimulants to keep his system going. His ravaged throat was sutured, reinforced and regrown, the Apothecaries administering intense regeneration chem-baths, cyborgisation surgery and a lengthy rejuvenat treatment. Although he survived the ordeal, Calgar was not unmarked by it, and ever after spoke with a faint mechanical burr to his voice.

The return of the Imperial ships to the docks above Saint's Haven was greeted with great jubilation by the citizenry below, and in the places not still fraught with battle, there were celebrations in the streets.

Although the people were still forbidden from looking upwards lest they catch a glimpse of the Great Rift, none could mistake the sullen growl and throb of the ships' engines.

The Imperial propaganda machine went into overdrive to explain the sudden presence of the fleet, insisting that it had returned to see Vigilus liberated, rather than admitting the truth of its retreat. At the onset of the mission, the Imperial vox-broadcasts had been so insistent that Calgar's armada would meet with unalloyed success, it was natural for the populace to assume that the enemy threat – the precise nature of which had been carefully obfuscated – had indeed been defeated.

There were those amongst the populace that knew the truth, however. These included the Sons of Vannadan – latter-day scions of the demagogue who had fuelled the rise of Storvhal's Tzeentchian pyroclastic cults during the War of Beasts. These Chaos followers claimed to be able to read the future in the flames. They spread the rumour that the Imperial fleet had been forced to return to Vigilus by the true inheritors of the planet – the worshippers of ancient gods from before the reign of the Emperor. With the words of Haarken Worldclaimer still ringing in their ears, the people of Storvhal and Hyperia gave gradual credence to these rumours, until an undercurrent of fear and doubt ran beneath the claims that all was well.

The Space Marines of Calgar's expedition made their return to Vigilus not in a triumphal procession, as the Ministorum would have had it, but as a Drop Pod invasion force. They hammered down from battle barges and strike cruisers by the dozen, contrails streaking the skies. This time they struck not at the Ork-held fringes of the hivesprawls, nor at the places where the banners of the Pauper Princes flew high, but at those areas claimed by Chaos. Many of the high spires and citadels were still being besieged, despite the aerial counter-assaults launched by Calgar's strike forces before the fleet had set off. In places, the sudden return of the Space Marines was enough to tip the balance, and several spires were reclaimed. But it was slowly becoming clear that the Adeptus Astartes were too late to truly have an impact on the rest. The rot had spread too far, infecting the hives from the top down.

Calgar, by this point, had healed well from his grievous injuries. As a prime example of the Adeptus Astartes – and a Primaris at that – his ability to survive trauma was second to none. Viewing dozens of dataslates and pict-thief relays at once in order to swiftly parse the maximum amount of relevant data, he spent long hours assessing the damage that had been inflicted upon the planet. It painted a grim picture indeed.

Dirkden was lost, abandoned to the Genestealer Cultists at Lord Calgar's command. Kaelac's Bane was likewise forsaken, its glacier miners having fled from the Drukhari menace haunting the blizzards. Mortwald had held out against the Ork assaults battering its trenches, but its wealthy rejuvenat clients and privileged aristocrats had withdrawn to their fortified palaces and left the common workers to the airborne attacks of Worldclaimer's Raptor hosts. Megaborealis was being torn apart by the forces of the Omnissiah, the heretic and the xenos. The Greater Omnissian Hoist – the orbital relay that enabled frozen water to be imported from asteroids – was in

the clutches of the Pauper Princes, thus robbing Vigilus of a vital water source. Dontoria Hivesprawl had been tainted by the plagues of Nurgle that had so recently infected Ultramar, and became host to a fast-spreading sickness that none could cure. Oteck's reservoirs, the site of intense war between the Pauper Princes, the Space Wolves and the Adepta Sororitas, had been proclaimed quarantine toxicus by the Deathwatch Kill Teams that had investigated their purity, and the ever-thirsting populace was being driven to the edge of madness by the shrieks of hunting Warp Talons. Storvhal, its geomantic sites tortured by the agents of the martyr Vannadan, was home to three erupting volcanoes, which were hurling billions of tons of ash into the skies to rain back down as smouldering cinders that burned the flesh. The planet was on the brink of total ruination, and the arrival of the inbound Chaos host would likely drive it over the edge.

THE WORLDCLAIMER

Abaddon's harbinger was known as the Herald of the Apocalypse for good reason. Upon arriving on Vigilus, Haarken Worldclaimer had used the thick cloud cover of the planet to his advantage, quietly and steadily conquering the spire tips of Vigilus while the defenders of the planet were concerned with the wars raging below. Once he had secured these hidden beachheads, he descended from the smog-blackened skies in glory. He slammed the Helspear into the planet's crust, and cried out that within eighty days and eighty nights, the planet would fall in the name of his dark master.

WAR IN THE DARKNESS

The coming of Chaos triggered an epidemic of fear and rage amongst the populace of Vigilus and, in places, rioting filled the streets. The reaction of many a soul, when faced with horror and near-certain doom, was to pray for divine intervention – and it was not only the Emperor that was worshipped upon that stricken planet.

The smog clouds above Vigilus parted under the bow wave of energy preceding the Chaos fleet, and the horrifying truth was revealed. The planet was under attack from precisely those forces Calgar's fleet was said to have defeated. Outbreaks of violent anger and unrest flared up in every hab-block. Some took to looting, while others went to ground, stockpiling food and water in the hope of riding out the storm.

Much of the populace of Vigilus found relief from the despair caused by the coming of Abaddon's fleet in the form of the Imperial Cult. The Adepta Sororitas and Ministorum Priests on the planet found themselves being followed around by crowds of devoted pilgrims,

ranging from ragged flagellants to organised gangs calling themselves frateris militia. All too often, these disciples proved as much a curse as a blessing for the Ministorum forces, for they gave little thought to strategy.

Meanwhile, many of those driven to near-madness by the ongoing war joined the side of the corrupters and despots, becoming part of the Chaos cults that flocked to greet their masters as the ships of the Heretic Astartes emerged from the pollution-choked skies. Still more sought solace underground. They embraced the fanaticism of the subterranean cults who claimed to be true native Vigilants, and in doing so, bolstered the ranks of the Pauper Princes. When

the Chaos ships arrived, the infestation welcomed a great influx almost overnight.

Abaddon had not taken the Pauper Princes into account when he had formulated his strategies of conquest, for the cult's war leaders had concealed their kin from psychic scrying as well as from mundane observation. Even as the Black Legion and their renegade allies fought to claim the hivesprawls from the top down, they encountered stalwart resistance from resurgent gene-sects seething up from below. In every false continent, the Chaos invaders were beset by the scions of Grandsire Wurm, for they would not relinquish the holdings they had worked so hard to acquire.

The Chaos invasion of Vigilus saw the xenocultist stronghold of Dirkden attacked in force. The continent's fate had been given to the infamous Night Lords, as well as elements from the Renegade Chapter known as the Scourged. Their mission was to capitalise on the fear and confusion engendered by Haarken Worldclaimer's Daemon-vox broadcasts and drive the hivesprawl over the edge into an abyss of madness and violence. It was a task to which the two forces were eminently suited.

Only a small force of Night Lords were part of the invasion – at that time the majority of their notorious brotherhood was near the Eye of Terror, attacking Craftworld Ulthwé. The Night Lords leader, Ramaghan Savasdus, had made a deal with Abaddon to ensure he was given Ashenid Non-Hive as the locale of his primary attack. He had learned from his skull-masked visionary brother, Vreanus, that the capital city's large criminal population might prove excellent

recruiting grounds for a new generation of warriors – or, if that failed, hardy slaves.

Yet even Vreanus had not foreseen the extent of the xenos corruption that ran throughout Dirkden. There was something about the psychic gestalt of the Genestealer hybrids that made it difficult for him, and those like him, to sense their presence. Whether this was a deliberate obfuscation on the part of the cult's Maguses or some innate echo of the Shadow in the Warp that precedes each Tyranid hive fleet, Vreanus could not tell. Either way, it proved to be a deciding factor in the wars to come.

When the Night Lords made planetfall, they slaughtered their way through the streets of Dirkden, torturing those who resisted them. They battled against the criminal fraternity of the continent for several days – for the lowest sinners and recidivists were the only ones who had stayed to claim the hivesprawl. Yet that corrupt

organisation was not all it seemed – its members were being controlled from the shadows. Savasdus, Vreanus and their warband found themselves fighting for their lives as thousands of Genestealer Cult hybrids emerged from false walls and trapdoors to fight alongside the criminals of the underworld. The bolters, blades and lightning claws of the Heretic Astartes took a horrific toll, many-limbed bodies piling so high the Night Lords used them as impromptu ramparts in the open-roofed halls of Ashenid Non-Hive.

Still the cult sent in wave after wave, intending to drown the invaders in sheer numbers. The cult did not risk its Purestrain Genestealer offspring against the Night Lords; instead the Primus Hollun Desh, sent from Megaborealis to secure the cult's holdings, led several claws of Aberrants and Metamorph Hybrids. The shock assault proved enough to break the Night Lords and the Scourged alike. Dirkden remained in the hands of the Pauper Princes.

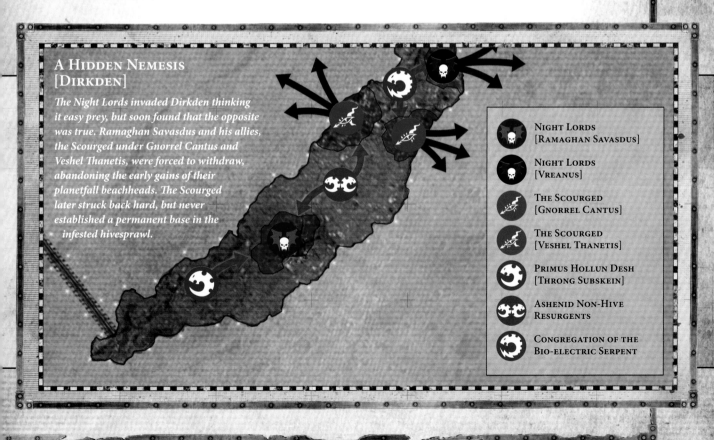

A Hidden Nemesis [Dirkden]

The Night Lords invaded Dirkden thinking it easy prey, but soon found that the opposite was true. Ramaghan Savasdus and his allies, the Scourged under Gnorrel Cantus and Veshel Thanetis, were forced to withdraw, abandoning the early gains of their planetfall beachheads. The Scourged later struck back hard, but never established a permanent base in the infested hivesprawl.

NIGHT LORDS [RAMAGHAN SAVASDUS]

NIGHT LORDS [VREANUS]

THE SCOURGED [GNORREL CANTUS]

THE SCOURGED [VESHEL THANETIS]

PRIMUS HOLLUN DESH [THRONG SUBSKEIN]

ASHENID NON-HIVE RESURGENTS

CONGREGATION OF THE BIO-ELECTRIC SERPENT

RETAKING THE HOIST

The Omnissian Hoist, that vast pulley mechanism by which the Adeptus Mechanicus drew ice-clad asteroids from space in order to harvest vital aqua meteoris, had been taken by a strike force of Purestrain Genestealers. With water so scarce, the Tech-Priests launched a concerted assault to reclaim it.

The war in Megaborealis had raged out of control for some time. Though the Genestealer Cult uprising had been contained in most of the continent's districts by methodical extermination teams of Skitarii, Kataphron servitors and Space Marines, the heaviest fighting had been concentrated around the vast technological miracle that ran through the core of the Stygian Spires and then high into space above them, known as the Greater Omnissian Hoist.

The Pauper Princes had taken the lower levels of the Hoist during the War of Beasts. Their invasion plans had been so thorough that their covert agents, who had infiltrated the Stygian workforce, had been able to extract the access codes for a hundred different vault doors. The upper levels, which were kept to a higher level of sanctification, proved far more difficult to seize. The alarm had already been raised by the unblinking servo-skulls that had first uncovered the xenocultist incursion, so the vital areas of the Stygian Spires were guarded by clades of Kastelan Robots programmed to hammer phosphor bullets into anything without a noospheric aura. However, a claw of Purestrain Genestealers had been able to bypass the Adeptus Mechanicus defences by worming their way up through water pipes to seize the upper levels of the Hoist. Within days, the primary source of Megaborealis' water had been cut off. A plan that had been generations in the making had finally been put into deadly effect.

At the tail end of the War of Beasts, the battle for the Hoist rose to new levels when the Iron Hands, masters of the armoured assault, made a methodical and precise attack on those holdings the Adeptus Mechanicus had designated lost to the xenos menace. Before they could make much headway, however, the presence of the Space Marines drew the attention of nearby Ork forces, who battered their way through the hivesprawl to join the fight. Within a matter of hours, the Space Marines found themselves battling two species of xenos at once. Without the adept calculations and compartmentalised war doctrines of their leader, Clan Captain Galkraan, they would have been swiftly overcome.

The Pauper Princes took advantage of the reprieve, rallying in the lower levels of the Stygian Spires. Then the Iron Hands strike cruiser *Darkspear* levelled a punitive barrage on coordinates relayed from Galkraan, reducing tracts of the Stygian Spires claimed by the Genestealer Cultists to blackened, smoking rubble. The way cleared, the Kastelan Robots and their Cult Mechanicus keepers began methodically working their way through the lower levels, guns blazing.

Meanwhile, Skitarii macroclades were despatched to take back the upper levels from the Purestrain Genestealers that had seized their sovereign domain. The Skitarii counter-attack hit home with impressive force. Unit after unit burst up from disused transit capillaries that led into the sanctified control centre, routes that had intentionally been left hidden by the warriors of the Omnissiah as contingencies should the main entry points be lost.

In a matter of moments, the Genestealers in the Hoist's control hub found that the tables had been turned. Dozens of xenos beasts were gunned down by the radium carbines and galvanic rifles of the Adeptus Mechanicus infantry. They fought with the fury of righteous zealots, so incensed were they at seeing their holy machinery profaned by xenos claws.

Acting on instinct, the Genestealers clambered up the walls like skittering spiders and ripped away the auto-lumens that bathed the control room in a pallid glow. Darkness descended as the lights were extinguished one by one, and with it came a horror from the void.

Emerging from the largest of the water pipelines came the original Patriarch of the Vigilus infestation, Grandsire Wurm. The xenos mastermind slashed his monstrous talons through the Skitarii with such force their bodies came apart in sprays of blood and sparking wire. Under his psychic control, the Genestealers and Metamorph Hybrids that fought alongside him sealed the vertical transit capillaries with deft twists of the circular wheel-locks. In doing so, they cut off the Skitarii reinforcements still climbing up those shafts to join the fight.

Eyes alight with an evil intelligence, the Patriarch hammered its gnarled fist into a glowing red icon on the primary control panel. The armoured shutters that were designed to seal the room off from the outside world began to descend, the plasteel plates sliding slowly into place with a series of loud metallic *thunks*.

However, before the control centre could be fully locked down, lances of neutron laser fire burst into the chamber, each a spear of blinding light in the gloom. Grandsire Wurm was caught by one of the beams, which blasted two of his muscular limbs from his torso. His brood of Purestrain Genestealers fared even worse; caught in a deadly crossfire, they were annihilated around him.

The vertical Skitarii assault had been a distraction tactic, and it had worked even better than expected. Anticipating that the Genestealers would be more than a match at close quarters, the Stygian Tech-Priests had sent their Onager Dunecrawlers up the outside of the hive-spire. With the metallic plates that guarded their giant talon-like legs humming with electromagnetic fields, they had been able to cling to the hive's metal skin and stalk slowly up its near-vertical slopes right to the top. The surprise assault had come not a moment too soon. Much to the relief of the Tech-Priests overseeing it, the Dunecrawler assault proved so effective that it cleansed the Hoist's upper levels of xenos taint altogether.

The symbol of the Pauper Princes was emblazoned on over three hundred captured Imperial battle tanks – whether wrought in iron or spray-marked in industrial paint, it indicated a deadly betrayal of the Astra Militarum. Even so, during the War of Nightmares, those same tanks fought hard against the Chaos scourge.

TO CAUTERISE THE WOUND

In Hyperia, the Imperial response to the Chaos invasion of the hive-spires was swift and focused. When ever more reports came in detailing a heretic presence on the other false continents, it became clear that wider and more drastic measures were needed to deal with the encroaching darkness.

Word of each new assault reached Saint's Haven via armed couriers, skyflare semaphore and intel cylinders from the moon of Neo-vellum, and the leaders of the Adeptus Astartes drew up overlapping response plans. Though they had made many tactical gains in the spires of Hyperia and further afield, the grand strategy had to be revised, over and over, as it became clear that Abaddon had brought a dark alliance of Renegade Chapters and Traitor Legions to bear against Vigilus. Even as the Space Marine lords pored over charts and dataslates of enemy dispositions, ten-thousand-year-old traitors who had devoted their immortal lifespans to the conquest of the Imperium stalked the hivesprawls with bolters roaring death.

Though there were many at the Vigilus Senate who had only heard the names of the forces attacking the planet as whispered legends – if that – to Marneus Calgar they rang like a litany of disaster from his worst nightmares. Here the ancient enemies of the Imperium were writ large. The Black Legion were present to some degree in all of the false continents, their midnight-black armour emblazoned with that most dreaded of sigils, the Eye of Horus. They were not alone, for Abaddon had marshalled an assembly of traitors like no other.

The Word Bearers, their crimson armour covered in the unholy script of Lorgar, were attacking the armoured spire-convents of Hyperia with zealous fanaticism.

Their foot soldiers advanced in massed phalanxes with their bolters laying down overlapping fields of fire, Havoc heavy weapons specialists blasting away at the Repulsor and Exorcist tanks sent to intercept them.

The Iron Warriors made drop assaults from vast, heavily armoured warships that hung in low orbit, the principal site of their aggression the well-defended trench networks of Mortwald. Masters in the art of siege warfare, they brought pinpoint lascannon fire against the bastion networks and Fortresses of Redemption that had held back the greenskin invaders for so many years. One by one these defences cracked, for the Iron Warriors struck with terrible

speed and strength. The Imperial Fists made haste to the front lines to hurl them back, but they could not be everywhere at once, and the feints and charges of massed Chaos Cultists kept them pinned amongst the trenches while the true strength of the traitors hit home elsewhere.

The Night Lords descended upon Dirkden, the Scourged alongside them. Though he hoped that they would be assailed by the Genestealer Cultists that had engineered the false continent's downfall, Calgar knew the vile scions of Konrad Curze would not be defeated so easily, and even if hurled back would be likely to refocus their assault on the Hyperia-Dirkden Fortwall and move into the regions south of Saint's Haven.

The Lenkotz Chain, including the false islands of Tzardonica and Luthvren Isle, was overrun by a strange machine-parasitism, and anarchy was brought to the streets by Abaddon's Arch-Lord Discordant, Vex Machinator. The water purification plants there were rendered hopelessly corrupt by the aura of raw Chaos he carried with him, which unleashed havoc upon man and machine alike.

Dontoria was in the grips of an epidemic. Plasteel shanty structures rotted in every hab-block, devoured by a rapacious rust-curse even as the flesh of the humans within blackened and turned to foul slurry. Giant, bulging blisters appeared on the citizens of Grodholev Subsprawl, often in patterns that mirrored the Great Rift. When the blisters burst they spilled out tiny, writhing creatures, Daemon maggots that grew swiftly into waddling Glitchlings whose aura infected machines as well as flesh.

Supernatural plague was an enemy that the Space Marines knew they could not fight. With heavy heart, Calgar considered the fact that Dontoria too was all but lost.

CALGAR'S FIRES

Calgar was left little choice but to take extreme action, for the assault of Abaddon and his allies was as devastating as it was swift. Yet having so recently conceded Dirkden to the Pauper Princes, he balked at the idea of giving up territory to the Chaos assault. The matter was discussed with vehement passion in the Vigilus Senate, but at first no one could agree on a course.

In the end, it was Lucienne Agamemnus IX, the Planetary Governor, who helped make Calgar's mind up for him. The upper levels of many hive-spires, taken over by the forces of Chaos, had been lost. She suggested that a deal be struck with the Adeptus Mechanicus, and their industrial machinery brought to bear to cause a seismic disruption of immense magnitude. Using Tectonic Fragdrills and bore-hives, they could topple the highest edifices across Vigilus. Calgar was not convinced. Not only would the tumbling buildings crash down to crush thousands of citizens, and the fissures opening up in each hivesprawl damn tens of thousands more, the effect upon morale would be crippling. Furthermore, Lucienne had stood in direct opposition to the works of the Adeptus Mechanicus for decades, and a reversal of policy would be seen as a sign of desperation. In response, Lucienne instead proposed a systematic program of arson, starting at the throat of each of the largest hive-spires. The fires raging upward would cleanse the traitors from the tips of each stronghold without the Imperial forces having to commit another bullet. Calgar agreed, albeit with a heavy heart. He ordered it done, and Ministorum-sanctioned Adepta Sororitas fire teams moved to enact his orders within the hour. The conflagrations known collectively as Calgar's Fires were set in every hive to pierce the smog-cloud layer, and one by one, the spires of Vigilus burned.

CALGAR'S FIRES

| CULTIVATED INFERNO | HIVE-SPIRES | SMOG LAYER |

INSIDE THE SWIRL

'There are truths upon Vigilus that have remained hidden for aeons. So closely guarded are they, so deeply buried, that the planet's people have no idea they even existed in the first place. Their hiding places have become blind spots, areas forgotten by all except the cautionary legends of grand-mamzels and the last of the Vigilant seers. Yet in those secret places can be found the salvation of the planet – or, if it falls into the wrong hands, its damnation.'

- *Valle de Geer, Elder Seer of the Burning Wheel*

The secret within the Vhulian Swirl was to affect the War of Nightmares in the most profound of ways. What had long been ignored suddenly became the focus of a new military campaign.

The giant dust storm to the east of Hyperia Hivesprawl was avoided by almost all on Vigilus – even the greenskins and the cultists of the Pauper Princes gave it a wide berth. Those whose curiosity had driven them close to its boundaries had found the ferocity of the weather system a deadly barrier, and those who lived to tell of it proved a further disincentive for any future would-be explorers. The whipping, high-velocity winds that howled in a great circle around the eye of the storm carried with them billions of tons of particulate matter – grains of sand, flinders of rust, and splinters of rock – that could shred the skin from a man in a matter of seconds. The storm raged on decade after decade, as ceaseless as the Jovian Red Spot in the Sol System. The Swirl was a region so hostile to life, so terrible in its anger, that only those with protective equipment, like Adeptus Astartes battle plate, had any chance of making it through to the eye of the storm beyond. But there were some who had braved the journey, and thereby found the secrets that lay deep within.

When the Space Marines arrived during the second phase of the War of Beasts, the Aquilarian Council, Vigilus' governing body at that time, had insisted that

to study the Vhulian Swirl was a waste of resources. Though it birthed smaller storms that span out across the wastes like the cells of some vile canker budding from the parent mass, the planet's leaders were convinced it was not worth investigating, as every attempt thus far had ended in failure.

The Dark Angels ventured to explore it nonetheless, for they had reasons of their own to search the most remote regions of the planet. At first they had travelled in rugged transports, driving in a sidelong chevron formation so one vehicle could provide cover for the next. When the transports had choked and died, their gears and pistons fouled by sand, the Space Marines had sent forth strike teams on armoured bikes, high-powered vehicles with a profile low enough to slip through the relentless winds. On these they made it further still, but not far enough.

The bikes too were fouled by the swirling particulate and ultimately brought to a halt, their machine spirits screaming in anger when their throttles were gunned to no avail. Vowing to reclaim their metal steeds before the end, the Space Marines had then advanced on foot, fighting with every dogged step to reach the Swirl's heart. But they were not to find it. The area covered by the Vhulian Swirl was vast, and with visibility so poor and the storm's electromagnetic interference playing havoc with their sensors, they were forced to concede defeat and return to the wider war. Yet it pained them to do so, for they sensed that something of great import was concealed within that terrible storm – and they were right.

For millennia, the Swirl had hidden an ancient stronghold of dark rock. Known by the nameless masons that had built it as the Citadel Vigilant, it had been claimed long ago by a warband of the Fallen. Those ancient traitors of the First Legion had been conducting investigations into the nature of Vigilus for centuries, and using the planet as a staging post for their own agendas. The remote and hostile locale, twinned with the psychic shielding provided by the Fallen Librarian Osandus, had made it extremely difficult for anyone to uncover the secret at the heart of the Swirl.

Abaddon was the exception. The Despoiler had signed a blood-marked pact with the Fallen leader centuries ago, and using this parchment his Sorcerers were able to track the psychic signature to Vigilus, like bloodhounds on the scent of their prey. After Abaddon had helped the Fallen escape a force of Dark Angels in the Pandorax war zone, Osandus had sworn fealty to the Despoiler. The Warmaster had suspected that the allegiance of the Fallen Librarian would be useful in the future, and the events upon Vigilus were to prove him right. The time to call in the debt was now.

VHULIAN SWIRL
Anomalous
weather system
in perpetuity
<declared In
Nominis Abhorrens
by the Aquilarian
Council>. Divinatos
level aptus
non, Subtithe
level aptus non.
Clearance zone
of official
cartographicus
border at least
3.2 leagues.
Satellite etching
from Neo-vellum
inconclusive due
to omnipresent dust
storm coverage.

Thought for the
day: Leave Well
Enough Alone.

THE VOIDCLAW

VOIDCLAW
Macro-Artefact
(carbon signature
indicative of
Dark Age of
Technology).
Similarities to
Hadronite large-
scale graviton
array (cf. Noctis
Labyrinth).
Generates anomaly
comparable to
micro-analogue of
collapsed star.
Atomic density of
yield unknown.

At the spine of the Citadel Vigilant was an ancient weapon known as the Voidclaw, a device of incredible power. Its Fallen guardians had a dire use in mind for it – but the Despoiler had plans of his own.

Upon reaching the planet's orbit, Abaddon's flagship, the *Vengeful Spirit*, took up a geosynchronous position above Storvhal, the vast ship revolving about its axis to level a punishing broadside at any Imperial craft that came too close. So mighty was the Gloriana-class battleship that it smashed aside all challengers with no more effort than an Ogryn swatting a gadfly. Though the Imperial Navy mounted an initial foray against it, cleared by the Chapter Masters who identified its hated silhouette, the giant warship inflicted such terrible losses they were forced to withdraw. Ultimately, the admiralty reasoned it better not to provoke the vast relic ship, for it only attacked when approached, and otherwise hung over Storvhal, seemingly inert.

Abaddon, on the other hand, was far from inactive. He had formulated an approach to the Citadel Vigilant that bypassed the swirling tempest entirely. With the sorcerous teleportarium arrays of the *Vengeful Spirit* focused onto the psychic spoor of Osandus, the Warmaster and his hand-picked Terminators – the Bringers of Despair – descended in a strike force no more than fifty strong. They appeared outside the gates of the Citadel Vigilant in a blaze of dark splendour, and called for an audience with those inside. For a long and tense minute, they had no reply. Abaddon had already started stalking forward, Drach'nyen raised in his great gauntlet, when the upper drawbridge clanked down and a hooded figure emerged.

The parley that followed was not the exchange of old friends, nor even old allies. It was fraught and terse, with the gun barrels of a hundred Fallen pointing down from the ramparts. The Black Legion showed not a moment's hesitation, nor a twitch of their guns, not even when the artillery emplacements and macro-cannons of the Citadel Vigilant tracked slowly towards them. Although all were on high alert, their guns remained silent.

Instead, a war of words began. It was a battle that Abaddon was well equipped to fight, for the Despoiler had brokered deals with the lords of Renegade Chapters and the Daemon Primarchs of the Traitor Legions. Some amongst the Black Legion claimed he had even spoken with the Ruinous Powers themselves, and maintained his sanity – or most of it – in the process.

It was for control of the Voidclaw that Abaddon bargained. The weapon at the heart of the citadel was like no other. It did not fire projectiles, but instead forced a breach in the fabric of space-time itself, focusing a beam of crushing energy upon a single point to open a gravitic anomaly smaller than a pearl. Though tiny, this singularity could bypass all known types of force field. The potential devastation that could be unleashed was incredible. The gravity of that anomaly was so strong it could draw all matter around it into its ravening nothingness, a fierce void from which nothing and no one could escape.

To the Fallen, the Voidclaw was a weapon to be unleashed upon their bitterest enemies – provided they could lure them into the right place at the right time, for the spire-like device was intended to engage warships, not armies. To Abaddon, however, it was a tool with which he could reshape the Nachmund Gauntlet.

The Despoiler outlined a plan to Osandus whereby the titanic weapon would be fired not at an enemy target, but at the area of space equidistant between Vigilus and its moon, Neo-vellum. Though small, the resultant gravitic anomaly would have a profound effect on both worlds, drawing countless tons of loose matter high into their orbits.

Vigilus, its status as a functioning sentinel world already precarious, would be plunged into an era where even gravity was turned against it. More than that, the Voidclaw's fell effects would alter the Nachmund Gauntlet beyond recovery.

THE MAD VENDETTA OF OSANDUS

The Fallen Librarian, Osandus, was at first reluctant to allow Abaddon access to the Voidclaw, as that extraordinary invention was intended to be his secret weapon against the Dark Angels. This was a device so powerful that even when dormant it caused an anomalous weather system to whirl around it. It was so ancient and strange that Osandus did not fully understand it, though he had made psychic communion with its spirit, and had reached a rapport with the malevolent weapon-sentience.

The Librarian's plan had been to gather an army of the Fallen so large that his former kin, the Dark Angels, had no choice but to investigate in force. Osandus allowed them to learn of the gathering through the deliberate confessions of Fallen captives, warriors who had willingly sacrificed themselves to further the wider strategy. Thus, the Librarian ensured that the correct information was revealed at the right time, luring the First Legion's remnants to Vigilus – in all probability upon the space-going fortress monastery known as the Rock. Once that great warship entered orbit, the Voidclaw would be unleashed. The Librarian intended to coax the Rock into committing to an orbital bombardment, trusting that the ancient force fields around the citadel would protect his warriors as he returned fire with the Voidclaw. Should the device open a singularity within the Rock, it would crush the space-going fortress from the inside out. Yet Abaddon's plan for the destruction of the Nachmund Gauntlet was so compelling in its vision and scope that Osandus came to see its virtue – to strike back at the Imperium as a whole would be an even sweeter prize.

With the chanting of sacraments and the shattering of ancient wards, the Voidclaw was brought to shuddering, crackling life. Dust whirled into a high spiral, the ground shuddering as the entire citadel was rocked to its foundations. The air itself screamed as the Voidclaw went to work, and a tiny singularity was torn in the fabric of realspace high above the planet.

FALSE TIDES

When unleashed, the Voidclaw had a horribly deleterious effect on Vigilus. Just as a moon affects the waters of the world below, the gravitic anomaly pulled everything upon Vigilus towards it, destroying a great deal in the process. The disruption it caused spiralled quickly to the level of a global catastrophe.

The terrifyingly strong lure of the Voidclaw's gravitic singularity – known thenceforth as the Vhulian Anomaly – had countless consequences for the Imperial war effort. The effects were so dire that the Vigilus Senate was flooded with intel from across the world, and the streets of Saint's Haven thronged with messengers and petitioners from every active front. Subsidiary war rooms were opened in chambers throughout the Governor's palace, each one a triage and solution centre for a separate theatre of battle. Yet even with Marneus Calgar's prodigious strategic acumen coordinating them, the Imperial commanders found themselves unable to categorise the ever-changing face of the War of Nightmares, let alone reverse its course. By the time one disaster had been reported, two more had begun to unfold.

The first to feel the anomaly's baleful pull were the fleets that hung in orbit around Vigilus. In the hours before the Voidclaw's thrumming engines had activated, the admirals of the Imperial fleets had watched in confusion as the Chaos ships had changed course, taking up new positions that appeared to have no strategic value. It was Arch-Commodore Vensatoria that first noticed that they were all facing away from the Vhulian Swirl, but she could not guess why.

Only when the gravitic singularity opened did the Imperial admirals realise that the change of orientation was for good reason. The Chaos ships had shifted to points where they could counteract the effect of the anomaly with their engines. The same could not be said for the Imperial fleet. Outrider ships, tugs and cutters that were near the gravity well of the singularity found themselves veering off course to crash into the leviathan ships they were supposed to be escorting.

Planetside, strings of explosions erupted as all manner of hell broke loose. The Vhulian Swirl was stretched up into a vast spiralling

THE DRAINING

Water too was drawn by the false tides of the gravitic anomaly. The theft of this priceless resource was as much a part of Abaddon's plan as any other consequence, for though his power-armoured Legions could survive with next to no liquid intake, the lack of it would cripple the Astra Militarum and further undermine the planet's morale. Combined with the uneasy pulling feeling that every citizen now had in the pit of their stomach, the phenomenon would bring the hivesprawls to the point of total societal collapse.

At first, only trickles of water escaped the reservoirs and sumps on the planet's surface. Then these turned to streams and tributaries of the precious liquid that snaked their way from every hivesprawl and into the arid wastes, still bound by Vigilus' mass but lured by the anomaly's pull. Much of the water was lost, absorbed by the porous landscape. But where the source of each outlet was significant – as was the case with the giant reservoirs that dotted across the planet's surface – a glittering river wound its way towards the Vhulian Swirl. In some places, new and shallow seas formed and flowed across the desert.

The movement of the water was all but impossible to stop. Hundreds of thousands of dehydrated citizens staggered and struggled with one another as they used tureens, tankards, ration tins, and even cupped hands to scoop up as much of the aqueous bounty as they could.

Initially, these citizens did so with a sense of triumph and wild hope. That most precious resource, usually guarded fiercely by the rich and influential, now seemed free to anyone who could harness it. Slowly it dawned on them that the water was painfully finite, and that time was short. Scuffles broke out over every newly formed rivulet, fist fights turning to knife duels, then even to gun battles in the streets. Wherever water flowed on towards the Swirl, behind it came thirsting masses of wide-eyed unfortunates.

The Imperium's grip on Vigilus, already drastically undermined by the serial invasions that had battered its surface, had been compromised once again. With the military echelons forced to prioritise their own water supply, a deadly drought amongst the populace seemed inevitable.

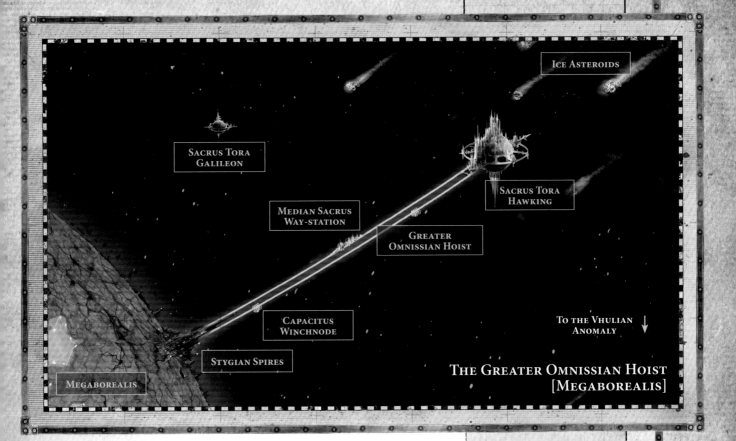

ICE ASTEROIDS

SACRUS TORA
GALILEON

SACRUS TORA
HAWKING

MEDIAN SACRUS
WAY-STATION

GREATER
OMNISSIAN HOIST

CAPACITUS
WINCHNODE

TO THE VHULIAN
ANOMALY

STYGIAN SPIRES

THE GREATER OMNISSIAN HOIST
[MEGABOREALIS]

MEGABOREALIS

cone towards the anomaly, a gigantic talon of dust that could be seen halfway across the planet. Anything small not tied or bolted down was drawn towards that great storm by the force of the anomaly that hungered above it. In Hurrikane Rekk, the closest Ork scrap city, every loose nut and screw began to roll in the same direction, heading out of the city in streams of metal – much to the bafflement of Ragzakka's Meks and the delight of those Grots enterprising enough to chase them down for profit.

As the planet's tectonic plates shivered and buckled, the spires of Megaborealis, Hyperia, Dirkden and Storvhal tumbled and fell. Thousands of lives were lost with each collapse, burning rubble cascading through the streets. Meanwhile, the Greater Omnissian Hoist warped and snapped as the Sacrus Tora Hawking space station to which it was connected was drawn towards the vortex.

Neo-vellum was also affected, though the alteration of its course was invisible to the eye. The acid swamps that blighted its surface slid and bubbled as they were caught in the anomaly's pull. The bridges and transit-ways that had linked each scriptorum were eaten away by the rising caustic lakes, and they too fell, toppling into the vitriolic muck to be dissolved.

In the depths of space, the nebulas of cosmic dust that swirled at the edge of the Vigilus System closed in, imperceptibly at first, but then at great pace as they were drawn towards the Vhulian Anomaly. Above Vigilus, the light of Astravigila became dimmer with every passing day, masking the planet below in gloom, and worsening Imperial morale still further. With one act of parley, by calling in a singular debt, Abaddon had struck a blow against the Vigilus System that would be almost impossible to counter.

'This is a war that cannot be won! What good are even a score of Space Marine Chapters if all they can do is claim victory over the desiccated corpse of a once-great world? We shall all be dead by the time they slay the monsters that come from the spires! How can we feed ourselves, our children, if even the water that we crave is being drained by dark magic? All is lost! We can but look to our own survival in the last few days of this apocalypse! Death to those who would hinder us!'

- Lemuas nach Sodheim, Civic Leader and Almsman of the Twenty-Headed Hydra

THE IRON FIST CLOSES TIGHT

Vigilus was being choked by the forces Abaddon had unleashed upon it. What had once been a world at war was now becoming a living hell – but it was not only the Imperial forces that were under pressure.

While the gravitic curse Abaddon had levelled against the planet Vigilus was bending the laws of physics to the cause of anarchy and disruption, the doomsday creeds his invading forces spread everywhere they went – along with the strange warp-summoning structures his allies were building across the planet – were having much the same effect.

The Word Bearers, that most devout of Traitor Legions, were given the task of summoning the energies of the Cicatrix Maledictum to the planet using arcane edifices known as Noctilith Crowns. The Death Guard were charged with spreading their plagues across Dontoria with renewed vigour, while the Night Lords were fighting hard in Dirkden, and the Iron Warriors were engaged with their old foes, the Imperial Fists, for control of Mortwald.

However, the Chaos forces did not go unopposed. The Imperials, though reeling, were not yet defeated. Denied their eyries and spire-tips by the controlled infernos known as Calgar's Fires, the Chaos invaders had taken the war into the cities and the parched wastes beyond. Some of the Traitor Legions, the World Eaters foremost amongst them, were content to slaughter and destroy – as the defenders of the Giants, a series of massive crenulated plateaus in northern Oteck, found to their cost. Others, such as the Alpha Legion, engaged in a devastating array of covert actions, while the more devout Legions pursued a war of indoctrination into the cults of

dark worship. Now was the time for all-out war, and neither traitor nor renegade shirked from their duty to cause as much carnage and madness as possible.

Rather than trying to take on all of his foes at once, Calgar and the leaders of the Vigilus Senate made use of their local knowledge to wage a campaign of misdirection and entrapment. Though the confusion, rioting and panicking in the cityscapes precluded any cogent military plan there, out in the wastes, the relatively open landscape was a canvas upon which Calgar could work a strategic masterpiece.

By manipulating the demeanours of their foes, the Imperial forces would drive one enemy into another, thus, ideally, obliterating both. It was a tactic inspired in part by Kryptman's Gambit – a strategy only to be used in the direst of circumstances. Yet it was effective.

Amongst the Space Marine forces that had fought during the War of Beasts, there were many who had learned first-hand of the reckless attitude of the Orks, and knew enough of the madcap, velocity-obsessed mentality of the

Speedwaaagh! to roughly predict its movements. Conversely, the Orks had learned afresh that a foe clad in power armour would always give a good fight and, to the greenskins, one Space Marine was much the same as another, no matter what sigils it wore or what cause it fought for.

Armed with this knowledge, Calgar and his fellow Chapter Masters ordered their forces to mount a series of fighting retreats. Enacted with impressive precision, they led the battle-hungry World Eaters, Crimson Slaughter and Red Corsairs out of the cities and into the wastes. This frequently meant leading the foe through relatively open terrain, and in doing so the Imperials suffered heavy losses – not just from Ork gunners in the cities taking opportunistic shots at these easy targets, but from Chaos invaders who had taken up positions in the higher storeys of the hivesprawls to level firepower

against Ork and Imperial alike. Yet this was a price worth paying, for the action opened a new front that would absorb a great deal of the Chaos attack's focus.

The Orks of the Speedwaaagh!, their eyes drawn to the explosions and trails of fire in the distance, made haste for the devastating clashes between loyalist and traitor that were now erupting in the wastes. Fully anticipating the tide of vehicles they would summon with the spectacle of open war, the loyalists withdrew swiftly and in good order, extracting via Thunderhawk Gunship and bulk lander while the jeers and bellowed challenges of their traitorous cousins rang in their ears.

The Chaos forces, not having as much in the way of aerial assets, were not able to evacuate in time from the kill zones into which they had been lured. They were quickly set upon by the Orks of

the Speedwaaagh!, who relished the fresh challenge of these new opponents. The first handful of greenskin vehicles were gunned down and cut apart by the Chaos troops as they turned their fury upon the advancing Speedwaaagh!. But close behind the first Ork vehicles came a score, then a hundred more. The Heretic Astartes could not hope to stop them all.

In the space of a few scant hours, the smoke pillars reaching high over the wastes had drawn thousands more roaring, belching, bullet-spitting vehicles to the open war zones. Even the World Eaters found themselves hard pressed, for the Orks were emboldened by speed and numerical superiority to such an extent that they could not be broken. So it was that the xenos bane that had torn Vigilus asunder during the War of Beasts proved to be an effective defence in its own right for the beleaguered Imperial forces.

INFERNAL MACHINES

Megaborealis' foremost blackstone cache – Silo XV of Thunder Sump – was protected by a vast refractor field. In order to destroy the substance within, Abaddon would have to deactivate this aegis. The Warmaster of Chaos sent in a vanguard of Daemon Engines, but they met resistance of a different kind.

Though they did not truly understand the nature of their hoard, the Tech-Priests of Megaborealis jealously protected the spear-like blackstone deposits they had unearthed from Vigilus' crust. The enigma of their construction, and the strange filigree of channels and holes that ran through them, hinted that they may have been fashioned by an alien race. They were an intoxicating source of potential knowledge.

Almost as soon as the first shipments of blackstone had been transported to safety from the deep mining shafts, Silo XV of Thunder Sump had been fortified as a permanent vault for their storage.

The silo was protected not only by stout fortress walls and a permanent garrison, but also by a large domed force field. This was no Bastion shield network, but an even more precious relic – a macro-grade refractor field. It generated a barrier that could turn energy, be it kinetic, thermal, nuclear or otherwise, into harmless flashes of light.

Abaddon had yet to release the wrecking ball of his Daemon Engine hosts, and by that time they were straining at the leash. The Brazen Beasts, worshippers of the Blood God, were known for their preponderance of possessed engines of war, and their fondness for launching several spearhead assaults at once. They had reached

the planet not in a flotilla of ships, but in one massive, twisted spacecraft – the *Cerberite*. That space-borne colossus had once been their Chapter's battle barge, but had languished so long in the Eye of Terror it was itself now more like a hideous, colossal, half-living Daemon Engine.

The mutated battle barge came in dangerously low to push through Silo XV's macro-grade refractor field, flames licking around its underside as that ancient protective shield fought against the *Cerberite*'s sheer mass. Fire was of little import to a machine forged in the hellscape of the warp, and Heldrakes peeled off from eyrie-like nests of ribbed cables.

Vast gargoyle mouths yawned open at the ship's fore, the klaxon roars of scrapcode so intimidating that machine spirits in a thousand barriers and vault-seals quailed and yielded their locks in terror. From the ship's flanks uncoiled clanking, ridged pseudopods made of linked metal plates that stretched down to anchor the ship to the spires of Megaborealis. Down from the steep ramps came entire hosts of Daemon Engines, their numbers such that they pushed through the defences of the Tech-Priests that hammered fire into their ranks.

When they attacked, they did so as a vast claw gouging at the Adeptus Mechanicus lines, each spear-tip led by a towering titan of war. The speed of their attack was as much a weapon as their strength, for though Megaborealis still had countless clades of defenders active, they not could bring enough assets to bear in time to stop the shock assault. The Brazen Beasts had amassed no fewer than three Lords of Skulls, demi-humanoid monstrosities that ground through whole congregations of Electro-Priests with skull-embossed tracks. Packs of Forgefiends thundered alongside them like giant hounds accompanying some godly hunter, using their vast metal claws to bat aside the Kataphron Breachers that drove forward to intercept them with crackling blasts of energy. As a concentric circle of Kastelan Robots formed up around Silo XV, many-legged Venomcrawlers scuttled towards them, their bulbous

abdomens emanating strange aetheric forces as they pounced on the towering automatons and stabbed at them with piston-driven legs. The Adeptus Mechanicus, having armoured their stronghold against all conventional attacks, had discounted one aspect of the Chaos assault – sheer daemonic savagery.

The coming of the *Cerberite* had also caused other forces to rush to the site of the battle. Over the latter phases of the War of Beasts, Megaborealis had been occupied by greenskins as well as Chaos worshippers, and they were eager for a fresh challenge. The Ork Warboss Krooldakka, having circumvented the still-burning wastelands of the Seeping Delta to investigate the 'glowy fing' that was Silo XV's refractor field under bombardment, drove his foremost Blitz Brigade through a hail of Skitarii firepower to get to the mine workings of western Megaborealis. A fleet of massive flatbed Trukks carrying the giant metal creations of Big Tanka smashed through the pitted sprawl of Thunder Sump and bullied their way into the silo districts beyond. The armoured assault ploughed through the Chaos Cultists and renegades that formed the body of the Brazen Beasts army without a moment's hesitation.

Though he lost dozens of Battlewagons to the heavy firepower of cannon-armed Daemon Engines on the way, Krooldakka was not to be stopped. With boxy Ork vehicles and Chaos war machines exploding all around him, he bellowed a mighty Waaagh! that drove his Speed Freek followers into a frenzy. The vehicular rampage ground a path to the commanders of the enemy force through sheer bloody-mindedness. When a Maulerfiend stormed into Krooldakka's path, he climbed atop his wagon's cab, ripped the head from the metal beast with his power klaw, and then, as the fiend flailed in its death throes, spat down its neck. The Speedwaaagh! ploughed onwards.

THE HARD FALL

With Krooldakka's flatbed megatrukks unloading their Deff Dread and Gorkanaut cargo, the battle at Thunder Sump swiftly turned into an engine war. Fat-bellied walkers traded bullets by the thousand with the white-hot projectiles that were churned out from the hades autocannons of Heldrakes and Forgefiends. The vanguard creatures of the Brazen Beasts, who by this time had ripped their way through the Kastelan Robots guarding Silo XV and set about destroying the refractor field generators, were too focused on their task to turn back. The Ork Warlord was deft enough to evade the reach of the Lords of Skulls, darting from one wreck to another and even using the slab-like side of a broken Onager Dunecrawler as a shield as he closed with the Brazen Beasts' commanders. The Warpsmith Ghorba Daemonbind, the creator of many of the vanguard beasts, found himself assailed by the bleeding, roaring Ork leader – and met his end at Krooldakka's claw. It was only when the twisted Chaos Knights that formed Daemonbind's shock troops finally broke the Adeptus Mechanicus defenders with a massed charge and destroyed the silo's refractor field that Daemonbind had his revenge from beyond the grave.

With the silo laid open and its field dispersed, the Despoiler's mighty flagship – the *Vengeful Spirit* – gave voice to its thunderous displeasure once more. This time the bombardment of cyclonic torpedoes hit home with planet-shattering force, obliterating Silo XV, the blackstone inside it, the Brazen Beasts vanguard, the Speedlord Krooldakka and everything else within a mile-wide radius.

CULTS AND CONQUESTS

The bow waves of fear that rippled out from each new disaster to affect Vigilus had alarming secondary effects. Many citizens sought the solace of greater powers other than the Emperor, joining cults that promised sanctuary in this most tumultuous of times. All too often, they were rewarded with damnation.

The influx of the common people that swelled the cults on Vigilus promised a new phase of war. Mania was matched against savagery, wide-eyed desperation against callous hate. Everywhere a new and sorry tale was unfolding, and Mortwald was no exception.

The coming of the Chaos fleet and the War of Nightmares that ensued pushed the aristocracy of Mortwald into a state of near panic. When the baleful effects of the Voidclaw made the continent's plight all the more dire, extreme measures were taken by the ruling aristocracy. Its defenders had spent a great deal of their resources in repelling the Orks from the Deinos Trench Network and the Tzeller

Line. Despite being bolstered by the Imperial Fists, several of their successor Chapters and Imperial Knights from not only Dharrovar but also Voltoris, the defenders had achieved little more than an uneasy stalemate. Meanwhile, they had lost ground to the uprising of the Pauper Princes that had blighted the southernmost regions.

The reaction of Lord Deinos Agamemnus and his fellow aristocrats was to stockpile all the food and water they could muster in the inner keeps and citadels of Mortwald's richest districts. This was perhaps understandable from a survivalist mindset. But the continent's rulers took their acquisitive mores to inhuman

extremes, donning high-tech Spyrer warsuits and hunting the representatives of Mortwald's poorer classes whenever they petitioned for a fairer spread of resources.

The stockpiling continued until the aristocrats holed up in Immortalis Spirehive had more food than they could eat in a hundred lifetimes. They also had enough water to wash it down twice over, despite the effects of the Vhulian Anomaly draining many of their open water reservoirs. Their endless wealth and connections with the aqua magnates of the planet were a powerful combination. Cults of luxury and youthful immortality came into being, focused

THE NOCTILITH CROWNS

The ring-like structures of blackstone known as Noctilith Crowns brought a loathsome new energy to the war effort. The crowns had been constructed on Nemendghast, perfected en route to Vigilus in the guts of Abaddon's forge ships, and raised on the sentinel planet by work gangs of indentured Chaos slaves. Where the Black Legion's Masters of Possession determined there was a site of geomantic significance, the crowns were aligned to the exacting specifications of Abaddon's ritualists, and driven into the surface of the planet with long steel spikes.

Wherever the Noctilith Crowns were planted, the minds of Chaos psykers flared with a frisson of forbidden power. Those who had any form of psychic sensitivity found strange new phenomena manifesting around them when they approached these sites. Even slaves and cultists without a flicker of psychic potential were assailed by searing visions.

The Noctilith Crowns were designed to bring the raw forces of the warp to the planet. They had been created from deposits of noctilith stone harnessed by the Black Legion over the course of their dark crusades from the Eye of Terror, imbued with Chaos energy, and distributed across the galaxy. This too was part of the Despoiler's greater plan.

Over the course of the Gothic War, the Warmaster of Chaos had learned that blackstone could be polarised either to attract the energies of Chaos, or to repel it. That knowledge had informed his grand strategy ever since. Where there were deposits of blackstone polarised to repel Chaos energy, Abaddon would do everything in his power to destroy them. Where there was blackstone that could be polarised to attract Chaos energy, he would seize it and turn it to his advantage. By chiselling into the stone blasphemous phrases and runes in the dark tongue, a Sorcerer could align its aura with the dimensional bleed of the warp.

Channelling these unpredictable energies using a Noctilith Crown could lead to a tremendous psychic backlash. In places upon Vigilus, more power than any mortal could possibly use flooded into the minds of those supplicants that sought to harness the Crown's supernatural aura. This too served the greater cause, for where a psychic disaster struck, the raw stuff of Chaos was soon to follow.

around the rejuvenat clinics that Mortwald's rulers now sought only to use for themselves. The consequences were dire indeed. Not only did the outlandish selfishness of the Mortwald elite trigger a wave of rioting that destabilised any regions still in Imperial hands, but in plumbing the depths of decadence they brought the perverted scions of Slaanesh to their door.

The Flawless Host, renegades so obsessed with their own excellence they were convinced they could do no wrong, were infamous even amongst their own kind. Having caught the scent of excess upon the aether, they made for Mortwald's richest sites. They used the still-valid access idents carried by their craft to bypass the layered defences and visit the most beautiful of Mortwald's buildings unhindered, licking their lips in anticipation of the feasts to come.

The glut of violence that followed was so disgusting in its obscenity it defies description. The rulers of Mortwald had been found guilty for the crime of imperfection – not for their excessive hoarding and sickeningly callous natures, but for not going far enough. The Flawless Host were glad to show Lord Deinos and his peers the meaning of true excess, summoning Daemonettes to aid them whenever a household guard regiment or rival cult moved against them. Each proud Mortwald spire soon burned from within, its rotten heart exposed for all to see.

The outskirts of Mortwald – and the western parts of Oteck Hivesprawl that were also starved of resources – fared little better. The people of these regions had felt the injustice and greed of their 'superiors' most keenly. Whipped into a frenzy of indignation by the cult leaders that had inveigled their way into the

continents' outskirts, they mounted a gory revolution that saw the people turn against their rulers and take their heads. Soon enough, these mobs turned into blood cults – and from there into worshippers of the Dark Gods. Shorn of reason, convinced that their absent rulers were the true evil and that their only hope lay in defection, they followed the Chaos Space Marines into battle whenever the traitors launched a new assault.

Though the sanctified Ecclesiarchal regions of Hyperia were once known as the domain of the hale and the sane, the coming of Chaos changed that forever. The fear sown though its people by the widely broadcast ultimatums of Haarken Worldclaimer introduced a seed of doubt that was soon to be fed and watered by that most difficult of dangers to fight – rampant plague.

It was the Death Guard of the Dolorous Strain, led to battle by Gurloch Thrax, that first split off from the Dontoria invaders and made it to Hyperia. There they operated from inside the same rusted water-crawler they had used to bypass the city's defences, venturing out to spread disease and despair every night. Ultimately, it was not the Imperial defenders of Hyperia that challenged them, but the Thousand Sons heading north from Kaelac's Bane – yet by the time the Dolorous Strain were neutralised, plague was already running rampant across the Dubchec Crevasse region.

VILE REVELATIONS

The Death Guard that had first infected Dontoria had gone to ground, working in the shadows to spread disease. At the onset of the War of Nightmares, they boiled out of their hiding places to renew their attack.

The Death Guard of Dontoria's Pravdus Subsprawl region, led by the methodical and ever-careful Plague Surgeon Zoculinsus, had sown the seeds of conquest by introducing the Gellerpox to the planet. Though the quarantine methods of the Adeptus Astartes and their Militarum Tempestus allies had slowed the servants of Nurgle, the search parties sent after them had been put down, and the firebomb tactics designed to scour the tunnels of their presence had claimed no more than a half dozen of their number. The cordon, although largely effective against man-sized targets, could not hold back the Sludge-Grubs, Glitchlings and Eyestinger Swarms that were birthed from the Gellerpox, and so the plague spread further and further afield, until Dontoria was as much the province of Nurgle as it was of the Imperium.

The role of the Death Guard was much greater than purely infecting the sentinel planet – their mission was to spread a star-spanning contagion across the entire sector and through the Nachmund Gauntlet, using Vigilus as a staging post. From Dontoria's principal spaceport, Litmus Dock, they sent freighters full of infected mutants further into space, some of them reaching the Vigilus Mandeville Point, despite the best efforts of the Rogue Trader du Languille to stop them. Over the course of the second and third stages of the War of Beasts, these plague vessels made translation into the warp and reached fresh war zones to infect.

Years later, when the hordes of Chaos invaded Vigilus, three of those scab-hulled freighters returned from their mission to bolster the armies of their infected brethren. They were so caked with filth and feculence they looked more like slowly descending meteors than spacecraft as they bellied down at Litmus Dock once more. They landed uncontested, for the spaceport was now firmly in the hands of the Death Guard. There they opened their voidlocks to disgorge groaning mutants of every size and description.

THE PURGE OF DONTORIA

Dontoria was soon contested once more, but this time the conflict was caused by a schism in the Chaos ranks. The Purge, a powerful band of renegades and followers of Nurgle, had made planetfall in eastern Dontoria – and found it utterly repulsive. The Heretic Astartes of this strange brotherhood believed in the destruction of all forms of life, for since their fall to the Ruinous Powers they saw all living things as either corrupt, or potential vessels for corruption. They believed that only by extinguishing all life in the galaxy could a new order rise, and that the quickest way to achieve this was with poison and pandemic.

This philosophy had begun with the noble desire to eradicate all evil, but when the weakness of man, the fallibility of mortals and the inevitability of entropy made itself evident everywhere they went, those who would become known as the Purge judged Humanity to be irredeemable. That stance only became more absolute as they saw flora, fauna and even the land itself as a potential source of evil. All life was inherently flawed, and had to be extinguished no matter the cost.

Those of the Purge that took this extremist stance did not foresee that they would come into conflict with other worshippers of Nurgle by killing every living thing they came across. But many of the Plague God's followers wanted to propagate life, no matter how foul. For the Death Guard, Dontoria ought to be a dark, fecund paradise, not a scorched and lifeless wasteland.

The Purge made landfall at the Great Choke, seeing its rampant pollution and smoke-belching industrial centres as the ideal epicentre for a wide-scale attack. They set to work slaughtering citizens and Gellerpox Infected alike, hurling the corpses of the slain into the furnaces of the Great Choke's manufactorums alongside noxious concoctions of their own making. The greasy black soot that billowed from the chimneys was thick, cloying, and far too toxic to breathe. Entire districts of the Tzimitria Subsprawl were swathed in this foul miasma, and tens of thousands suffocated in the space of a few days – even the plants and insect life withered and died. The Purge looked upon their works and saw them to be right and true.

Over the course of the next few months, the Purge continued their heretical works, capturing entire districts and turning their furnaces to the purpose of extreme pollution. The air in eastern Dontoria became near impossible to breathe; those with lungs already ravaged by the poor air quality of the Big Fug died in droves. The hardier citizens fled as best they could, only to be torn apart by the Gellerpox Mutants that roamed the streets.

What had once been a teeming metropolis, so full of life, quickly turned into a blackened, soot-stained wasteland, with many of its districts populated by little more than skeletons. The Death Guard, who had worked hard to sow the seeds of Nurgle's ever-growing garden across the western hivesprawl, looked upon their neighbours in eastern Dontoria with distaste, then resentment, and finally – when the Gellerpox itself began to die out – with open hatred. They put aside their joyous slaughter of the Imperial military and went to war against the Purge, besieging their industrial citadels with a will that even the Iron Warriors assailing Mortwald were said to have respected.

Bitter infighting ravaged the scions of Nurgle, but it was the citizens of Dontoria that paid the highest price. Chaos had taken the hivesprawl on every level, from the fleets battling above it to the plague-ravaged populace, to the microbes mutating and dying in the charnel battlefields below – and the conflict showed no sign of abating. None amongst the Death Guard or the Purge were able to truly claim victory, for they were locked in a bitter stalemate that not even Calgar sought to disrupt. Abaddon, watching from afar, was content, for Dontoria had fallen.

OF MAN AND XENOS

Time was running out for Vigilus. Even the most close-minded and intractable soul could see the planet was on the brink of destruction. The warlords of the Imperium, with their forces committed to a man and all reinforcements cut off by the Great Rift, had no option but to take drastic measures to survive.

In every war zone across Vigilus the situation was dire. Much of the planet was ablaze, thick black smog choking the air and making breathing difficult for anyone venturing above ground level. Water had all but run out, with the vast majority of the citizenry having access to perhaps a thimbleful at dawn and another at dusk. Were it not for Lucienne Agamemnus' inspired solution of tying its distribution to clocking in at day's beginning and clocking out at day's end, the infrastructure of the planet would have collapsed altogether. To travel from one region to another was to invite being preyed upon by speeding Ork hunters or shrieking Heldrakes, and with the calculations of Neo-vellum's Datasaint thrown askew by the Vhulian Anomaly, long-range communication had become next to impossible.

The forces of Chaos, invading in such number they could not be held back, were crushing Imperial defences and xenos-claimed territories alike. Spires were toppling every hour as the planet's tectonic plates, tortured by the Vhulian Anomaly, fought against one another to grind closer to that cursed singularity. Perhaps worse still, reports were sent from Neo-vellum's surviving relay stations that the perimeter of the Great Rift was expanding, like a roiling thunderhead creeping over the horizon and into ominous proximity. When reports from the admiralty of the embattled Imperial fleet in orbit around the planet were collated and parsed, it appeared certain that the Cicatrix Maledictum was encroaching upon Vigilus. Some even claimed to see leering faces in the depths of the malevolent phenomenon.

Over this period, several senior Astropaths reported visions of a pitiless clawed hand crushing a throat – interpreted by them as the narrow passage of the Nachmund Gauntlet being closed by an influx of Chaos energy. Abaddon's plan to bring Chaos in every form and fashion to Vigilus was working, and at a frightening pace.

Many drastic courses of action were considered by the members of the Imperial war council. There were those upon the Vigilus Senate who advocated for quarantine measures up to and including Exterminatus, the wholesale eradication of all life upon the planet. But Vigilus was a linchpin of the entire sector, and the Nachmund Gauntlet could not be yielded without abandoning countless light years of the Imperium Nihilus. The Primarch Guilliman himself had stated that Vigilus would not fall, and the Ultramarines there would rather fight to the last bolt than concede victory and make a liar of their primogenitor. After long hours of circular arguments and impassioned debates, it was the precedent set by Roboute Guilliman that showed the way, inspiring

Calgar to an act of diplomacy that made his fellow Chapter Masters uneasy in the extreme.

The forces of the Pauper Princes and Krooldakka's Speedwaaagh! had taken a significant toll on the Chaos invaders; the troop dispositions and after-action reports trickling in to the war rooms of Saint's Haven painted a picture of battles unfolding where not a single Imperial asset had been assigned. Yet wherever the xenos won a victory, they turned their guns on the Imperial troops soon after. There were tales circulating of Ork mercenaries offering their services to the Astra Militarum in exchange for the tanks of their armoured companies – and even dataslate reports, requested personally by Pedro Kantor of the Crimson Fists, of one commander who took them up on their offer. The misguided Commander Nerrogh van Thrynn had won back the outskirts of the Magentine Veils using a combined force of Astra Militarum armour and belligerent Ork mercenaries, but earned himself a death sentence at the muzzle of a Commissar's bolt pistol in the process.

The senate's view was that a lasting alliance with the savage enemies the Imperial forces had battled against during the War of Beasts was out of the question. The greenskins were too unpredictable and bloodthirsty to count on when a foe as dangerous as the Heretic Astartes was at the door. As for the self-proclaimed true inheritors of the planet, the Pauper Princes, it was unanimously agreed those xeno-tainted hybrids were so repugnant that they could only ever be greeted with flame and fury. But the fact remained that the Imperium was fighting a losing battle. Though more manpower was undoubtedly en route from the wider Imperium – for even under the tyranny of the Great Rift, Mankind's armies were all but inexhaustible – the chances of it arriving in time to make a difference were dwindling with every passing night.

Of the perfidious Aeldari, none spoke. The possibility of a pact hung in the air, for Roboute Guilliman had forged an alliance with that ancient xenos race in living memory, from the very heart of Macragge. But to truck with the alien was to invite disaster, this every officer in every war room knew, and some had witnessed first-hand. Even now the wild-eyed xenos were using their sleek jetbikes and grav-tanks to mount speeding raids upon Hyperia. Calgar's own Extremis Guard had paid the price for attempting to deal with the vengeful Aeldari of Saim-Hann, losing three honoured veterans before Lieutenant Eothrus and his brothers had driven them off. The blood of the fallen Macraggians still stained the marble flagstones less than a hundred yards from the central debating circle where the war council was taking place.

Emotions roiled in Calgar's chest. With every new account of disaster that reached him, he felt forced to set aside his doubts. On the second night after the onset of the Vhulian Anomaly, Calgar marched out of the senate, his Victrix Guard by his side, and the remonstrations of intractable senate members ringing in his ears. Rendezvousing with elements of the 1st Company, the Lord Macragge made his way to the main bridge crossing the Ring of Nothingness. There the Aeldari forces were still waging war upon the Tempestus Scions and their Adepta Sororitas allies, for the warriors of Saim-Hann had a score to settle with the Imperium. During the War of Beasts, their leader, Autarch Rhyloor, had been slain. His death had been sanctioned

by the Aquilarian Council, who recognised no difference between the Asuryani of the craftworlds and the vicious Drukhari raiders that had long tormented the people of Vigilus. This murderous act the warriors of Saim-Hann would see avenged a hundred times over, and for them the matter would not be settled until every human associated with the death of the Autarch lay dead.

Upon locating the Aeldari, Calgar joined the fight – firing to kill only when necessary, and instead attempting to bring the xenos to bay, to pin them down, to suppress and surround those who might otherwise escape on arrow-swift craft from the next phase of his plan.

At a critical moment during a brief lull in the fighting, the Lord Macragge called for parley. Calgar's gambit would likely have come to nought, had this Saim-Hann force been led by any other than the visionary Farseer Keltoc. He was the former advisor of Spiritseer Qelanaris, whose brother's death had triggered Hyperia's cycle of blood vengeance in the first place. Yet as much as he also longed to avenge that crime, he had another agenda. A ceasefire was called, and the stage set for a historic confluence of interests.

THE PENUMBRAL PACT

The prospect of a deal between the Ultramarines and the Asuryani was unthinkable to many. Had it not been for the alliance Primarch Guilliman had once secured with the ambassador Yvraine, such a truce would have been considered all but impossible. Yet Calgar's daring and complex plan was put into motion.

Farseer Keltoc had scried the course of Vigilus' future, and had found dire hints of the effects it would have upon the wider galaxy. With the empire of Mankind fully divided, Abaddon would claim the Imperium Nihilus for his own, and the Great Enemy of the Aeldari race would reap the rewards. That Keltoc would not allow. Though ostensibly a member of Clan Moirec's war party, he had come to the planet seeking another way.

When Calgar's stentorian tones echoed around the cracked marble walls of Saint's Haven, he was not greeted with gunfire as Lieutenant Eothrus had been before him.

Instead, Farseer Keltoc held up a hand, sending a psychic pulse to his warriors instructing them to hold their fire and listen to the Space Marine leader.

The Chapter Master spoke eloquently of Macragge, of the dire threats facing the Imperium, of the Black Legion – and of a priestess of the Aeldari God of the Dead. That last topic caused even the most truculent Saim-Hann Wild Riders to lower their blades. For a time, the battle between man and xenos was waged with words – and then, as the sun set over the burning spires in the distance, it was not waged at all. The rapport the Chapter Master

reached with the Farseer that day led to the two forces uniting in their hatred of the common enemy, and their alliance lit the dark fate of the planet Vigilus with a flickering flame of hope.

The Aeldari of Saim-Hann were not known for their forgiving nature. Precisely how Calgar won their allegiance he never disclosed, and the actual exchange between Keltoc and Calgar was never made a matter of Imperial record, despite Guilliman's insistence that historitors accompany all Ultramarines missions. In fact, the records of the interchange between Calgar and the Aeldari Farseer were

A DEADLY CARGO

The first stage of Calgar's master plan involved the acquisition of all six of Deinos Agamemnus' personal Deathstrike missiles. These had been collected with painstaking care by the Vigilant historium enthusiast over the last century and a half, and were safely kept in a gene-locked hangar vault. Lord Deinos had boasted on numerous occasions that two of his Deathstrike devices were fitted with much-feared Vortex warheads, and that should he so choose, he could rip apart a rival hive in a matter of hours, consigning the survivors to a living hell as they were dragged screaming into the empyrean.

Calgar drafted a large and ornate parchment bearing the words of the Primarch Guilliman himself, and the vow that Vigilus would not fall. To this he added his own addenda, then signed with his full array of titles in his function as Regent of Ultramar, Heir Apparent of the Tetrarchy, and Chapter Master of the Ultramarines. He flew to Mortwald through blood-red skies in the Thunderhawk Gunship *Eagle's Fury* to land with as much pomp and circumstance as he could muster. Lord Deinos, at that point taking refuge from the horrors that the Flawless Host had visited upon him and his fellows, was coaxed

from his Proteus-class bunker by an appeal to his pride; after all, to have the Chapter Master of the Ultramarines request an audience would bolster his status immeasurably. Calgar presented the Primarch's Writ to Deinos Agamemnus, and formally requested he turn over all six of the Deathstrikes for use in the war effort.

Lord Deinos refused point blank. The gigantic missiles were not for firing, he said, but for display, and he had gone to great pains to keep them in mint condition. He would invoke every legal barrier and bureaucratic mechanism he could find to ensure the requisition fell flat.

At this, Calgar's temper snapped. He grabbed Lord Deinos by the arm and lifted him high. Ignoring the sound of breaking bones and noxious smell of fear that emanated from the fool's gold-braided pantaloons, he asked again through gritted teeth. This time, Lord Deinos acquiesced, opening the gene-locked vaults and handing over the contents to Marneus Calgar. Within a matter of hours the vault was empty, and the Deathstrike missiles were sequestered in the holds of rugged transport craft.

immediately expunged, never to be entered into any official account of the War of Nightmares. Even now the Ultramarines cannot speak of what was said between the two leaders as they talked beneath the massive triumphal arch to the west of the Statue of the Great Templar. Only the Victrix Guard heard the details of the bargain that Calgar struck there, and they were sworn to secrecy. Yet three things about that fateful parley are known. The first is that the Farseer Keltoc and his senior chieftains accompanied Calgar back to the Governor's palace that day. The second is that, from that moment on, the doors of the Vigilus Senate were barred and guarded by two members of the Victrix Guard, who had orders to let none pass. The third is that those members of the Aquilarian Council who had presided on the day of Autarch Rhyloor's death were never seen by anyone again, Lucienne Agamemnus and Proctor Commander Venedar amongst them.

Considering the matter of honour settled, the vengeful Aeldari of Clan Moirec joined the Imperium in hurling back the Chaos invasion. Not only that, but they lent to the war effort a very special vessel – *Vaul's Ghost*, a near-invisible stealth ship that had plagued the Imperial shipping lanes around Saim-Hann for decades. It was Calgar's intention to use the Aeldari stealth vessel to intercept the *Vengeful Spirit* in orbit high above Storvhal, and by using himself as bait, ensure the Warmaster of Chaos had his eyes fixed elsewhere. Calgar's plan was to strike at that which Abaddon held dearest. The Warmaster of Chaos had already demonstrated a callous disregard for his Heretic Astartes brethren and utter contempt for the chattel that fought alongside them; that much could be seen in Dontoria, Megaborealis and Storvhal. But there was one war asset he held dear, aside from those he carried on his person – and this was Calgar's target.

Should the Lord Macragge's plan unfold as intended, the ends would justify the means. Should it fail, the planet itself would be forfeit – as would be the Nachmund Gauntlet, and almost certainly Calgar's life.

When the other Chapter Masters heard of what the Ultramarines intended, they took the news with disbelief at first, but then with a grudging acquiescence. It was known to both the Crimson Fists and Necropolis Hawks that the Aeldari had no love for the Great Enemy, for they had seen the two foes clash before. It would be a fine day for the Imperium if two of their oldest foes could neutralise each other in one fell blow.

'You talk of disaster, and I know well why you might. A hundred battles, a billion corpses, with more joining the carrion pile with each passing second. There is panic, cowardice, and nightmarish desperation in every hab-block – and fuel is being poured on the fire wherever you look. Yet this planet is still defended by the Imperium's finest. We hold the keys to its survival. I assure you, we will be equal to the task, no matter what sacrifice it takes.'

– Marneus Calgar, Chapter Master of the Ultramarines

37

DISTRACTION TACTICS

As the Chapter Masters of the Vigilus Senate made preparations for their counter-attack, a strike with which they intended to cripple Abaddon's defences, the Aeldari were fighting a war of their own. Scores of lightning-swift warriors rushed to enact Farseer Keltoc's scheme of subterfuge and misdirection.

The Wild Rider armies of Saim-Hann, the curving silhouettes of their craft graceful and glorious even under the darksome skies, raced across the wastelands of Vigilus at extreme velocity. Beyond the spires and towers of Hyperia, they made the perfect bait for the Ork Speedwaaagh!. Being bright red and travelling at breakneck pace, they caught the eye of every Speed Freek in the vicinity, and soon had the Ork racers on their tail, the greenskins' crude but effective guns spitting bullets in great streams.

Dozens of Wild Rider clans took part in Farseer Keltoc's great initiative, a process he likened to the Aeldari myth known as the Goading

of the Yggh-Bulls. The Saim-Hann Asuryani purposefully slowed down whenever they outdistanced the Ork vehicle columns; after all, an Aeldari jetbike is far swifter than even the most souped-up Ork hot rod with its afterburners blazing. Only the Shokkjump Dragstas of Mekstop City – built in a frenzy of copycat creativity after the warp-kut incident at the Hyperia-Dirkden Fortwall – were able to get the better of the Saim-Hann riders. At Glaive Point, the Ork speedster known as Da Red Bullit teleported ahead of the foremost Aeldari vehicles – a unit of Warlocks with bright trailing pennants known as the Seven Snakes – and punched them from the sky in a storm

of corkscrewing rockets and plasma rounds.

But for the most part, the Wild Riders led the Orks a merry dance across the wastelands of Vigilus. When the greenskins were all but frantic with the desire to wreak havoc, the Aeldari led them straight into the teeth of the Chaos Space Marines who were establishing strongpoints across the planet. Just as the bullets began to fly and a dangerous crossfire threatened, the daring Saim-Hann riders turned their craft to a vertical heading, speeding up into the safety of the clouds – or into the electrical storms summoned by Farseer Keltoc for precisely that

THE SERPENT'S LURE [MORTWALD]

- - → **SAIM-HANN WILD RIDERS ROUTE OF ATTACK**

→ **SAIM-HANN VERTICAL ESCAPE VECTOR**

IRON WARRIORS SIEGE FORCES

➤ **SPEEDWAAAGH! ATTACK VECTOR**

✶ **MAJOR CLASH**

The Aeldari, riding swift-moving jetbikes and anti-grav skimmers, antagonised the Ork Speed Freeks to the point they were engaged in three separate running battles. Weaving north and west, they crossed one another's paths to ensure a series of collisions in the Ork ranks – and then drew the rest on a pell-mell course towards Iron Warriors siege forces before making a vertical escape and leaving one foe to fight the other.

purpose. In their wake, they left the greenskins and the Heretic Astartes fighting a sudden battle that none had anticipated, but from which neither side would back down. The crowning glory of Keltoc's tactics unfolded when his Wave Serpents, their shields crackling at maximum yield to blunt the thunderous Ork firepower raining down around them, led seven full Blitz Brigades in a headlong charge towards the super-heavy assets and Traitor Titans of the Legio Decapitorum.

With the battle-maddened Orks to the rear and the stoic Imperial defenders to the fore, the Chaos forces found themselves broken in a score of war zones. It was a development that could not be ignored, and it drew the focus of a hundred warlords eager to earn Abaddon's favour. Only Keltoc, Calgar and the Imperial Navy attaché to the Ultramarines Command knew that the battle for New Vitae Docks was the only critical clash at that time. The

Mortwald aerial base was sending every Valkyrie and bulk lander that it could scramble into low orbit, despite being under heavy siege from the Iron Warriors. Though the vast majority of the craft had nothing of note in their cargo bays, six of them contained the Deathstrike missiles that Calgar had prised from the wretched grip of Grand Castellan Deinos – and amongst them, the two Vortex warheads with which the Chapter Master intended to deal Abaddon a deadly blow.

In the orbital battle between the outmatched Imperial fleet and the far larger Chaos armada, a grander tale was unfolding. The tattered remnants of the Imperial Navy made a concerted attack on the Chaos fleet, darting in wherever

there was a blind spot like a pack of killer cetaceans harassing a pod of vast armoured leviathans. They paid a heavy price, losing a good eighty per cent of their number to the relentless, overlapping broadsides of Abaddon's fleet, and yet their foray did enough damage in return to seem credible as a last-ditch assault. Those pilots, crewmen and voidsmen-at-arms that gave their lives for Calgar's great initiative died unsung, but their contribution to the war effort was as great as any soldier or general fighting planetside to keep the wolves from the door.

Ultimately, however, there was only one ship that mattered. *Vaul's Ghost* rendezvoused with the vessels transporting the Deathstrike payload as they safely reached orbit, and transferred the Mortwald munitions into its own cargo hold. Then it made its heading the *Vengeful Spirit*, and with it went the hopes of the Vigilus Senate and their strange Aeldari allies.

DEMISE OF A LEGEND

A confrontation that had long seemed inevitable was drawing near. Marneus Calgar's plan was to challenge the Warmaster directly, knowing that Abaddon would not refuse the chance to deal such a symbolic blow to Imperial morale. It was a high-risk ploy, but Lord Calgar was convinced it was worth it.

The battle for Saint's Haven was the stuff of sagas and triumphal monuments. Its tale resonates throughout the history of the Imperium, for it was a clash not just of blades and armour, but of ideologies – and even, some have said, of the gods themselves.

Calgar had put into place a battle plan that had such a slim chance of success that even his closest warriors and advisors had balked at it. Yet there was little other choice. The planet was in turmoil. Even where the Imperial leaders had been able to turn the warmongering of the xenos invaders to their advantage, they had bought but a minor reprieve – or precipitated a situation where one foe was dealt with, only for another to rise to prominence. By the best estimates of the Neo-vellum vitae-scryer gestalts, the planet's population had been halved, and then halved again. But Calgar would not countenance the extreme solution of Exterminatus. He was challenged by Raquilon Zandtus, Chapter Master of the Necropolis Hawks, whose approach to diplomatic matters was to quote the long tracts of the Codex Astartes that reinforced his chosen points. Calgar countered that his own plans were already in motion, and that the Primarch himself had stated Vigilus would not fall. He would not see that maxim turned into a lie.

Marneus walked out from the Vigilus senatorium and climbed the high steps of the Governor's palace. His footsteps left crimson smears on the marble slabs, for even here there had been recent bloodshed. He reached the Eyrie of Reflection – the highest level of Saint's Haven that was not ablaze – and there marshalled the Victrix and Extremis Guards into a living fortress. The deep azure of their battle plate glowed orange in the flames of the spires above. His words conveyed by vox-skull servitors to the laud hailer networks of the Ecclesiarchy, he issued his decree. It was a challenge to Abaddon himself – face him in single combat. To the victor would go the planet itself.

The Warmaster heard news of Calgar's rash gambit soon enough, for Haarken Worldclaimer and his Raptor host still haunted the upper levels of Hyperia, and made haste to convey the message to their master. As Calgar's words were relayed, Abaddon smiled, his long canine teeth glinting red in the twilight. In one hand Abaddon wielded Drach'nyen, a Daemon sword of pure murderous intent that could eat the souls of those it struck, and on the other he wore the Talon of Horus, that same baleful device that had claimed the life of the Primarch Sanguinius so long ago. What chance did a mortal warrior, barely a few centuries old, have against such ancient evil?

The Citadel Vigilant was a structure replete with ancient technologies, for its construction dated back to the early Imperium. The Fallen knew well what power lay in such artefacts. Amongst them was a fully functioning teleportarium, coaxed into life by Osandus and his technomantic allies. It was this asset that Abaddon used to strike directly at Calgar, his elite Terminators and their Daemon-possessed thralls alongside him.

Chapter Master Calgar stood in the open atop the palace of Saint's Haven, no longer protected by the scryer-baffles and enigma circuits that had until now shielded him from swift assassination while he commanded the war effort from the Vigilus Senate. Abaddon appeared in a blaze of actinic light, already striding forward to meet the loyalist Space Marine in combat as the flash of lightning that heralded his arrival faded. His Bringers of Despair teleported with him, appearing in a crackling dome of force with their combi-bolters laying down a hail of explosive bolts.

The Ultramarines had been expecting such an assault, having seen a similar tactic on their flagship. They took a single step backwards, then charged as one,

shield bashing the nearest Chaos Terminators away from their master in order to press the attack. Their counter-assault was devastatingly effective. By the time they were driven back by Abaddon's Chosen, twelve millennia-old traitors lay dead and bleeding on the ivory stairs. But the Ultramarines had lost eight of their own number in the process. Worse, Abaddon had closed in on their Chapter Master.

The burning spires above the duellists lit the sky red-black, the clouds of smoke forming strange and unsettling shapes as Warmaster and Chapter Master duelled to the death. Calgar dodged and feinted, giving ground behind fallen statuary and dropping to rise once more. The Armour of Heraclus gave him greater movement and reaction speeds than any warsuit he had worn before. By hammering out bolt rounds from the Gauntlets of Ultramar, he kept his foe from bringing the deadly sword Drach'nyen to bear. The Reivers, Suppressors and Scouts watching through their gunsights knew that the Chapter Master was deliberately holding back, though none took a shot. With every second that the two combatants spent testing the other, watching and learning so as to find the perfect moment to strike, Calgar's plan grew closer to fruition. To force Abaddon to retreat now would risk ruining everything.

Incensed, Abaddon let loose with his combi-bolter, explosive ammunition thundering from the Talon of Horus to envelop Calgar in a storm of flame. One of the flagstones gave way under the Chapter Master's weight, and for a moment he was thrown off-balance. Suddenly Abaddon was there, body to body, his Talon of Horus ripping away one of Calgar's priceless gauntlets to expose a forearm splintered and shorn of skin. Balling his injured fist, the Lord Macragge punched his assailant in the face hard enough to crack his jaw. The follow-up blow, a thunderous uppercut from Calgar's remaining power fist, lifted Abaddon clean from his feet and cracked his breastplate.

The Warmaster's face contorted with anger. The air screamed around him, tendrils of daemonic effluvia licking like flames from his blade. In came Drach'nyen; Calgar made to block with his gauntlet, but the sword cut right through it, severing two of Calgar's fingers in the process. The blow rent apart the armour behind it, slashing open the Chapter Master's primary and secondary hearts in a single blow.

Just as Calgar fell to the ground, Haarken Worldclaimer called to Abaddon across a codified vox link. The *Vengeful Spirit* was critically wounded, and seconds away from destruction. It was effecting an emergency warp translation, and they had only moments before it vanished from the Vigilus System altogether.

> 'Warmaster. The *Spirit* has been stricken amidships. The weak fool at its helm has ordered flight into the warp, likely using the attack to claim our flagship for himself. We must return, or risk losing it forever!'
>
> - Haarken Worldclaimer

FALLEN SKIES

The short but bloody duel in the spires of Saint's Haven had reached its deadly conclusion, and Calgar lay defeated. But all was not as it seemed. A succession of vital sacrifices had been made in good faith by devoted servants of the Emperor, and their consequences were finally becoming clear.

The Daemon sword Drach'nyen screamed in denial as Abaddon turned away from his fallen victim. Motioning the Bringers of Despair to gather around him, he sent forward a horde of Daemon-possessed monstrosities to cover his departure. He had achieved that which he had come to do, he had lain low his ancient rival, and now another duty beckoned – for the *Vengeful Spirit* Abaddon prized above even the Blackstone Fortresses he had claimed over the course of his Black Crusades. If it translated at speed into the roiling tides of the warp without him, there was every chance it would be forever divorced from its rightful commander and inheritor.

Dark flames formed a hexagrammatic symbol around Abaddon and his bodyguard, then a blinding red light enveloped the masters of the Black Legion, and they disappeared. There was a sulphurous stink of dark magic, lingering in the air like ozone after a storm, and he was gone.

The Possessed fiends the Warmaster left behind moved towards Calgar, stalking like scavengers approaching the corpse of a great beast. Amid the detritus of the battle the Lord Macragge lay cold as stone upon the flags, his skin white as alabaster. The Chapter Master's hearts were pierced through, and dark blood drizzled from the great

fissure split in his armour. Worse still, the Possessed were able to punch a hole in the defences of the Victrix Guard, one fell creature tearing its way through to stand above him, claws raised.

Any normal Space Marine would have died then and there. Yet within the Lord Macragge's mighty breast, his Belisarian Furnace triggered. That miraculous organ pumped restorative stimulants into his system, giving him one last burst of energy before death claimed him completely. It was the inner strength of the Adeptus Astartes and the arcanoscience of Belisarius Cawl matched against the hellish powers of the Chaos Gods.

Calgar got to one knee as the Greater Possessed loomed over him, then stood up fast. His remaining Gauntlet of Ultramar, although damaged, was still functioning. He batted the creature away with a backhand blow, then levelled a punishing salvo of explosive bullets that ripped it apart, the device still cycling as it clicked empty. Then the mighty warrior fell back once more, blood running from his wounds.

The Victrix Guard and the remnants of the Extremis Guard rushed around him to form a shield, their bolters thudding death into the last of the Possessed. Down from the skies came the Stormraven Gunship *Hope's Blade*, its frontal hatches yawning to allow a pair of veteran Apothecaries to jump down to the flags. They sprinted over to Calgar and brought their narthchiums to bear upon him, filling his ravaged system with stabilising elixirs and life-giving suspensions of blessed vitae. Calgar, his face contorted in a rictus of agony, stood tall. He saluted his men, told them to take the fight to the traitors in the streets, and then finally allowed himself to be escorted into the emergency med-suite that awaited him within the Stormraven.

Calgar survived that fell day, his secondary heart salvaged by the secret arts of the apothecarium even though his primary heart was cloven through. He was not seen on the front line of the battlefield from that point on, but continued to command the armies of the Imperium from the heart of the Vigilus Senate. Though he was diminished in stature by the grievous wounds he had suffered, his mind was as strong and sharp as ever. The Lord Macragge had denied Abaddon his prize, not through sheer force of arms, but through courage and honour. Yet Vigilus was still fighting a losing battle – not for victory, but for survival.

THE SLOW BLEED

With the Black Legion's elite teleporting back to their flagship and the colossal Gloriana-class vessel making transition into the warp, the shape of the war for Vigilus changed radically. The Imperial Navy, emboldened by the disappearance of the enemy's most powerful asset, drove through the gaping hole in the Chaos cordon to level broadsides at a fleet still reeling from the empyric bow wave of the *Spirit's* emergency translation. Word spread to the Chaos armies planetside that Abaddon had begun a withdrawal, and soon the Chaos troops began to look to their own self-preservation. After all, the planet was all but destroyed – and there was plenty more of the Imperium left to bring down in flames.

HEROES OF THE VOID

The attack on the *Vengeful Spirit* had been exceptionally costly for the Imperial Navy. So many assets had hastened to the Vigilus war zone that the nearby worlds of Neo-vellum, Omis-Prion, Geotrope XII and Falsehood had been entirely denuded of warship support. In the case of Omis-Prion, lately assailed by the ancient xenos threat of the Necrons, the planet had been brought to the brink of catastrophe. Yet High Command judged the sacrifice worthwhile.

Assets diverted to Vigilus reinforced the battered Navy there. Though a few score ships shored up the holes in Calgar's tattered cordon around the planet's equator – now stretched painfully thin – the majority renewed the assault upon the *Vengeful Spirit* over the course of a three-day void battle. Not one of them was able to deal the ship a telling blow, for it seemed every torpedo was intercepted, every lance blast turned aside by some mystical force field. In return, the vast fortress had brought its guns to bear in a series of devastating broadsides that had blasted scores of craft into nothing more than clouds of spiralling scrap metal.

Included amongst the *Vengeful Spirit's* defences was a coven of Sorcerers that scried the echoes of the warp for threats, and warned the vast battleship's command crew in time to intercept them. Even they were not powerful enough to foresee the nature of the threat posed by *Vaul's Ghost*, however, for the Aeldari craft was equipped with complex psychic baffles as well as hologrammatic stealth technology. By the time the Sorcerers were able to determine the source of the attack, it was too late.

Vaul's Ghost crashed into the side of the *Vengeful Spirit* at great speed, all six of the Deathstrike missiles in its hold detonating in a chain explosion. The blast ripped a gaping hole in the battleship's flank, and the Vortex warheads combined to create a whirling maelstrom that began eating away at the vessel. Too large to come about, the ship was slowly being ripped apart by the hole in realspace that Calgar's grand strategy had engendered. Klaxons blared as the ship prepared for an emergency translation into the warp. Eliminating the threat of the *Vengeful Spirit* was a vital blow that changed the course of the war entire.

PLANET IN FLAMES

Though the Warmaster himself had withdrawn from the battle, his legions rampaged across the planet still, sowing anarchy wherever they went. The fate of Vigilus remained dire.

With the departure of Abaddon and the elite elements of the Black Legion, a sense of relief could be felt all across Hyperia Hivesprawl, as if a choking gauntlet had been removed from the throat of the Imperial war effort. Without their overlord to unite them, the Heretic Astartes war parties fought in an uncoordinated fashion, and this was quickly exploited by the Space Marines. In places, the disparate armies of traitors and renegades fell to utter disorder, battling each other for the spoils of war and fighting to scavenge intact power armour from fallen heretic and loyalist alike.

The battle for Megaborealis continued to rage. The Adeptus Mechanicus had plenty of reserves in store, which they had accumulated when a civil war between the dynasties of Stygies VIII and the Agamemnus clan had seemed inevitable. They had enough water, promethium and raw manpower to fight on against Genestealer Cultist and Chaos invader alike. Whenever the Skitarii Legions wavered, their Tech-Priest masters would instil in them an iron resolve using remote data-tethers, and they would fight on. The priests of Stygies VIII had spent centuries unearthing the xenos-crafted wonders of the planet, and they had no intention of abandoning their treasures.

However, when the World Eaters joined the fray, the Skitarii were outmatched, and even the Kataphron Breachers and Kastelan Robots found that their firepower could not drive the foe back. Only when Fabricator Vosch made a formal alliance with the Iron Hands, yielding great swathes of information about Megaborealis

and the forces defending it, did the Imperium turn what had been a slaughter into a decisive counter-attack. The Skitarii's superior numbers and the Iron Hands' calculated strategies allowed the joint Imperial force to divide and compartmentalise the enemy, foiling them one after another with sacrificial feints, delaying tactics and overlapping withdrawals – then hammering them from afar with artillery strikes until there was not a single heretic left standing.

On the western reaches of Megaborealis, Silo XV had been ravaged, much of its blackstone reserves blasted to flinders by the bombardments of the Black Legion. But the Adeptus Mechanicus had secreted several minor caches of blackstone all over the planet that the Chaos Space Marines never found, and there was still a great deal of the strange mineral known as noctilith buried in Vigilus' crust. The planet's astonishing ability to hold open a channel of reality between the blackstone spears in its crust and those of Sangua Terra, its twin world on the other side of the Cicatrix Maledictum, had been diminished, but not destroyed.

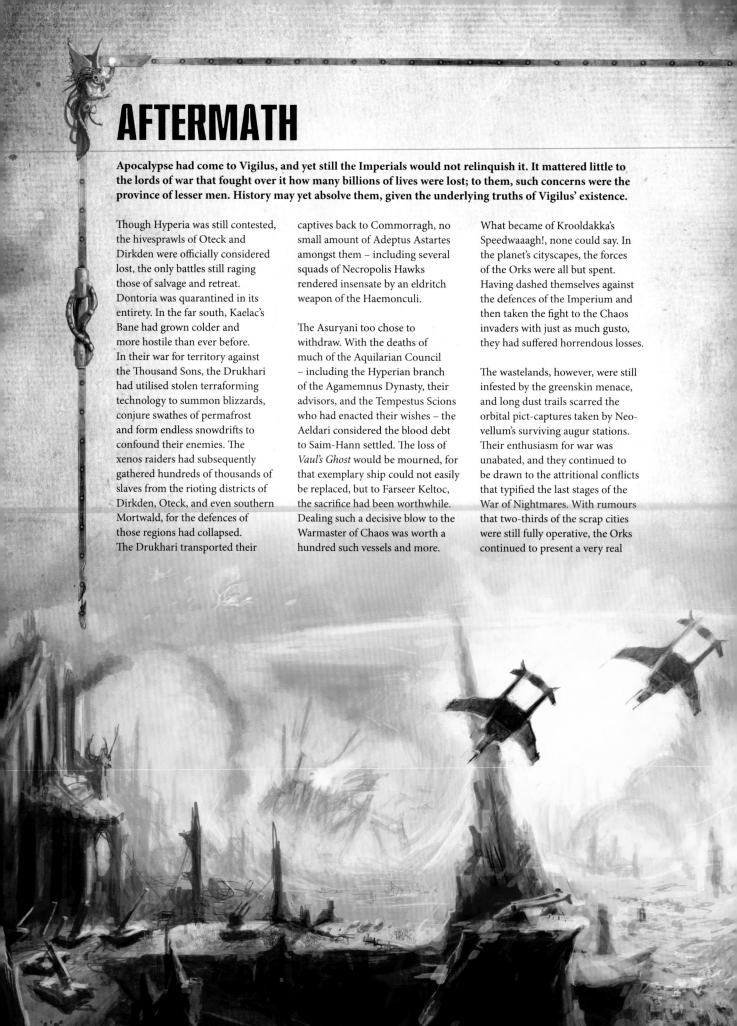

AFTERMATH

Apocalypse had come to Vigilus, and yet still the Imperials would not relinquish it. It mattered little to the lords of war that fought over it how many billions of lives were lost; to them, such concerns were the province of lesser men. History may yet absolve them, given the underlying truths of Vigilus' existence.

Though Hyperia was still contested, the hivesprawls of Oteck and Dirkden were officially considered lost, the only battles still raging those of salvage and retreat. Dontoria was quarantined in its entirety. In the far south, Kaelac's Bane had grown colder and more hostile than ever before. In their war for territory against the Thousand Sons, the Drukhari had utilised stolen terraforming technology to summon blizzards, conjure swathes of permafrost and form endless snowdrifts to confound their enemies. The xenos raiders had subsequently gathered hundreds of thousands of slaves from the rioting districts of Dirkden, Oteck, and even southern Mortwald, for the defences of those regions had collapsed. The Drukhari transported their

captives back to Commorragh, no small amount of Adeptus Astartes amongst them – including several squads of Necropolis Hawks rendered insensate by an eldritch weapon of the Haemonculi.

The Asuryani too chose to withdraw. With the deaths of much of the Aquilarian Council – including the Hyperian branch of the Agamemnus Dynasty, their advisors, and the Tempestus Scions who had enacted their wishes – the Aeldari considered the blood debt to Saim-Hann settled. The loss of *Vaul's Ghost* would be mourned, for that exemplary ship could not easily be replaced, but to Farseer Keltoc, the sacrifice had been worthwhile. Dealing such a decisive blow to the Warmaster of Chaos was worth a hundred such vessels and more.

What became of Krooldakka's Speedwaaagh!, none could say. In the planet's cityscapes, the forces of the Orks were all but spent. Having dashed themselves against the defences of the Imperium and then taken the fight to the Chaos invaders with just as much gusto, they had suffered horrendous losses.

The wastelands, however, were still infested by the greenskin menace, and long dust trails scarred the orbital pict-captures taken by Neo-vellum's surviving augur stations. Their enthusiasm for war was unabated, and they continued to be drawn to the attritional conflicts that typified the last stages of the War of Nightmares. With rumours that two-thirds of the scrap cities were still fully operative, the Orks continued to present a very real threat to those that would venture across the wastes.

Worse still, word had spread to Ork hordes across the galaxy that Vigilus was the site of a really good war. From systems all across the Nachmund Sub-sector, Ork fleets set their course for that embattled world, hoping to join the fun before it was too late.

The Pauper Princes fought tooth and nail for their hard-won holdings. First- and second-generation hybrids fought alongside Purestrain Genestealers and even Grandsire Wurm himself to hurl back the Chaos invaders, winning bloody victories in some theatres of war even as their followers were pitilessly put down in others. They still infested Dirkden from top to bottom, but ultimately their uprising had been premature, and over the course of the War of Nightmares their long-planned conquest was left in tatters. The xenos cultists looked to the skies every hour, hoping for a sign of their Tyranid deliverers, come from the void to claim the planet for their rightful bounty. But they saw only Chaos, their eyes drawn inexorably from the darkness of empty space to the oppressive horror of the Great Rift.

The Imperium's foes had slaughtered one another to the point that it seemed the united Imperial forces would be able to endure the storm that had battered the planet for so long. Its propaganda machine ground slowly back into action, claiming each new victory – whether a minor skirmish or the collapse of an entire front – as a critical turning point in the planet's fortunes.

The Preachers and Commissars of the Imperial war effort talked of hope amid the terror, as one Chaos force after another withdrew. They spoke of a victory all but won, and of how it was always darkest before the dawn. Even though the choking soot in the air and the raging wildfires on every horizon told a different story, the long journey towards recovery had begun.

Though the Imperial presence upon Vigilus had been reduced to little more than a shattered collection of traumatised survivors, the planet itself endured. The Nachmund Gauntlet, though it had been narrowed by the destruction of much of the planet's blackstone, was still intact, and a corridor of realspace still existed between the Imperium Sanctus and the Imperium Nihilus.

When the remnants of Neo-vellum's Lunar Choir re-established a psychic connection across the rift, there was great rejoicing. The planet had not been cut off from the light of Holy Terra, and the grace of the Emperor was still upon it. Only when the lords of Neo-vellum received clear visions from the other side of the Great Rift did they feel a shadow of trepidation settle upon their hearts. The messages spoke of a monstrous evil, first seen during a battle for the stars themselves. It could destroy a world purely with the power of its blazing lance. That lance was covered in blood from a holy crucible.

The meaning of the vision was scrutinised by a dozen senior Astropaths. The 'battle for the stars themselves' was the Gothic War, a Black Crusade so violent that suns died in its wake. The 'blood from a holy crucible' spoke of Sangua Terra, whose name translated from High Gothic to 'the Blood of Earth', the crucible in which the human race itself was born. And the lance, ready to destroy a world – that lance was no less a weapon than that wielded by Abaddon's former flagship. That fell craft's name was spoken in hushed tones, its import clutching at the heart with a cold claw of dread.

The *Planet Killer*.

WAR ZONES

The landscape of Vigilus changed drastically following its initial invasion, riven by widespread quakes and scorched by wildfires. The machinations of Abaddon were to break the planet completely.

Vigilus was once the domain of several Imperial institutions, all held in a precarious balance by the Pact of Fire and Steel. The Adeptus Mechanicus had sovereign rule over Megaborealis, while the Ecclesiarchy had the majority of its presence in Hyperia Hivesprawl. Dontoria, Oteck and Dirkden were ruled over by the seconds of the Agamemnus Dynasty, each keen to feather his or her own nest at the expense of their peers. Mortwald, the planet's breadbasket and home of the famed rejuvenat clinics that brought the planet so much wealth, was ruled over by Deinos Agamemnus, brother of the Planetary Governor, Lucienne.

The planet's false continents, already more interested in looking to their own fortunes than presenting a united front, became even more isolated over the course of the War of Beasts. Some fought losing battles, others doggedly hung on to their independence by defending their most critical locales, but all were assailed by the xenos threat to some extent. The planet hung in limbo – even when the Imperial defenders were reinforced by the Adeptus Astartes and the alien usurpers hurled back on a score of fronts, there was nowhere on the planet that could be called free of xenos presence. The land masses burned, and the skies, already thick with pollutants, turned black with the choking chemicals of industrial zones aflame.

Into this hellish twilight of war came Abaddon's invasion. Once more the false continents burned, and this time, the lines between attacker and defender blurred more than ever before. Many gave up

hope entirely as word of the Chaos incursion spread throughout the populace, joining redemptionist cults and even offering themselves to the Chaos forces in the hope of buying their own survival. Many were accepted, or at least allowed to live, by the traitors and renegades that stormed through their homesteads – only to be expended as cannon fodder when the Imperial troops launched their counter-attacks.

When Abaddon seized the Voidclaw in the citadel at the heart of the Vhulian Swirl – and used it to open a pinpoint singularity between Vigilus and Neo-vellum – he altered the landscape of the planet beyond recognition. Cascades of rubble, wrecked vehicles, and anything that was not secured to a solid installation rolled through the streets towards the wastelands above which the gravitational anomaly had opened. More importantly, the waters of Vigilus trickled towards the site, harnessed by this new force to ensure the populace had virtually no drinking water. An epidemic of thirst spread across the planet, adding further fuel to the panic caused by the tectonic disruption beneath the already tortured surface of the planet. The Chaos Space Marines revelled amongst the carnage – deliberately spilling slicks of promethium that, when ignited, crept across the wastelands as lakes of fire – while their ships high above toppled burning hive-spires into the cities below with sustained heavy barrages.

The planet was consumed by terror and anarchy, and there was little chance of its salvation.

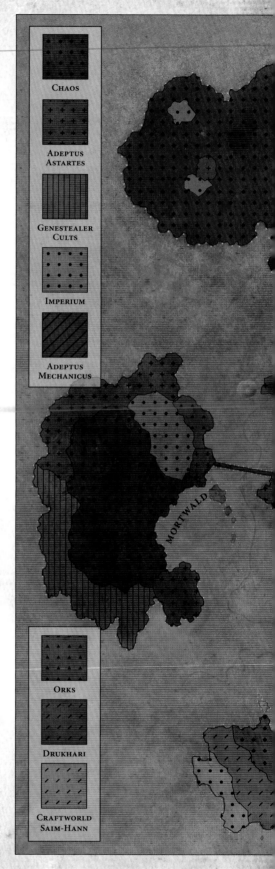

CHAOS

ADEPTUS ASTARTES

GENESTEALER CULTS

IMPERIUM

ADEPTUS MECHANICUS

MORTWALD

ORKS

DRUKHARI

CRAFTWORLD SAIM-HANN

DONTORIA HIVESPRAWL

The Chaos invasion saw massive swathes of Vigilus' false continents fall, for the Imperial defences had already been severely weakened by the xenos threat. The War of Nightmares was typified by desperate rearguard actions and tense city-fighting that saw the death toll spiral high.

MEGABOREALIS

STORVHAL

VHULIAN SWIRL

HYPERIA HIVESPRAWL

ECK HIVESPRAWL

DIRKDEN HIVESPRAWL

KAELAC'S BANE

18.643 POST VCM

WAR OF NIGHTMARES: PHASE 1

DONTORIA HIVESPRAWL

Once the most populous of all Vigilus' hivesprawls, Dontoria was ravaged by disease and torn by constant battle. From the opening phases of the War of Beasts, its people, too poverty-stricken or oppressed to flee, died by the million.

Dontoria Hivesprawl once teemed with human life. Not only had this false continent expanded so much over the last few centuries it almost encroached on Mortwald and Megaborealis, it had also spread into the wastelands beyond. Before the War of Beasts, Dontoria had been considered one of the three most vital components of Vigilus' infrastructure, its endless amount of manpower a vital boon in the planet's defence. Over the course of the War of Nightmares, that same population density became a bane. The plagues unleashed upon that metropolis – amongst them the much-reviled Gellerpox – spread from one district to another, and with horrible swiftness due to the citizenry being so densely packed. The Ultramarines knew well the

dangers that the scions of Nurgle posed to a planet's populace, having faced them before. Together with the Necropolis Hawks, the Iron Hands and the Crimson Fists, they quarantined the heart of Dontoria. Yet despite the efforts of the Imperium to maintain the cordon, in the space of a few weeks dozens of active war fronts fell to deadly sickness.

Dontoria's major source of water, Lake Dontor, was claimed by the Genestealer Cult during the War of Beasts. Over the course of the War of Nightmares it was polluted by the agents of Nurgle to such an extent that even the most hardened xenocultist metabolism could not process it. Bereft of drinkable water, and afraid of contracting a

lethal plague, the citizens that made their livelihoods on the fringes of Dontoria fled into the wastes, taking their chances with the Ork menace instead. In an effort to protect the quarantine, Space Marine kill teams eliminated many such interlopers, lest they carry sickness to the other hivesprawls.

Eventually, however, the Space Marines were redeployed to other war zones, for they were deemed too valuable to waste on garrison duties. Dontoria was left in the hands of their Astra Militarum allies. This proved a costly mistake, for ultimately the continent fell entirely to plague – a foe that the firepower of the Imperial Guard could not defeat. Dontoria was thus abandoned by the Imperium.

DONTORIA

[Firewall Extent]

Vostoyev Subsprawl

New Horizon

Infection Genesis Zone

Litmus Dock

Pravdus Subsprawl

Beta-Industrium's Citadel

Munitorum Shanties

[Firewall Extent]

Grodholev Subsprawl

Gellerpox Zone [Quarantined]

The Great Choke

Hab-Zones Overrun

Lake Dontor [Polluted]

Tzimitria Subsprawl [Ork Presence]

Missionary Point

Mesha's Delta

Hallordwight Subsprawl

Guardia Periphery

Smog Field

Stump Subsprawl

Gork's Landing [Contained]

Noctilith Crown Site

Warp Breach Incident

VIGILUS

DIRKDEN HIVESPRAWL

Dirkden was called the cursed continent. After a disastrous political standoff with Hyperia in 145 previo, its fortunes took a sharp downturn. During the War of Nightmares, it held out against the Night Lords and the Scourged, but only because the area was so thoroughly infested by Genestealer Cultists.

Dirkden was known as a place of ill omen even before it fell to the insurrection of the Pauper Princes. It was as symbolic of the Imperium's flaws as Hyperia was an inspiring incarnation of its might. There no statues were raised to the Imperium's glory, only the half-completed and skeletal tangle of metal that was Ashenid Non-Hive. Despite being abandoned partway through its construction, that monument to failure became home to millions of impoverished citizens nonetheless. They built scaffolds, gangways and cabling of their own to fill the megastructure, the edifice becoming more like a moundspider's conical web than the solidly built hive cities of nearby Hyperia. It was a haunted place even before the coming of Chaos.

The Dirkden gangs that made Ashenid Non-Hive their home came from a criminal dynasty that stretched back a dozen generations, encompassing everything from protection rackets to kidnapping, gunrunning, dealing in banned substances and even wholesale murder in the case of the wide-scale arson attack known as the Long Inferno. The criminal families that ruled the Ashenid region were engaged in nefarious activities the Adeptus Arbites had long ceased attempting to curtail. To aid their smuggling missions, they established an extensive network of tunnels that linked the hive's mining sites, all the way from the Rescalid Underworks in the south-west to Glaive Point in the north. It was often said upon Vigilus that there

was as much of Dirkden Hivesprawl under the ground as there was above it.

Decades before the war, the city's council failed to capitalise on Dirkden's connection to Hyperia via the fortwall after a disastrous trade deal. Sabotaged by leaders of the criminal dynasties, the council slid into disgrace, and was ultimately deposed. After that, Dirkden was largely written off by the Imperium's armed forces as a wasteland that was more trouble than it was worth. It became a haven for the subterranean operatives of the Genestealer Cult ever after.

Early in the War of Nightmares, this rotten vista was invaded by the renegades known as the Scourged.

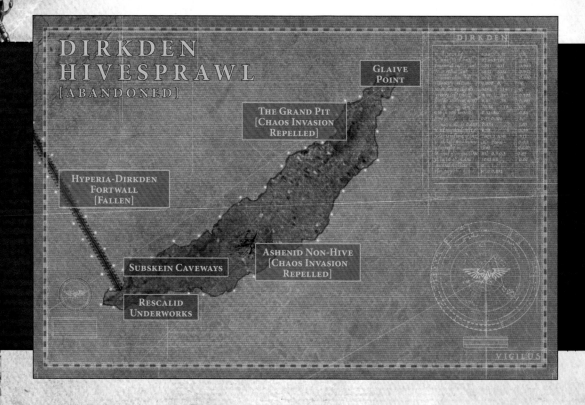

DIRKDEN HIVESPRAWL
[ABANDONED]

GLAIVE POINT

THE GRAND PIT
[CHAOS INVASION REPELLED]

HYPERIA-DIRKDEN FORTWALL
[FALLEN]

SUBSKEIN CAVEWAYS

ASHENID NON-HIVE
[CHAOS INVASION REPELLED]

RESCALID UNDERWORKS

VIGILUS

Their sudden attack even threatened the sanctum of Grandsire Wurm, who at the time was deep in the Subskein Caveways, feasting in a ritual intended to empower him further. The assault was pitiless and sudden, the renegades slaughtering a great many hybrids of the first and second generations as well as whole broods of Purestrain Genestealers. If it had not been for the Pauper Princes' eagerness to martyr themselves, hurling their bodies in front of their beloved leaders whenever a gun was aimed towards them, the ruling elite of the Dirkden gene-sect might have been crippled at a stroke.

As it was, the cultists counter-attacked with seething fury, their numbers such that the Scourged found themselves pushed back. The visionary renegades had prescience enough to sense each ambush before it came, however – using their supernatural ability to perceive lies, they could see through every façade and misdirection, and it was this that kept them alive.

Their uncanny ability also allowed them to see the great lie at the heart of the Genestealer Cult. The Chapter Master of the Scourged, Gallus Herodicus, sent a psychic message to his lieutenants, enabling them to uncover that deadly deception and, in doing so, turn it into a weapon.

High above the Patriarch's genesis pool, where a great many cultists were gathered, an image flickered – a mirage conjured by the foremost Sorcerers in Herodicus' warband. It showed what would be the final fate of the Pauper Princes. The sky was filled with grotesque bio-ships, and the ground teemed with the blade-limbed xenos beasts known as Tyranids, who set about massacring human and Ork alike with terrifying efficiency. The Pauper Princes cried out in glee, faces beaming in rapture at the vision. Then, in the mirage, the Tyranids turned on their loyal worshippers, exhibiting the same savagery with which they had cut down the Imperial citizenry before them.

The Pauper Princes in the chamber watched as their future selves were disembodied, then messily devoured. The Scourged believed that, when faced with the truth of their existence, the cult would self-destruct, and utter bedlam would break out. But the devotion of the Pauper Princes was bone deep, and not easily shaken. The cry went up – 'Lies!' – until the roof of the cavern shook and dust trickled down from above. Confronted by a horrible reality, the hybrids of Dirkden burrowed further into their delusion, their strange faith strengthened all the more by this challenge to it.

The Scourged were attacked with renewed ferocity, and a full half of their number slain by claw, bullet and talon. They did at least cause such disarray that Savasdus and his Night Lords were able to evade the throng attacking them and make a bid for freedom. Despite appearing dilapidated, the false continent was effectively a fortress, and far harder to break than any had imagined.

REPORT 129NN6GAMMA1
ASHENID NON-HIVE

Construction abandoned 820 previo. Evidence of clandestine structures and unauthorised levels, pipeways, sluices found on levels 0A,1 to 131A,1. Adeptus Arbites class nonquam sub-terra. Caution advised in persecution of sites known for population density.

MEGABOREALIS

Megaborealis was the sovereign domain of the Adeptus Mechanicus, whose industry beneath the planet's crust had revealed a vital secret. Assailed during the War of Beasts by the Genestealer Cultists seeded there, the hivesprawl also become a primary focus of Abaddon's invasion during the War of Nightmares.

From the ravaged lands of Megaborealis, the Tech-Priests of Stygies VIII had delved deep beneath the surface of Vigilus. What they sought had been long hidden – of the Priesthood of Mars, perhaps only Belisarius Cawl knew its true nature. Yet it was vital to the future of the planet, and the continued existence of the Nachmund Gauntlet itself. Every towering bore-hive, every abyssal mine or delver-crevice, was listed in the Neo-vellum datastacks as producing a variety of conventional minerals, but in truth they were all turned to the extraction of the same substance. For beneath Vigilus' crust were deposits of the arcane mineral noctilith, also known as blackstone by the Skitarii that safeguarded it.

The planet's crust was pitted with dozens of sphere-like hollows that were filled with suspensions of black liquid. These spheres appeared like bubbles in the planet's strata, and if there was a pattern to their dispersal, none could discern it. Within these, strange blackstone deposits floated, each shaped like a javelin or needle, always pointing in the same direction no matter the planet's position around Astravigila. The Tech-Priests observed that these needles always faced down the throat of the Nachmund Gauntlet, but it was Fabricator Vosch who concluded that the blackstone in fact created the gauntlet by projecting a long range contra-empyric field. The richest nodes could be found under Bore-hives Ultris and Scelerus, and

Mineworks West 23. When the rest of the hivesprawl was burning in the fires of war, assailed by Ork invaders, Genestealer Cultists and the daemonic machineries of the Brazen Beasts, the Tech-Priests ignored Calgar's order to withdraw from these vital zones. Even the Stygian Spires, site of the space elevator that provided Megaborealis precious water, were considered of secondary importance by comparison. To the Adeptus Mechanicus, discovering the secret of the blackstone was more important than life itself. Were it not for their layered defences and single-minded devotion to their cause, Abaddon would likely have torn their bounty from the planet within the first few days of his invasion.

THE OMNISSIAN HOIST

The Greater Omnissian Hoist was linked to the Stygian Spires, largest of all Megaborealis' bore-hives. Its lowest reaches were the sites of fierce fighting between the Adeptus Mechanicus and the Pauper Princes – and even when that had been concluded, a new war front opened in the space station high above.

The taking of the Greater Omnissian Hoist in 9.972 post by the Pauper Princes had been a strategic master stroke. Even as the main body of their cult was taking punishment from the Iron Hands sent to relieve the Stygian Spires, the Purestrain Genestealers had conquered the Hoist's control centre. Before that level was subsequently liberated by an Onager Dunecrawler counter-assault, some of the xenos creatures had ridden the vast pulleys out of the construction and into space, towards the mining station of Sacrus Tora Hawking.

The first phase of the War of Nightmares saw a brief space battle between the up-gunned ships of the Magma Hounds Renegade Chapter and the cannon servitors of Sacrus Tora Hawking. Though the space station had an arsenal of lance batteries and torpedoes, it took a heavy bombardment from the Magma Hounds and their allies. As a static target, it was easy prey for the swift-moving craft in the Heretic Astartes armada, and while its defenders fought bravely, they were ultimately overcome by the volume of firepower sent their way.

The Magma Hounds could almost certainly have completed their mission to destroy Sacrus Tora Hawking with an orbital bombardment, but instead they launched boarding torpedoes, sent on a vertical assault vector into the uppermost surfaces of the space station. Each cylinder cut through the station's outer hull with its melta array, slamming its clamps through the resultant hole and disgorging a dozen power-armoured killers into the corridors beyond. They sought one thing – the blood of the foe.

The servitors and mining personnel aboard the station fought hard against the renegades, but were soon outmatched. Only when the blood-hungry Magma Hounds reached the upper terminus of the space elevator did they find heavy resistance – not from the Skitarii or worker clades that ensured the ice-locked asteroids reached the planet below, but from the Genestealers that had infected them.

In the close confines of the space station, the renegades suddenly found it was they who were fighting a losing battle. Around every corner and behind every automat door panel lurked another xenos monstrosity hungry for the kill. Realising they had strayed into a fight they could not win, the Chaos Space Marines detonated a clutch of melta charges and breached the

space station's hull, the equalising pressure blowing them and their alien nemeses out into the darkness of space.

Though many of them were later recovered, the Magma Hounds never reached the surface of Vigilus during the War of Nightmares. Neither did the last asteroids that Sacrus Tora Hawking had captured for processing upon Megaborealis far below. When the Vhulian Anomaly's gravitational pull buckled and twisted the Hoist's skeletal superstructure – ultimately wrecking its carbon fibre winch apparatus – another of the planet's principal sources of water was cut off completely. For everyone but the water magnates selling aqua to the highest bidders in the hivesprawls below, it was a dire turn of events indeed.

MORTWALD

Following the invasion of the Speedwaaagh!, Mortwald was hammered by relentless waves of attacks by the barbarous greenskin hordes. At the time of Abaddon's invasion it was still holding out, though the extreme measures taken by its rulers attracted a new kind of predator that conquered from within.

The verdant land of Mortwald formed the principal source of food for the planet Vigilus, its sprawling irrigation networks dotted with thousands of cactus farms and forests of succulents that could thrive even in the arid atmosphere. That alone made it vital indeed, especially when combined with its extensive underground hydroponics suites. The continent's reputation for grandeur, however, came from the rejuvenat clinics of Ageless Weald, Immortalis Spirehive and Rejuvenis Strongport.

The upmarket medicae facilities of the rejuvenat clinics provided anti-thanatosic and youth-giving phoenicius treatments to those visitors rich enough to extend their lifespans a few decades – for an astronomically high price, of course. Together, these sites supplied the false continent with a near limitless supply of wealth, ensuring that the ruling elite could live in the luxury to which they had long ago become accustomed. It was that same opulence that would bring about the downfall of Mortwald's most well-defended fortresses and citadels.

The coming of the Chaos fleet, and the War of Nightmares that ensued, pushed the aristocracy of Mortwald from their habitual complacency into a state of near panic. The false continent's defenders had committed almost all of their resources against the Orks attacking the Deinos Trench Network and the Tzeller Line. Despite being bolstered by the Imperial Fists, several of their successor Chapters, and contingents of Imperial Knights from Dharrovar and Voltoris, the Imperial forces had achieved little more than an uneasy stalemate. Meanwhile, in southern Mortwald, the Imperium had lost ground to an uprising of the Pauper Princes that had gradually conquered the Biosanctic Fleshplants during the War of Beasts. Deinos Agamemnus and his fellows had sent elite Astra Militarum regiments stationed in that province to combat them. So it was that when the Iron Warriors made planetfall to the east of the Deinos Trench Line at the onset of the Chaos invasion, the defenders of Mortwald had very little in the way of military resources with which to stop them.

It was at that point that the Renegade Chapter known as the Flawless Host breached Mortwald's richest areas, taking sadistic pleasure in the ease with which they were able to overcome the household guard of each aristocratic dynasty. A slew of atrocities was to follow as the Flawless Host punished the rulers of Mortwald for the crime of being imperfect. At much the same time, the Iron Warriors launched a devastating assault on the trench lines that had held so long against the Ork menace of the Western Scrap City Cluster. Mortwald teetered on the brink of disaster.

It was the Black Legion that finally pushed the false continent into a state of cataclysm. They had sent the Flawless Host to Mortwald not merely to indulge their taste for luxury, but also to shut down the automated defences that protected the war zone. The Flawless Host, having only relatively recently turned renegade from the Imperium, still utilised

many of the same craft with which they had waged war in the name of the Emperor. Though these ships were now gilded, bejewelled and painted in an eye-watering array of hues, they still possessed the Adeptus Astartes idents that allowed them to bypass the cogitators of the automated defence networks. Approaching the most well-defended areas of Mortwald, the Flawless Host systematically destroyed every anti-air asset that these spires could bring to bear against an aerial assault.

Upon receiving word that the false continent's defence batteries were taken care of, the Black Legion descended upon Mortwald by the thousand. The Terminator lord Thorosgar Bear-fist bypassed the Deinos Trench Network and the Imperial Fist line entirely, launching a devastating attack on the defenders of Electros Hive and Djodrolev Hivestar. Zhune Tzang, a skilled Master of Possession who had enjoyed Abaddon's favour for several months, pushed his own

assault into the Emerald Strain, while sending a contingent of Slaaneshi Daemons to invade Electros Hive alongside Bear-fist. The Black Legion commanders had picked the sites of their assaults well, for there were countless miles of civilian territory between them and the Space Marines that defended the outskirts. By the time the Necropolis Hawks and Imperial Fists had closed in, the streets of Mortwald were running with blood.

REPORT 191AS6BETIC8
MORTWALD
Coordinates: 181W-232E-112S-882N
Area: 92380232.1 hectarids
Population: 19.7 billion
Climate: Equatorial
Governance: Dynastic (secundus)

Trench networks compromised as of 1.823 post. 32% defence network ceded to xenos invaders (cf. Tzeller Line, Viridian Forests, Biosanctic Fleshplants). Rejuvenat industry ceased ad infinitum (pending emergency requisition by citizenry platinum level and above). As of 14.782 post evidence of +++REDUCTIO INQUISITORIA MAJORIS+++ across Deinos Trench Network. Evidence of +++REDUCTIO INQUISITORIA+++ in upper spires of Electros Hive, Djodrolev Hivestar, New Vitae Docks, Immortalis Spirehive.

Voschian Canal
network active as
of 872 previo.
From that date
supply of vital
energy to all
hivesprawls near
constant. Evidence
of pyroclastic
cults active
throughout War of
Beasts Exoneratus
as per order of
Fabricator Vosch,
Planetary Governor
Agamemnus. Later
reclassified as
condemnatus by
order of Chapter
Master Marneus
Calgar of the
Vigilus Senate.
Mount Colossid,
Hive Magmathermid,
Hekatoria Volcano,
Vulcanid Geohive
listed as In
Daemoniad Nihilos.

STORVHAL

Shimmering on the horizon of Hyperia could be seen Storvhal, a land of volcanoes and energy farms. As the War of Nightmares got underway, its calderas began erupting with warp-infused firestorms.

The volcanic continent of Storvhal once provided an endless stream of energy to the continents of Vigilus. Its geothermic farms, built to harness even the most violent eruption and turn it into raw power, were known for their searing temperatures and diligent, burn-scarred workers. But amongst extreme environments grow extreme viewpoints and strange creeds. The fact that so many workers met their end in a bubbling vat or river of lava lent credence to those who believed that Storvhal had a spirit of its own, and that it fed on human sacrifice. With each geo-spasm that racked the false continent's fault lines and set off a chain of eruptions or overflows, more lives were claimed, and the superstitious notion reinforced over again.

In the third stage of the War of Beasts, the claims that there were fire-devils frolicking in the flames were put down to hallucinations brought on by the Great Rift. It was almost impossible not to glimpse the celestial phenomenon of the Cicatrix Maledictum, especially at night, and there was copious evidence it could affect the sanity of those who witnessed it.

Only when Haarken Worldclaimer's message boomed down from the ash clouds above Storvhal did the idea that there might be some truth to the sightings of magical beasts existing in the fires gain any real traction. Within hours, the word that had only ever been whispered amongst the workers or scratched on the inside of basement walls was being spoken out loud – 'diabolus'.

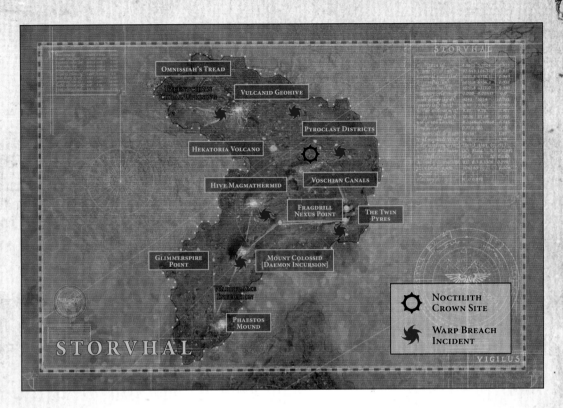

STORVHAL

OMNISSIAH'S TREAD

VULCANID GEOHIVE

PYROCLAST DISTRICTS

HEKATORIA VOLCANO

VOSCHIAN CANALS

HIVE MAGMATHERMID

FRAGDRILL NEXUS POINT

THE TWIN PYRES

GLIMMERSPIRE POINT

MOUNT COLOSSID [DAEMON INCURSION]

PHAESTOS MOUND

STORVHAL

⬡ NOCTILITH CROWN SITE

✶ WARP BREACH INCIDENT

VIGILUS

Storvhal was host to many pyroclastic cults that met in secret when their Tech-Priest overlords were elsewhere. They all worshipped fire in one form or another, whether as an incarnation of the Omnissiah's wrath, a bringer of calm at the end of a hard day's work, or as a means to read their future. Some of these cults were corrupted by Chaos. The largest, known as the Sons of Vannadan, after its founder who had given his life in battle against a strike force of Aeldari, was famous for the prophetic insights it gleaned from the fire-sprites dancing upon Mount Colossid. Only when Abaddon's fleet entered low orbit did the cult reveal its true colours, rising up against the Skitarii that sought to suppress it. Even as they were under heavy fire from the Adeptus Mechanicus, the most psychically gifted of their worshippers completed a great ritual of fire and blood on the top of Phaestos Mound. They opened a warp gate – a split in reality that looked much like the Great Rift in microcosm – and conjured a host of Tzeentchian

Daemons that spilled down the flanks of the peak. The psykers, rejoicing that their faith in the Dark Gods had been rewarded, saw dozens of Chaos Cultist uprisings flock to their banner. With the energies of the Great Rift running wild, Phaestos Mound, Omnissiah's Tread and even Mount Colossid began erupting with multicoloured flame and bolts of kaleidoscopic lightning, instead of the cherry-red lifeblood of the planet.

If it were not for the quick decisions and callous efficiency of Fabricator Vosch, the false continent would likely have been consumed by empyric energies. There were dozens of Tectonic Fragdrills across Storvhal; many had fallen into the hands of the Genestealer Cultists, but many more were still under Skitarii control. Vosch ordered them to be activated as one, and even sent targeted binharic overrides to enrage the machine spirits of those under enemy control. Many of these drills were positioned over geomantic nexus points. Instead of being carefully

activated to bleed the earth of magma, as they did whenever the volcanoes of Storvhal were on the verge of a critical eruption, they now burrowed into the planet's crust in a destructive frenzy. With every Fragdrill gnawing into the earth as one, the boiling undercurrents of magma flowed in great measure, filling the Voschian Canal network to maximum capacity and sending huge pulses of energy down the macrofibres and cables that connected Storvhal to the hivesprawls. The volcanoes boiled over, the rage of tortured tectonic plates spilling from their fiery throats. In a matter of hours the Daemons and cultists that had claimed the uppermost calderas of the volcanoes were crushed by tons of ash and pumice, or consumed by pyroclastic energies. Even the massing Daemons of Tzeentch were sent shrieking back to the warp. Hundreds of thousands of workers and Skitarii died along with them, and the industry of Storvhal was crippled – but for Vosch, it was a price well worth paying to deny the forces of Chaos.

OTECK HIVESPRAWL

The central hivesprawl of Oteck was once a thriving example of an Imperial metropolis. After the opening of the Great Rift, it was torn asunder, its hab-blocks the site of constant battle between the agents of the Imperium, invading Orks, usurping Genestealer Cultists, and the Chaos onslaught.

The vast urban nation of Oteck Hivesprawl once had a great deal of influence over Vigilus. It harboured the five great reservoirs of Greigan, Mysandren, Ostaveer, Trevig and Agamemnus, known collectively as the Hollows. With the sentinel world being so arid, Oteck's resources were always in high demand. Water was not Oteck's only bounty, either – it also housed a treasure trove of data, pertaining to every aspect of the planet and its neighbours in the Vigilus System, in the Turingsbane Datahives. There was a persistent rumour that insights into the fabled Standard Template Constructs were hidden within the depths of those labyrinthine vaults. The Adeptus Mechanicus had long sought full access to that bounty of data,

despite having signed the Pact of Fire and Steel that forbade them unaccompanied access to its secrets.

Because of its rich resources, Oteck had a disproportionately high concentration of the Adeptus Arbites – the judges, juries and executioners of Imperial society. Their law enforcement and precinct networks were further bolstered by the Adepta Sororitas assigned from Hyperia in the east. Together with the Space Wolves of Haldor Icepelt, it was the Sisters of Battle that bore the brunt of the intense fighting around Greigan Hollow. The Deathwatch, specialists in the art of hunting xenos, quarantined the Hollows after they were found to be tainted by the Genestealer Cultists that skulked in the dank tunnels

beneath the fortified reservoirs, but many citizens drank from them nonetheless, risking a bullet for just one draught of precious water whenever the garrison's backs were turned.

When Abaddon used the eldritch technologies of the Voidclaw to open a tiny singularity at one of Vigilus' Legrange points – a zone equidistant between planet and moon – he disturbed the gravity of the world so much so that its water supplies were irrevocably drawn towards the Vhulian Swirl. The Hollows were drained in a single week, the water crawling up the walls of the reservoirs to flow towards the great dust wastes beyond the hivesprawl like glittering snakes on some strange

Report V345/sygma/0

OTECK

Coordinates: 181W-232E-112S-882N
Area: 63783410.9 hectarids
Population: 22.8 billion
Climate: Sub-Equatorial
Governance: Dynastic (tertius)

(cf. War of Nightmares) Hollows Greigan, Mysandren, Agamemnus, Ostaveer, Trevig declared condemnatus as per Ordo Xenos allied directive 887.Genecurs'd (cf. Deathwatch). Secondary insurgence ref. Pauper Princes 59% eradicated. Alpha Legion presence detected (cf. multiple instances of <REDACTIO EXTREMIS> presence signifiers in Siltid River region, Hive Zontanus, Ellerophosus Hivebelt). Mortwald-Oteck Fortwall compromised, Tzardonica and Lenkotz Chain aqua farm processors at 12% optimum. Assets under review. Likelihood of total loss of control at 82% (current estimate) and climbing.

migration. Oteck's people, who also felt that tug so strongly it was a fight not to let themselves be pulled eastward, fought each other to scoop up the water from the rivulets that spread through the streets, filling canteens, tureens, and empty promethium barrels with as much aqua as they could salvage. The Militarum garrison, at a loss, could not stop the water making its slithering voyage towards the swirl, and so remained at their posts. Even with the stuff of life just waiting to be claimed in the streets, and cultist uprisings blossoming all over the hivesprawl, they knew better than to abandon their duty – for the Commissars did not look kindly on such things. The citizens all but tore themselves apart over the departing resource, clawing at one another tooth and nail to claim the water for themselves.

With the eyes of Oteck's law enforcement elsewhere, the Tech-Priests of Megaborealis and Storvhal redoubled their efforts to claim the Turingsbane Datahives

for themselves. Thankfully for the Imperial war effort, they were successful – for what the Tech-Priests found down there in the dataslate tunnels was potent enough to change the face of the ravaged planet once and for all. Through diligent cross-referencing and acts of painstaking archeolexicography, the Tech-Priests of Stygies VIII unearthed ancient records of the Citadel Vigilant – and, more pertinently, construction dataslates for the doomsday device known as the Voidclaw.

In their research on the Citadel Vigilant, the Tech-Priests found iconographical links to the original incarnation of the First Legion. Fabricator Vosch himself sent a carefully encrypted message to the Techmarines of the Dark Angels, keeping his information purely technical so as to avoid any questions as to its origins or ownership. In doing so, he gave the Dark Angels the keys they needed to bypass the Voidclaw's defences – and, if needed, to destroy it.

'ALL THAT TIME, WE FOUGHT TO PROTECT THE AQUEOUS RESERVOIRS AT THE HEART OF OTECK HIVESPRAWL. WE SOUGHT TO CONTROL THE HOLLOWS, DESPITE THE FACT THEIR BOUNTY WAS ALREADY POISONED BEYOND RECOVERY. YET THE TRUE TREASURE OF THAT GREAT METROPOLIS WAS BURIED FAR DEEPER – A BOUNTY OF INFORMATION FROM THE EARLY DAYS OF THE IMPERIUM, UNDILUTED AND GLORIOUS. IT WAS THE FONT OF KNOWLEDGE FROM WHICH WE SUPPED THE DEEPEST, AND IN DOING SO, SALVAGED THAT WHICH WAS SO NEARLY LOST FOREVER.'

- Excerpt from the journal of Meta-Geologue Xanthran Tarendos (latter volume, War of Nightmares)

21.119 POST – A WORLD CROWNED BY CHAOS

The Noctilith Crowns were perfected by Abaddon and his original Master of Summoning, the Darkling Liege Narcus Tharanda. Though single devices had been used to blight a dozen worlds before Abaddon's alliance reached Vigilus, the crowns were first deployed en masse when Abaddon set foot upon Vigilus and deemed it the right time to make use of his hard-won resource. Each was painstakingly carved with runes in the Dark Tongue of Chaos, bathed in the blood of hundreds of sacrificial victims, anointed with the oily residue of scores of rendered-down psykers and installed in great iron housings before being bulk-lifted down to the planet's surface and sunk deep into Vigilus' crust.

21.226 POST – THE EMPYRIC CURSE

The Noctilith Crowns, aligned so as to channel the empyric force of the Great Rift as the planet turned, established a continent-spanning network of psychic amplifiers that thrummed with Chaotic energy. Wherever they resonated the strongest, the visions and nightmares that had troubled the people of Vigilus began to manifest in reality as warp-gheists, ethereal horrors that plagued the citizenry for a hundred miles around each site. The anarchy that resulted only added fuel to the fires that looked set to consume the planet entirely.

THE VHULIAN SWIRL

At the heart of the Vhulian Swirl was a secret of such power it changed the face of Vigilus forever, summoning a gravitic anomaly high above the dust storm that wreaked utter havoc on the war below.

A massive, swirling dust vortex so vast it birthed lesser storms to ravage the wilderness around it, the Vhulian Swirl was always something of an enigma to the populace of Vigilus. All citizens at least knew to stay well away from that ever-whirling tempest – not that the average person had the liberty to be able to stray far from their allotted task and hab-block – for it was a potent presence in Vigilant folklore, treated more as a baleful creature than a simple storm. To approach it was to run the risk of having one's skin – and the flesh beneath – stripped away by the fierce abrasion of hurtling particulate. It was rumoured, although few could confirm it, that the lands about were littered with bones – the scattered remnants of those too stupid or fatally curious to stay away. Even those Orks that

braved its outskirts, careening around the perimeter as part of the Speedwaaagh!'s daredevil races, learned to avoid the giant ochre-black walls of dust that formed the Swirl proper.

At the beginning of the War of Nightmares, none on the Vigilus Senate truly knew what caused the Swirl's existence. Very few of their warriors had ventured inside its reaches to find out, and even fewer had returned. Some called the Swirl a natural phenomenon, but that could not have been further from the truth.

Over the course of the war for Vigilus, the Swirl's secret was finally revealed. At the heart of that great storm stood the Citadel Vigilant, a monument built as much from the fabled mineral noctilith as it was

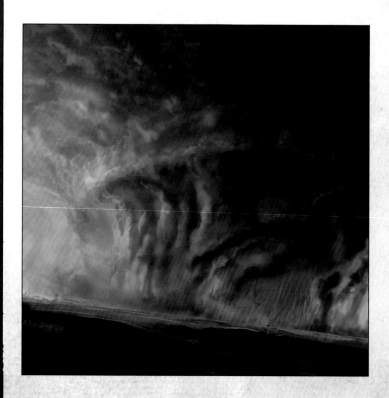

A WOLF AT THE DOOR

In the early stages of the War of Nightmares, Wolf Lord Krom Dragongaze's Great Company arrived in force above Vigilus. The Fenrisian battle barges smashed a path through the outer ring of Ork scrap-hulks, but the Fierce-eye was drawn to the largest greenskin vessel in range, the immense rokkit krooza marked *Worldsmasha*.

Seeking to announce his presence on the embattled world with a fitting act of glory, the Wolf Lord and his Rimeguard teleported aboard the ship. The Space Wolves cut a bloody path through the Ork Meks that controlled the *Worldsmasha*'s immense rokkit arrays, and the Wolf Guard Wulfrik Stormsmite placed melta bombs on key points along the krooza's sprawling ammunition yards, while Dragongaze sought out and beheaded the Big Mek captain with a swing of his frost axe.

The Space Wolves exfiltrated moments before a chain reaction demolished the upper decks of the *Worldsmasha*, sending it into a spiralling death dive

into the wastes of Vigilus near the Vhulian Swirl. The doomed ship struck like a cyclonic warhead, destroying several warbands of Ork Speed Freeks and a number of the greenskins' crude scrap-forts on the outskirts of Hurrikane Rekk. Lord Dragongaze considered this a fitting spectacle with which to herald his arrival on Vigilus.

Upon reporting to the Vigilus Senate, Wolf Lord Krom immediately clashed with Lord Marneus Calgar, who was then organising the defence of Vigilus from his command centre within the Aquilarian Palace. The Chapter Master vetoed the Fierce-eye's demand for an aggressive assault upon the remains of Hurrikane Rekk, for the Wolf Lord was keen to finish what he had started, and claim a significant victory for his Great Company in the process. The heated argument between the two Space Marines grew bitter, but was averted when news arrived of an Ork incursion into the temple districts of Hyperia. The Fierce-eye set off at once to defeat this new threat – much to Calgar's relief.

---

obsidian and hypersteel. The lack of weathering upon its slick black walls implied that the monstrous keep had been built in recent years, but in truth it had been constructed long before Humanity had quested out into the stars on the Emperor's Great Crusade. There was said to be something alien about its appearance, and the peculiar spire atop it – which housed a weapon with the potential to cause cataclysmic destruction – shimmered with energies that hurt the eye.

The Citadel Vigilant had long been the stronghold for a coven of warrior mystics that, thousands of years ago, forsook the Adeptus Astartes in search of deeper truths. They were known as the Fallen. Protected by the strange temporal aegis of that place from the vagaries of time, they sought to unlock the secrets of the citadel – and the minerals in the planet's crust beneath – but were never truly able to confirm their suspicions that noctilith was tied to the power of the Dark Gods.

Some amongst the Fallen of the Citadel Vigilant believed they could drive out the taint of corruption from the souls of the afflicted by chaining the victim to a slab of noctilith, charged to repel the energies of Chaos, for a year and a day. Others claimed that the planet was vital to the future of the Imperium, and that they had been called there to act as guardians for the final day of reckoning.

The Despoiler, knowing full well the promise of the blackstone deposits in the citadel, made planetfall under the auspice of parley, and

even alliance. Such was his personal charisma and the lure of his carefully considered words that the Fallen joined his side voluntarily – for they saw in Abaddon a chance to sever their brothers in the Dark Angels from the holy light of Terra forever more, and in doing so, force them to embrace the bleak truths they had hidden for so long.

The activation of the Voidclaw saw the Vhulian Swirl turn from a massive whirling cyclone to a sucking vortex that drew up millions of tons of sand and detritus with every passing moment. Only the Citadel Vigilant itself remained unaffected, protected as it was by a force field of unprecedented size and strength that defied Imperial classification – but which made the structure as immune to the great tempest as a mountain is to a light shower. During the war, battle was to rage under that great aegis, the combatants giving everything they had to settle a millennia-old grudge – and in doing so, determine whether the planet was to survive, or to be consumed.

KAELAC'S BANE

Kaelac's Bane was typified by blizzards, ice predators and sub-zero temperatures that could freeze a man's eyes shut. During the War of Beasts, it was abandoned by the quarrymen that had mined it for water, and since then formed a base of operations for warriors who cared not for mortal concerns like temperature.

Kaelac's Bane was once thought of as the salvation of the planet, for in its glaciers and ice wastes were countless tonnes of water waiting to be thawed and purified for the consumption of the populace – but that endless promise was claimed only by the rich. Once its vast macrocraters had been properly treated to work as quarries, and a freight infrastructure put in place to carry that bounty – mined in vast cuboid structures – to those who could pay the right price, the icy realm provided water only to the upper echelons of Vigilus. That privilege was to change over the course of the War of Beasts, and again with the coming of Chaos.

Deep in the western reaches of the icy wilderness was an area

designated Quarantine Cryofernus by the Imperial authorities, for those who strayed within its perimeter did not come back out. For a while it was believed that the cause was the giant ice mantises that hunted in the blizzards. These predatory creatures were lethal indeed, and caused a great many deaths amongst the Skitarii and cybernetic quarrymen that hewed their aqueous fortune from the glaciers. But it was in truth the Drukhari – pitiless Aeldari raiders that preyed on isolated groups and took them back to the twisted city of Commorragh – that were responsible for the most losses. At the heart of the Quarantine Cryofernus was a webway portal, elegant and slender in the fashion of Aeldari architecture. When

activated by one with the correct arcane knowledge, it opened a shimmering gateway that led to the labyrinth dimension, allowing raiders to cross vast gulfs of space to reach Vigilus undetected.

It was not only the Drukhari that knew of this portal's existence. The Thousand Sons, that Traitor Legion whose tragic fall from grace rendered them armoured spirits led by inhuman Sorcerers, had delved deep into the mysteries of the webway. Though they possessed only a fraction of the Aeldari's mastery, they had found a route to Vigilus, their progress guided by their strange god Tzeentch.

As Abaddon's invasion got underway, the Thousand Sons

Report 10134t6/betic9*9

KAELAC'S BANE

ARCTIC ANOMALY — CARNELIAN ALERT

<COORDINATES/DIMENSIONS
CURRENTLY UNDER REVIEW>
Population: 4.1 million
Climate: Arctic
Governance: Industrial
(Adeptus Mechanicus)

Non-standard polar region
climate, provenance inconclusive
(cf. Kaelac Mining Consortium,
Stygies VIII aqua reclamation).
Quarantine Cryofernus declared
and extant (Coordinates:
176W-198E-12S-98N). Evidence

of xenos infestation (Aeldari
subcategory 3.2 betic) — mining
operations to proceed within
acceptable parameters where 95%
or greater level of automation
is viable. Enforced diaspora for
all other site assets (Glacia
Betus Macroquarry, Kaelac's
Bane Geoscrying Installation,
Heliostrike Impact Crater,
Glacia Omicroid Macroquarry).
First phase War of Nightmares
evidence of continent expansion
and severe temperature drop.

Evacuation figure projection
estimates operation complete
with only 68% total losses.

began to emerge from the webway portal by the hundred. The off-white tundra of the Dearthland Permafrost was compacted by the crump of power-armoured feet marching in unison, as the unfeeling automatons strode through the Ice Mantis Drifts, their inferno bolters ripping apart any indigenous predators foolish enough to approach. The Drukhari had long seen Kaelac's Bane as their rightful territory, and the webway gate was a vital means of bringing reinforcements to Vigilus that they were not prepared to sacrifice. As such, they engaged the Thousand Sons in a series of hit-and-run strikes. They rode the blizzards, screaming out of the white nothingness to slice and stab at the Rubricae and their sorcerous masters. Yet these battles did not go well for them, for what is crippling pain to one whose mortal remains are little more than dust sealed in a suit of armour?

Only when the Drukhari retreated to the Quixotine Loop did they find the key to their nemeses' defeat. Those strange islands of ice, seemingly featureless yet guarded by an array of force fields and moats disproportionate to their military value, hid a strange secret. The Drukhari, able to bypass the protective barriers with a subsidiary webway portal, found a complex mechanism the size of a hab-block that their foremost mind, Archon Khaeva the Inscrutable, concluded was a primitive but effective terraforming node. Within a few hours, the Archon had revived the machine and turned it to its most extreme setting.

The Drukhari did not know it, but the ancient device had been the invention of Kaelac himself, the first explorer to attempt to mine the continent for water. It had been his demise, for its terraforming technology had proved all too effective, the pioneer freezing to death in the glacial wilderness.

For the Drukhari, however, it worked with startling efficacy. The terraforming engines chugged and chuntered as they worked their way back to full capacity and, gradually at first, then with startling speed, the arctic wilderness of Kaelac's Bane began to grow colder still. Its borders expanded, fingers of ice forming across the wastelands in thin sheets.

In the heartlands of Kaelac's Bane, the temperature dropped so severely that the blizzards formed thick snowdrifts, then hard prisons of ice. This master stroke proved far more effective against the Thousand Sons than any number of toxins or artfully delivered sword cuts, for the silent phalanxes of Rubricae that had taken control of the icy continent found themselves slowing to a crawl, stopping altogether, then becoming completely inert – frozen in place and, in some cases, trapped in a swiftly forming glacier. The Sorcerers of the Thousand Sons were forced to abandon their retinues and, hunted by gleeful Drukhari raiding parties, flee back through the webway portal.

KAELAC'S BANE

QUIXOTINE LOOP

TERRAFORMING ENGINE NODE

TUNDRIC PERIMETER

DEARTHLAND PERMAFROST

QUARANTINE CRYOFERNUS [DRUKHARI PORTAL]

GLACIA BETUS MACROQUARRY

GEOSCRYING INSTILLATION [NON-THETIC]

FIRST SIGHTING OF PALE STALKER

VENSTRAN IMPACT CRATER

ICE MANTIS DRIFTS

HELIOSTRIKE IMPACT CRATER

GLACIA OMICROID MACROQUARRY

DIVESTRUM BLIZZARD

CREEPING PERIMETER

NOCTILITH CROWN SITE

WARP BREACH INCIDENT

VIGILUS

NEO-VELLUM

Vigilus' moon was given over to communications, from the physical despatching of message tubes to the sending and receiving of astropathic communiques. It was infested by Genestealer Cultists over the course of the War of Beasts, and later wrenched out of its orbit by the Vhulian Anomaly, causing utter havoc.

Neo-vellum was once an exemplary facility dedicated to the arts of the scriptorum and the quill-servitor. A world of gas storms and acid swamps dotted with armoured, hermetically sealed population centres, it formed the information hub for Vigilus. Its vantage point in the celestial vault gave it independence, and allowed the satellite a degree of omniscience over the activities on the planet below. Unfortunately, over the course of the War of Nightmares, the old saying 'Neo-vellum sees all' was to be proven decidedly false.

Neo-vellum's information engine, an immense thing of cogs, pneumatic tubes and orreries, could despatch a message tube to a given site on the planet below with a

relatively high degree of accuracy. Yet when the Great Rift opened the skies, its calculations went badly awry, and the psyker choir of Neo-vellum's massive torus-shaped Choralium was plagued with horrible episodes of insanity.

To make matters worse, during the War of Beasts, the Pauper Princes sent two Purestrain Genestealers to the Administratum moon. Hiding amongst the toiling masses, each brood established its own gene-sect, while the scribes of Neo-vellum, taking solace in their scrollwork, were blind to the corruption unfolding in their midst. A strike clade of Skitarii requisitioned by Inquisitor Garalas of the Ordo Xenos purged many of the life forms, but many more escaped.

The gradual doom the cultists represented was superseded when the gravitic anomaly opened by the Voidclaw pulled the planet from its orbit. The acid swamps boiled, the emerald gas storms intensified, and the bouts of madness grew more frequent as the world was drawn ever closer to the tiny singularity that was the Vhulian Anomaly. Even for the most cybernetically augmented of the planet's workers, the sense of impending doom could be felt deep in every gut. Dire whispers led to panic, and then – despite the heavy-handed oppression of the scriptorum masters – to open rioting, with the surviving Genestealer Cultists adding to the furore. The scriptorums of Neo-vellum were soon aflame.

Report 943056/alphic0

NEO-VELLUM

ROGUE PLANETOID — VERMILION ALERT

Coordinates: High Orbit
Area: Lambda-class planetoid
Population: 17.2 billion
Climate: Toxicity level 23%
Governance: Administratum (cf.
Adeptus Mechanicus presence
escalating after Ordo Xenos purge.)

Administratum facility (platinum
level) compromised by known xenos
infestation. Subsequent purge
incomplete. Orbital trajectory
altered to spiral course converging
on Vhulian Anomaly. Point of
total destruction estimated as
40.333 post.

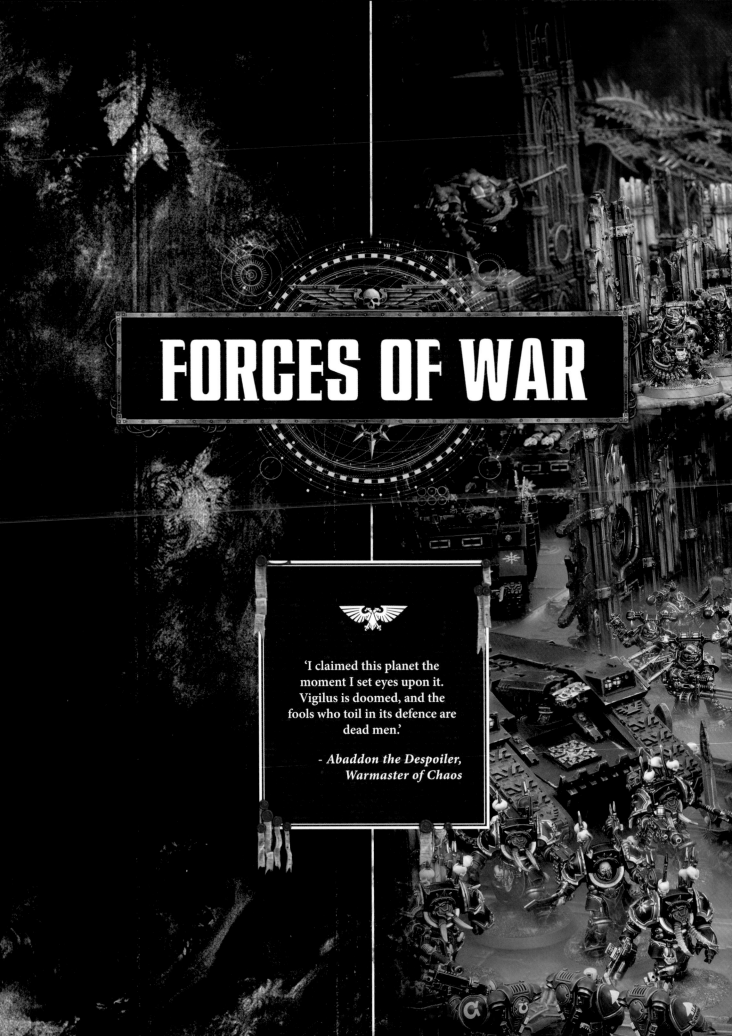

FORCES OF WAR

'I claimed this planet the
moment I set eyes upon it.
Vigilus is doomed, and the
fools who toil in its defence are
dead men.'

- *Abaddon the Despoiler,*
Warmaster of Chaos

FORCES OF CHAOS

The Chaos hosts that invaded Vigilus were disparate, and struck at every hivesprawl and island in a different fashion. Each Traitor Legion and Renegade Chapter had its own agenda, its own enemies it yearned to destroy. The only uniting factor was the ruthless efficiency with which they went about their murderous work.

In theory, with the looming presence and grand strategy of the Warmaster to unite them, the forces of Chaos should have proved greater than the sum of their parts. But where the Imperial armies were tightly marshalled and guided by a council of respected war leaders, the twisted scions of the Dark Gods were largely left to their own devices.

Abaddon had greater designs than acting as a disciplinarian to keep his unruly seconds in line – that would have been such a Sisyphean task that even to attempt it would have precluded any personal ambition or long-term plan. Instead, the Warmaster used his forces as agents of disruption, anarchy and despair, allowing them to spread the fires of war as they wished.

Ultimately, Abaddon considered the front-line engagements, executions and intricacies of the Long War to be distractions. His works, and those of the Daemon Primarchs, had torn Imperial space in half. He fully intended to make good on the promise of damnation he had written across the skies of the galaxy – and to do so, he would need to bathe Vigilus in such intense madness that its defenders had to fight on all fronts, at all times. Only then could he pursue his greater agenda without fear of a coherent counter-attack.

A DIABOLICAL STRATEGY

The planet's inherent ability to repel Chaos had made its secrets irresistible to the Adeptus Mechanicus, just as it had made it a priority target for the forces of the Dark Gods, who sought to destroy it. It was a cruel truth that for all their painstaking analysis, the Tech-Priests of Stygies had less insight into the noctilith substance than the Chaos warlords under Abaddon the Despoiler. Perhaps if the lords of Megaborealis had better cooperated with the Priesthood of Mars – and Archmagos Dominus Cawl in particular – they may have made better use of the bounty they had mined so fastidiously.

HERETIC ASTARTES

The armies that flocked to Abaddon's banner were beyond counting. Many hailed from the Eye of Terror, and had fought alongside the Warmaster's elite forces for time immemorial. Others were allies of opportunity, marshalled from nearby Nemendghast or Hearthlack – or even summoned from the depths of the Great Rift with promises of glories to come. Ultimately, all that mattered to Abaddon was that the planet be set ablaze.

BLACK LEGION

The Bringers of Despair ....1 warband (elite corps)
The Hounds of Abaddon ....1 warband (elite corps)
Lord Kadros' Champions...................................5 warbands
Drakkoth's Destroyers.......................................4 warbands
The Skull-eaters.................................... 4 warbands (Khorne)
The Bringers of Decay........................1 warband (Nurgle)
The Crimson Hurricane............2 warbands (heavy cavalry)
Thaskor's Chosen...............................2 warbands (Tzeentch)
Sons of the Cyclops .... 1 warband (Tzeentch)
Heralds of the Inevitable End ....2 warbands (armoured)
The Sixth Rapture...............................2 warbands (Slaanesh)
The Ironspines........ 1 warband (heavy Obliterator presence)
The Oathed.................................3 warbands (Nurgle-tithe)
The Unworthy Inheritors..................................2 Chaos cults
The Warmaster's Blades ....1 Chaos cult

DEATH GUARD

Apostles of Contagion......................7 warbands (cf. schism)
Carrion Hounds..2 warbands
The Rotworm Brotherhood....................................7 warbands
Bringers of Putrid Salvation........ 3 warbands (opportunist)
Seventh-day Morbidians.....................................4 warbands
Selminster's Curse..5 warbands
Dolorous Strain...1 kill team
Gellerpox Hordes ....4 pox-mobs

WORLD EATERS

Dhorngar's Goredrinkers....................................3 warbands
Crushers of Bone...12 warbands
Pistlehand's Daemoniforge............................ 1 warband

THOUSAND SONS

Xenash Capensis' Rubric Phalanx ....2 warbands
The Fractal Blades..1 kill team
Masters of Magnus' Will.................................. 1 warband
The Scions of the Great Architect........................ 1 warband

IRON WARRIORS

Anathraxis Warhost ....2 warbands
The Pitiless...3 warbands
The Hammers Relentless ....2 warbands
Siege-masters Olympian .... 1 warband

ALPHA LEGION

Sons of Deception............................2 warbands (infiltrators)
20th Alpharians .... 1 warband
The Armoured Serpents .... 1 warband (armoured)

WORD BEARERS

Holy Sons of Lorgar..3 warbands
The Runic Blazon..2 warbands
The Devout Horde.......................................1 worshipper host

NIGHT LORDS

Blades of Savasdus..3 warbands
Bleak Claw .... 1 warband
Vreanus' Killers .... 1 warband

FLAWLESS HOST

Lashdrum Monarchs...2 warbands
Villsid Skinsmen... 1 warband
The Luscious Few.. 1 warband

CRIMSON SLAUGHTER

Jackalan Echoes...3 warbands
Umidia's Call ....1 doppelgänger warband
The Spectral Curse............................ 1 warband (armoured)

THE PURGE

Nihilant Banes...................................2 warbands (cf. schism)
Eradicatus Corps ....2 warbands (cf. schism)

THE SCOURGED

Seers of Alltome..3 warbands
Gilded Manifestans ....2 warbands
Excorias Elite.......................................1 warband (sorcerous)

BRAZEN BEASTS

Daemonbind's Onslaught ....13 Daemon Engine packs
The Triad of Gore................................3 Lords of Skulls
Drakes of the Savage Roost ....5 Heldrake fear squadrons
The *Cerberite* ....1 Daemon-possessed battle barge

HERETICUS MILITARUM

The Machnorian VI 'Sighted' ....1 regiment
The Vostokh 13th Heavy Infantry ....1 regiment
The Pallisane 'Idolators' ....3 regiments
Jenen Ironclads .... 4 regiments
Feresk Truthsayers.. 3 regiments
Antivigil Bloodcorps... 2 regiments

TRAITOR LEGIO TITANICUS

Death's Heads .... CLASSIFIED
Fire Masters... CLASSIFIED
Legio Vulcanum II.. CLASSIFIED
Legio Decapitorum... CLASSIFIED

THE GRAND FLEET OF THE DESPOILER

The *Vengeful Spirit*
12 battleships
19 heavy cruisers
est. 34 cruiser squadrons
est. 84 escort squadrons

++CONTINUED IN FILE IMP.VIG/CHV1/1-19

Participants in second and third stages of Vigilus conflict codified 'War of Nightmares' codified in auxiliary dataslate Imp.Vig/Ons3/11-128.

The blackstone taken from the planet's crust had been charged by some arcane force to have an anti-empyric resonance, a fact that the sorcerous cabals advising Abaddon had learned from afar using scrying rituals and daemonic bargains. As to how this worked, none amongst either camp knew. Fabricator Vosch of Megaborealis had theorised it was xenos hands that had fashioned the stuff into strange spear-like shapes and aligned it in the fluid-filled bubbles of the deep geological strata, for he had heard of no such phenomenon on any other world catalogued by his peers. Those who had examined those linear mineral deposits closely had found evidence of mechanical processes so advanced no human artisan could have replicated them. The blackstone was rife with channels and holes that wound with labyrinthine complexity, each so regular it was as if they had been machined by some technological marvel. The micro-servitors sent into the holes to examine the maze of passages did not come out again.

The Adeptus Mechanicus did not allow their lack of understanding to hinder their progress in sequestering the material – for that was not their way. When Abaddon learned from Haarken Worldclaimer that the Tech-Priests had gathered the material and stored it in their most well-defended silos, he laughed long and loud, for unwittingly they had done much of the work for him. The planet's bounty was no longer buried deep in its crust – the excavation of the blackstone, something that Abaddon had feared may have taken several decades and hundreds of thousands of slaves to achieve, had already been done for him.

The Despoiler had learned the value of blackstone long ago, in the distant past of his kingship – indeed, many of his Black Crusades had revolved around its destruction. Whenever Abaddon located

noctilith structures that had been charged to hold back the forces of Chaos, he spared no effort to shatter them, for in doing so he severely weakened the metaphysical barrier between realspace and the warp. He had achieved this feat on a string of worlds across the Imperium. The Eldritch Needles of Nemesis Tessera, the Gates of the Kromarch's Citadel, the Black Obelisks of Monarchive – even the mysterious pylons of Cadia had been toppled when Abaddon had thrown every weapon at his disposal into the planet's destruction.

There was a pattern to these invasions. From a certain vantage point, they linked up to form a jagged diagonal line across the galaxy – the line that had split open and given rise to the Great Rift. The sentinel world of Vigilus lay on that same galactic fault line, and it was the priority of the forces of Chaos to destroy it. On Vigilus, Abaddon's plan was to obliterate the structures that protected the planet in order to expand the Great Rift, and to close one of the very few channels that allowed passage across its roiling mass.

Over the course of the Gothic War, the Warmaster's Sorcerers had found a way to turn blackstone from its natural state of neutral resonance – where it neither attracted nor repelled Chaos – to an alignment where it harnessed and stored the energies of the warp.

This technique required costly and dangerous rituals involving human sacrifice, percussive arrhythmical impacts and the inscription of dark runes upon the blackstone's surface. The cost in lives of these sorcerous processes was gladly paid by the Black Legion. Their ultimate agenda was to ensure the galaxy drowned in a rising tide of Chaos, and if the Nachmund Gauntlet were to be closed forever, the Imperium Nihilus would be brought a great deal closer to that dark fate.

With war raging across Vigilus, there was no time for Abaddon's Sorcerers to recover the deposits the Adeptus Mechanicus had unearthed – let alone perform the rituals that would turn them to the cause of Chaos – so he opted to destroy the precious resource instead, an act that would still devastate the Imperium. He ordered his shock troops – in the form of entire armies of Daemon Engines – to assault the blackstone silos in order to disable the force fields that protected them. Then, with that aegis down, his warships levelled an orbital bombardment to blast the blackstone into flinders of rock so small and so scattered they could no longer hold back the Great Rift with their metaphysical power.

Even as Vigilus was assailed, the other half of Abaddon's dual strike was unfolding in the reaches of the Imperium Sanctus. He believed that whatever ancient order had placed the blackstone spears within Vigilus' crust had deliberately created the Nachmund Gauntlet, and that similar – if not identical – deposits would be found in the earth of a twin planet on the other side of that channel. That planet was Sangua Terra. By taking war to these sites, and by destroying the blackstone spears that kept them sacrosanct, he would collapse the Nachmund Gauntlet entire. This was Abaddon's true intent – and upon Vigilus and Sangua Terra alike, every other slaughter, massacre and betrayal was merely a distraction.

DESCENT OF THE CERBERITE [MEGABOREALIS]

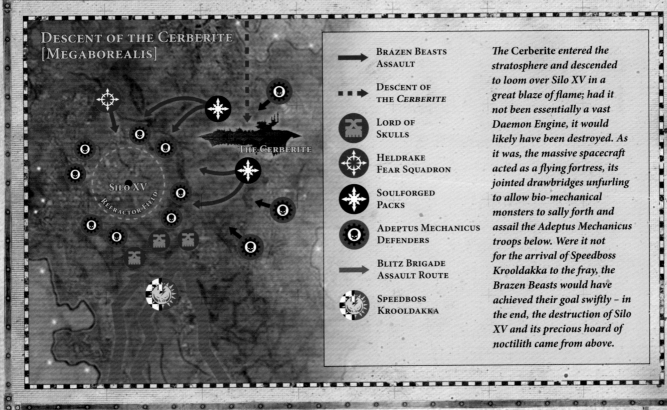

→	BRAZEN BEASTS ASSAULT
⇢	DESCENT OF THE *CERBERITE*
(skull)	LORD OF SKULLS
(star)	HELDRAKE FEAR SQUADRON
(chaos star)	SOULFORGED PACKS
(cog)	ADEPTUS MECHANICUS DEFENDERS
→	BLITZ BRIGADE ASSAULT ROUTE
(checkered)	SPEEDBOSS KROOLDAKKA

The Cerberite entered the stratosphere and descended to loom over Silo XV in a great blaze of flame; had it not been essentially a vast Daemon Engine, it would likely have been destroyed. As it was, the massive spacecraft acted as a flying fortress, its jointed drawbridges unfurling to allow bio-mechanical monsters to sally forth and assail the Adeptus Mechanicus troops below. Were it not for the arrival of Speedboss Krooldakka to the fray, the Brazen Beasts would have achieved their goal swiftly – in the end, the destruction of Silo XV and its precious hoard of noctilith came from above.

FORCES OF THE BLACK LEGION

The Black Legionnaires fought as a series of warbands, each centred around a charismatic leader figure. In turn, these dark champions formed a greater host that answered to Abaddon himself. Their attacks were so swift and vicious that few outside the Vigilus Senate had time to consider the strategy uniting them.

Long millennia as the master of the Black Crusades had taught Abaddon that the legions of Chaos were not fine instruments to be wielded as a surgeon wields the knife. Not even the Black Legion, his own brethren, whom he had brought back from the brink of disaster and slowly built into a force that could threaten the galaxy entire, could fully be trusted to obey his will when their thirst for carnage took hold. These forces were wrecking balls, sledgehammers, and jagged blades aimed at the throat. But what they lacked in subtlety, they more than made up for in the destruction they brought down upon their foes. As such, where the actions of his forces led to resources being wasted or misused, or schisms between allies developing, the Warmaster reacted with little more than a curled lip. Only the direst infractions did he punish, and even then through an intermediary.

The Black Legion wear a stylised Eye of Horus surrounded by the eight-pointed star of Chaos.

The Eye of Horus is a symbol so aligned with Chaos it sometimes takes on a gruesome life of its own.

The onyx armour of the Black Legion sends a stark message – framed in gold, it speaks of a dark majesty that has kept the Imperium on the verge of utter dissolution since the first Warmaster's heresy.

BLEAK EXECUTIONERS

Those that worked against Abaddon or deliberately flouted his rule were visited by his enforcers. These came in the form of the Bringers of Despair, his veteran Terminator bodyguard, and Ghordar Bann, a Master of Executions who had risen high in the Warmaster's favour on the killing fields of the tundra planet Truska. When Abaddon commanded that one of his lesser warlords be killed, it was often the axe of Ghordar Bann that took the head; the snowdrifts of Asavensus had been stained with the lifeblood of three such champions marked for death. The tally he claimed amongst the officer cadres of the Truskan Snowhounds was five times that number, his axe parting heads from necks with expert precision.

Each of the headsman's attacks on Vigilus was brief and terrifying. Teleporting from the sorcerous octagrams aboard the *Vengeful*

Spirit, Ghordar and a band of the Bringers of Despair would arrive in a flash of dark light before their mark. The Terminators would instantly blast away the guardians of the intended victim with combi-bolter and reaper autocannon, while Ghordar strode forward, axe raised. There was no escaping such a fate once it had been set. Ghordar Bann had ripped out his own eye in a lengthy and painful Chaos ritual, exchanging it in a daemonic bargain for limited warp-sight. By covering his remaining eye, he could see his intended quarry across time and space as a flicker of red light – and he could hunt the offender out no matter how well concealed they thought themselves to be. When Bann's inescapable axe descended, a head would roll, and Abaddon's reign of fear would be strengthened all the more.

Bann was sent against many Imperial captains and commanders over the course of the War of

Nightmares, though Marneus Calgar was not one of them. Calgar was a formidable opponent, and Abaddon did not intend to throw away the life of his promising champion on such an errand. More than that, he intended to claim the head of the Lord Macragge himself, and finally settle their ancient rivalry. That resolution was to lead to a climactic duel, and ultimately, decide the fate of the planet.

THE ARCH-LORD DISCORDANT

There were hundreds of war leaders in the Warmaster's inner circles, each with his own priorities and ambitions. Amongst them there was one who, above all others, sought to disrupt, divide and destroy all semblance of ordered thought. He was the Arch-Lord Discordant known in the Black Legion as Vex Machinator. It was his particular ability to bring Chaos to the foe that made him the heir to Abaddon's throne.

None knew the true name of Vex Machinator; much like a Daemon, he kept it secret so that none could have true power over him. Instead he was named for his practices. To everyone he encountered he brought strife, regardless of their allegiance – even to approach him was to feel vexation, confusion and dismay. He was like a living embodiment of Chaos, feeding on the bitter division he sowed amongst friends and foes alike, and in his

machinations he was as much a parasite as the giant scuttling Helstalker he rode to war. Nothing was immune to his corrupting aura; even machine spirits turned rogue in his presence, shrieking in scrapcode as their host engines and cogitators spat cascades of blood-red sparks. Aside from Abaddon himself, it was difficult to find an agent of Chaos that was more roundly hated.

As the Arch-Lord Discordant rode to war, hard-won alliances collapsed around him in suspicion and paranoia. Orders went unheard or unheeded, and tightly bound battle plans unravelled into discord. The warriors of Chaos were vicious and self-centred enough to fight on as individuals; indeed, for the World Eaters he fought alongside at Luthvren Isle, that was already their way of life. But those who thrived on discipline quickly came unstuck. When Vex Machinator led a charge of Juggernaut-riding Bloodletters and hulking Daemon

Engines at the Tzimitria Breach, the Cadians that stood against them could not focus their fire as they had been trained, and in their desperation fired at will. They wounded dozens of the foe, but spread their fire too thinly, and failed to put any of them down. They paid for that mistake with their lives, trampled into the arid wastes by brass-shod hooves.

Behind the battle lines, Machinator's Chaotic aura unbound those who would unite against Abaddon. A conspiracy to dethrone the Warmaster, painstakingly drawn up by the treasonous Daemon Prince Shamha Ygra-Thrysh, ended with the war leaders turning against one another shortly after Vex Machinator joined their ranks as a double agent. Not one of the conspirators survived the ensuing arguments. The Arch-Lord Discordant rode out of the fray alone, covered in gore, and even higher in the Warmaster's favour.

Hereticus Extremis Profile 1.A

ABADDON
THE DESPOILER

Warmaster-class Nemesis (Segmentum
Obscurus, Segmentum Solar,
Ultima Segmentum)

Heretic Astartes Grade Alpha-Alpha-Onus

cf. Ezekyle Abaddon <record incomplete>,
First Captain Luna Wolves (XVI Legion,
First Founding), Sons of Horus (Heresy
Designatus), Black Legion. Discrepancy
Alert 53% causal — see Genetor Majoris
Anzion's Disparate Individual Hypothesis,
Biomagus Suprema Tharazenth's Cloneson
Treatise, Torquemada's Median Tracts.

nb. — Archival request 92% likelihood of
fatal overload to non-Terragrade system
due to density of war record assimilation

cf. Planet Killer (Armageddon Gun)

cf. Bringers of Despair (elite traitoris)

cf. Fortress of Spite (Rebo System)

Opus Record Archives include key terms:

Warmaster, Arch-Heretic, Dark
Pilgrimage, Lord Ravager, Lord
Deceiver, Lord Corruptor, Lord Purgator,
Mournival, Flayerplague

Opus Record Archives include key locales:

Maeleum, Tower of Silence, Floating
Cities of Melphia, Uralan, Cadia, Cadian
Gate, Nemesis Tessera, Belis Corona,
Gerstahl, St. Josmane's Hope, El'Phanor,
Elysia, Tarinth, Jyrro, Mackan, Teekus,
Rithcarn, Cancephalus, Antecanis,
Monarchive, Helica Sector, Thracian
Primaris, Medusa, Relorria, Arx, Mordian,
Hydraphur, Parenxes, Pandorax, Lukitar

<RECORDS INCOMPLETE>

Thought for the Day: Damnation to All Who
Turn from the Emperor's Light.

THE CULTS OF DESTRUCTION

During the war for Vigilus, the Belis
Corona Warbeasts were set upon
the fortress networks of Hyperia.
Giant, lumbering cyborgs each
possessed of a driving obsession for
a particular form of killing, these
grotesque warriors were famously
unruly, but they had learned to fear
Abaddon's displeasure. The hulking
Mutilator known as the King of
Swords had once defied Abaddon –
until he had been cut in two with a
single blow from Drach'nyen. Since
then the Warbeasts had recognised
the master of the Black Legion as
their rightful leader.

The Cults of Destruction took
great pleasure in profaning the
holy ground of Hyperia with their
presence. So redolent with Chaos
were these creatures that their
footsteps left steaming, discoloured
marks on the sacred stones.
When the Obliterators at the fore
opened fire with their profusion of
cannons and heavy weapons, even
the statue-braced bulwarks that
guarded the Ring of Nothingness
were torn down, the garrisons
on their ramparts tumbling with
them. Counter-attacks launched
by the Adepta Sororitas kept the
Obliterators pinned, and where
their Exorcist missile tanks were
brought to bear, even felled them.
But each time the Sisters of Battle
closed within range to bring their
holy trinity of bolter, melta and
flamer to bear, the Mutilators that
thudded alongside their gun-
cyborg brethren would break into
a lumbering run to hit the Imperial
lines with battering-ram force.
Again and again the Sisters gave
ground, for to match that living wall
of blades was to go to a premature
grave. It was only when the Cult of
Destruction was goaded out onto
Phanatos Bridge that the Adepta
Sororitas were able to deal a lasting
blow, collapsing the causeway with
carefully placed munitions and
sending a dozen of the fleshmetal
monstrosities tumbling into the
darkness below.

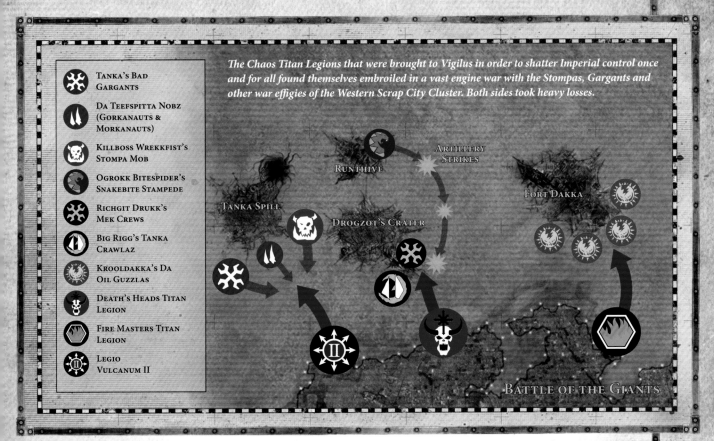

The Chaos Titan Legions that were brought to Vigilus in order to shatter Imperial control once and for all found themselves embroiled in a vast engine war with the Stompas, Gargants and other war effigies of the Western Scrap City Cluster. Both sides took heavy losses.

- TANKA'S BAD GARGANTS
- DA TEEFSPITTA NOBZ (GORKANAUTS & MORKANAUTS)
- KILLBOSS WREKKFIST'S STOMPA MOB
- OGROKK BITESPIDER'S SNAKEBITE STAMPEDE
- RICHGIT DRUKK'S MEK CREWS
- BIG RIGG'S TANKA CRAWLAZ
- KROOLDAKKA'S DA OIL GUZZLAS
- DEATH'S HEADS TITAN LEGION
- FIRE MASTERS TITAN LEGION
- LEGIO VULCANUM II

RUNTHIVE

ARTILLERY STRIKES

TANKA SPILL

DROGZOT'S CRATER

FORT DAKKA

BATTLE OF THE GIANTS

BATTLE OF THE GIANTS

The scrap cities of the Orks were at first all but ignored by the Black Legion's invasion. Only when the Speedlord Supreme, Krooldakka, took the fight to the Brazen Beasts in Megaborealis did Abaddon divert resources to make a punitive strike. He knew in his black heart that the Orks were simply too bellicose a threat to be ignored, and that they respected only brute strength. Luckily, that was something the Black Legion and their allies possessed in great measure.

The Chaos forces that had invaded Vigilus boasted not only Heretic Astartes, but also the Titan Legions of Imperial legend. The hivesprawls of Oteck, Dontoria and Megaborealis had proven so riddled with tunnels, mines and underhives that a god-machine could easily collapse an entire section of road with its weight, so they did not stray far into the cities. Instead, the Titan

Legions bombarded the sites from afar with their long-range cannons.

After Krooldakka's attack, these metal giants turned from their assigned sprawls and marched out into the wastes to do battle with the greenskin horde's Stompas, Gorkanauts, Morkanauts and Gargants. At Tanka Spill, Drogzot's Crater and Fort Dakka a war of metal monstrosities broke out, the battle raging amongst the looted hulks of the Freeblade Imperial Knights that had made their ill-fated assault during the War of Beasts. This time the Orks were outmatched, for the skill, savagery and raw firepower of the Chaos Titans that faced them saw three greenskin war effigies torn apart for every god-machine they brought down. Even at close range the Chaos Titans excelled, ripping the Ork machines asunder with coiling tentacles and long-taloned claws that punched, thrust and gouged at the heads of their adversaries.

The battle dragged on for days, for what the Orks lacked in quality they made up for in quantity and aggression alike.

The clash was immensely costly for both sides, but prevented the Orks from gaining the momentum they needed to launch a full Waaagh!. In this it allowed the main body of the Black Legion invaders to concentrate on tearing apart the Imperium's armies.

FORCES OF THE ALPHA LEGION

The Alpha Legion warbands on Vigilus were provided with an open mandate by Abaddon: wreak whatever havoc they pleased, provided it destabilised the Imperial military infrastructure. This was a war that perfectly suited the clandestine compulsions of this most devious and divisive of Traitor Legions.

To date, Imperial historitors have been unable to accurately assess the number of Alpha Legionnaires that operated on Vigilus. There is no way of determining the true damage they caused, for many records pertaining to the heretics' operations were mysteriously corrupted or erased.

Others were actively booby-trapped, data-gheists savaging the autosavants tasked with these records' recovery. It has been surmised, however, that the Alpha Legion was behind a string of uprisings by cells of Chaos Cultists throughout Hyperia. Elements of the Cadian 92nd and

the 187th 'Fanebreakers' suffered heavy casualties during a guerrilla offensive by fanatical heretic elements. Fragmentary reports persist of half-seen giants in blue-green power armour who supported the cultist onslaught, but not a single loyalist eyewitness survived to corroborate these tales.

The many-headed hydra of the Alpha Legion represents their fluid and duplicitous way of war.

The omnibetical symbols for 'alpha' and 'omega' are intertwined in some Alpha Legion iconography.

The symbol of the hydra speaks of a force that can never be defeated by traditional means.

The sea-green of the Alpha Legion is sometimes adorned with hydra designs and scale patterns. A common tactic is to mark out new recruits as if they were squad leaders, duping the enemy's snipers in the heat of battle.

CATASTROPHE AT HUB K-876

The Trinity Hives that towered over Hyperia Hivesprawl were crucial distribution centres for the aqua sanctus that sustained its populace. Efforts by elements within the Adeptus Ministorum had seen that precious resource continue to flow down to workers labouring in Hyperia's munitions manufactorums. Aqua sanctus was the divine fuel powering the workforce, who in turn fed the holy armaments of the Imperial defenders; such was the rationale of the charitable mission known as the Benevolent Hand. This collection of Ministorum Priests, frateris militia and Battle Sisters from the Order of Our Martyred Lady worked tirelessly – often in perilous conditions and with no official logistical support – to supply those who would otherwise have been ignored by self-interested Munitorum clerks.

It is unclear whether the Benevolent Hand were infiltrated by Alpha Legion operatives, or were simply fed misinformation to propel them into damnation. A sudden shift in activities indicates the point at which Ministorum volunteers grew suspicious of the source of the aqua sanctus coming into Hivespire Magentine. It can be inferred from recovered fragments of communiqués that the Benevolent Hand became convinced that, as a result of heretic sabotage, the water they were distributing bore a corrupting taint. After their warnings to the Munitorum fell upon deaf ears, the Benevolent Hand acted directly. They distributed weapons amongst their flock, attempting to halt and forcibly inspect a large shipment of water coming through Hub K-876 from outside Hyperia. Instead of heretical saboteurs, however, the Benevolent Hand found themselves faced by several platoons of Cadian 92nd heavy infantry who – thanks to a now untraceable tip-off – were expecting malicious interference from disguised heretical elements attempting to corrupt the water supply. Post-action analysis shows that the first shot, which turned a tense stand-off into a slaughter, was fired not by a representative of either Imperial faction, but by a concealed third party with a bolt-calibre sniper weapon concealed in the gantries above Hub K-876. This sparked a brutal firefight that saw the Benevolent Hand annihilated, the Cadian platoons savaged and the entire aqua sanctus shipment ruined. At a stroke, the water supply to the Magentine munitions workers was cut off, triggering an estimated twenty-four per cent drop in material output over the following weeks. Furthermore, it cannot be a coincidence that those same Cadian platoons, weakened by the Catastrophe at Hub K-876, proved unable to hold back a string of raids upon Hivespire Magentine by unidentified Heretic Astartes kill teams in the days that followed.

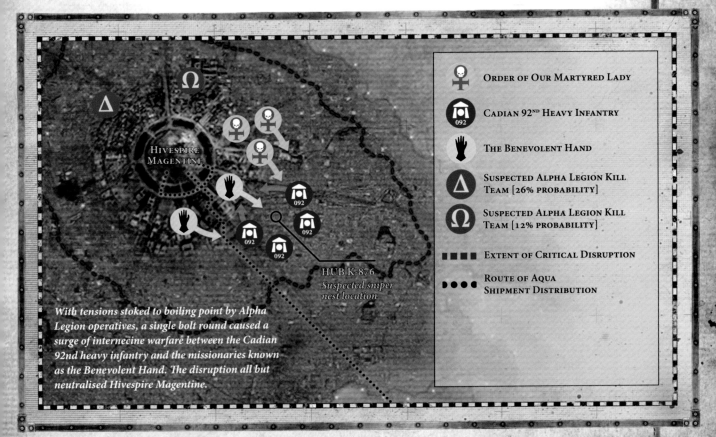

With tensions stoked to boiling point by Alpha Legion operatives, a single bolt round caused a surge of internecine warfare between the Cadian 92nd heavy infantry and the missionaries known as the Benevolent Hand. The disruption all but neutralised Hivespire Magentine.

HUB K-876
Suspected sniper nest location

ORDER OF OUR MARTYRED LADY

CADIAN 92ND HEAVY INFANTRY

THE BENEVOLENT HAND

SUSPECTED ALPHA LEGION KILL TEAM [26% PROBABILITY]

SUSPECTED ALPHA LEGION KILL TEAM [12% PROBABILITY]

EXTENT OF CRITICAL DISRUPTION

ROUTE OF AQUA SHIPMENT DISTRIBUTION

FORCES OF THE NIGHT LORDS

Masters of psychological warfare, the Night Lords had done a great deal to destabilise the planet in the third phase of the War of Beasts. When they indulged in open battle, however, they found themselves matched against a foe like no other – and brought to the brink of disgrace.

The Night Lords upon Vigilus were few, for the greater portion of their Legion was involved in an escalating war with the Asuryani, but they made a heavy impact nonetheless. The heretics initially invaded Dirkden Hivesprawl, hoping for easy prey, but soon found xenos in the shadows.

The Night Lords had taken that tumbled, crime-ridden sprawl as a perfect environment for their particular brand of warfare, and perhaps even a recruiting ground for new blood, for the Sons of Curze had long filled their ranks with hardened criminals. Their Raptor hosts gleefully hung the

corpses of their prey from the half-finished spires of Ashenid Non-Hive as their strike forces prowled the lower levels. They took note of those gangs and criminal overlords that put up a good fight and spared those that showed the most promise. The enterprise was profitable at first, as well as being

The winged skull symbol of the Night Lords has struck fear into the Imperium's worlds for millennia.

In some warbands, a winged skull on a field of crimson denotes a Night Lords war visionary.

The laughing skull device is often worn by Night Lords who specialise in stealth attacks.

The battle plate of the Night Lords is adorned with grotesque imagery intended to strike fear into the foe. Some members of this Legion even have tendrils of wild energy crackling across their power armour.

gratifying in terms of raw violence and terror – the Night Lords captured many slaves and selected no few criminal prodigies to bolster their own ranks.

Then the indigenous Genestealer Cult that had lurked beneath Dirkden's surface for generations rose up against the Night Lords invaders. Though the cultists had expended a vast proportion of their strength overtaking the hivesprawl continent, they infested every stratum of Dirkdenite society, and had multiplied exponentially in the darkness. No matter how many the Heretic Astartes killed there seemed always to be more. They proved far better armed and more tenacious than the Imperial troops that the Night Lords had encountered in the skeletal convoys fleeing the hivesprawl, and they carried heavy industrial weaponry and exhibited strange xenomutations as lethal as any chainsword.

For a time, the Night Lords slew every breed of hybrid that dared challenge them, but even they were not indefatigable. Eventually, the hunters found that they had become the hunted. Purestrain Genestealers burst out from smuggling cavities within false walls, Goliath Rockgrinders drove recklessly into the flanks of Rhino transport convoys, and street-level Brood Brother weapons teams took pot shots at the Raptors haunting the unfinished spires.

Each strike ended in a vicious melee as the Heretic Astartes fought back-to-back to slay their assailants with chainswords and lightning-wreathed claws, but whenever the cultists were outmatched they melted away into the shadows as if at some unseen signal. Ultimately, the Night Lords were forced to concede the continent, making off with what gains they could secure.

The heretics chose their targets with greater care on the eastern borders of Hyperia, waging a hit-and-run war against a foe they knew how to fight from long experience – the Adeptus Astartes. Engaging the Dark Angels of the 4th Company, they launched a series of smaller skirmishes, but did so with a far greater degree of fury – for their pride had been besmirched by the events in Dirkden, and their bitter ire mingled with aeons-old hatred.

This was a war for survival, for, after their failure in Dirkden, the Night Lords could not report back to Abaddon without news of victory in the wider war. The losses they had sustained in Dirkden were almost untenable, the raw recruits they had picked out from the populace were a long way from becoming true Space Marines, and the spoils of war had been few and far between. So the Night Lords fought with cunning and stealth instead of the dark predatory glee with which they had begun their campaign. Their kill teams struck hard from the blackest alleyways wherever the Dark Angels gathered, taking down one or two warriors before staging a fighting retreat and repeating the tactic elsewhere.

It was an effective mode of warfare, and it won the Night Lords a string of minor, but significant, victories. Only when the airborne elements of the Ravenwing tracked down and killed Varrus Hekatos, the Chaos Lord coordinating the ambushing strikes, did the Dark Angels manage to fight the Night Lords on their own terms.

SURVIVAL OF THE CRUELLEST

It was towards the end of the War of Nightmares that Praxis Empyrealus rose to power amongst the ranks of the Night Lords. The skull-masked Master of Possession had been Varrus Hekatos' advisor for years, but the two generally exhibited a cold and seething hatred for one another. Though few amongst the Night Lords knew it, it was Praxis who had set the fires in the formerly quiet Venderan Maze – Hekatos' base of operations. The leaping flames alerted the Ravenwing to the commander's presence and, after a costly skirmish where Land Speeders duelled with jump pack-equipped Night Lords in the tightly packed streets, both Hekatos and the Ravenwing Lieutenant Pinyus lay dead.

Praxis Empyrealus wasted no time. Summoning a flock of iridescent sky rays and several packs of warpfire-hurling Flamers, he corralled the Land Speeders of the Ravenwing by setting the skies afire. Then, taking an impossible risk by physically touching the Noctilith Crown he had raised at the heart of the Maze, Praxis Empyrealus blasted the agile craft from the sky with a storm of livid purple lightning. When elements from the 3rd and 4th Companies of the Dark Angels closed in, they were met by overlapping fields of bolter fire – the Night Lords had learned every nook and crevice of their lair well. Five Dark Angels died for every Night Lord that fell that day, a ratio that pleased Abaddon enough to overlook the disastrous attack upon Dirkden. The Night Lords withdrew from the front lines after that victory – though they maintained a presence throughout the rest of the war.

FORCES OF THE WORD BEARERS

Upon making planetfall, the Word Bearers applied every bit of their dark cunning and single-minded commitment to the execution of the Warmaster's grand plan. While the Black Legion were destroying the material keeping the Great Rift at bay, the Word Bearers were raising structures to attract it.

Abaddon tasked the Word Bearers with a vital part of his strategy – to seed the planet with the ring-like structures known as Noctilith Crowns. The Despoiler's grudging respect for the Word Bearers, and their commitment to the downfall of the Imperium, was made clear when he took the leaders of

that Legion into his confidence. Amongst them were the nine Chaos Lords and Dark Apostles known as the Coven Triplicatus. On his rune-circled artificer decks, Abaddon showed them dozens of Noctilith Crowns, and explained the reasons behind their creation. It was a plan of such impressive ambition and

devotion that the Coven Triplicatus knelt before him, offering their maces and accursed croziuses to him as knights would offer their swords to their liege.

It was no easy feat to raise the Noctilith Crowns; even to touch the great toroidal constructions was

The burning, infernal head is the symbol of the Word Bearers. Many variations were seen upon Vigilus.

The Bringers of Enlightenment, a warband under Deshamentus, raised many Noctilith Crowns.

The tomes depicted on the armour of the Word Bearers are symbolic of their blasphemous knowledge.

The deep crimson of the Word Bearers' armour is bracketed with frameworks of burnished gunmetal. Sometimes their armour is adorned in Colchisian script, each string of dark runes an excerpt from the unholy Book of Lorgar.

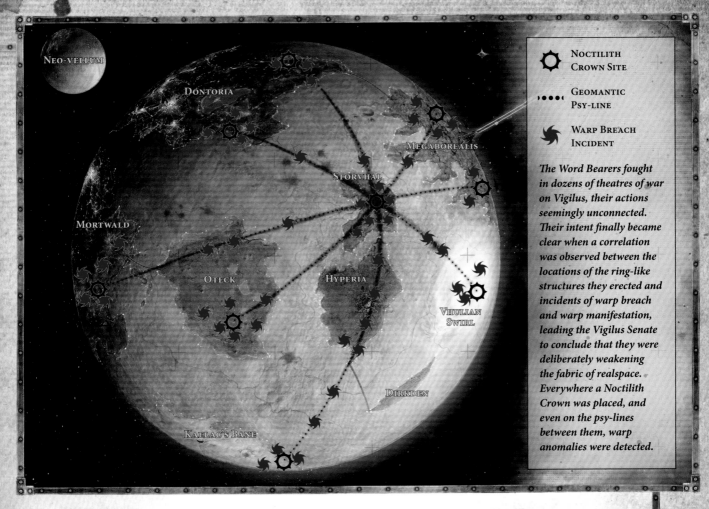

NEO-VELLUM

DONTORIA

MEGABOREALIS

STORVHAL

MORTWALD

OTECK

HYPERIA

VEHULIAN
SWIRL

DIRKDEN

KAELAC'S BANE

NOCTILITH
CROWN SITE

GEOMANTIC
PSY-LINE

WARP BREACH
INCIDENT

*The Word Bearers fought
in dozens of theatres of war
on Vigilus, their actions
seemingly unconnected.
Their intent finally became
clear when a correlation
was observed between the
locations of the ring-like
structures they erected and
incidents of warp breach
and warp manifestation,
leading the Vigilus Senate
to conclude that they were
deliberately weakening
the fabric of realspace.
Everywhere a Noctilith
Crown was placed, and
even on the psy-lines
between them, warp
anomalies were detected.*

to risk death by psychic overload. But like their Primarch Lorgar before them, the war leaders of the Word Bearers are consummate demagogues, dark preachers and charismatic leaders, and they have never been short of cultist devotees ready to give their lives to a cause. By raising slave gangs, each several hundred strong, the Word Bearers hauled the Chaos-attracting structures into place and had them hammered into the planet's crust. Thousands perished, but it was a sacrifice the Word Bearers made without a second thought. Those slaves whose latent supernatural ability blossomed into full psychic manifestation were dragged away and psycho-conditioned by the Legion's Sorcerers and Masters of Possession. The most stable of these vassal psykers were given prominent Imperial targets that they were to get close to before the implanted conditioning of their masters spurred their tortured minds into a devastating psychic overload.

Others were chained together and put under great duress until their communal agony caused them to rip themselves apart with wild psychic energy, and in doing so, form a gate through which the daemonic allies of the Word Bearers could enter realspace. Wherever such a site came to be, another Noctilith Crown was raised, attracting yet more Daemons to the planet's surface. It was a shockingly effective tactic, and with the Word Bearers fighting as a well-coordinated strike force in each site's defence, it provided a major source of reinforcements for Abaddon's war effort.

Only three of the numerous Noctilith Crowns that Abaddon had entrusted to the Word Bearers remained on the *Vengeful Spirit*'s artificer decks at the time of its emergency translation into the empyrean. Had they too been raised, it is quite possible the entire planet would have been swallowed by the warp.

'Let that pompous fool Abaddon think we do his bidding. It matters not. For all his vision, for all his might, he is still but a mortal, and one who has refused the ultimate blessing of the Ruinous Powers. No indeed, anointed ones – here we do the work of the Dark Gods, bringing devastation unto the universe that all might see the glory of the Primordial Truth. When the long night descends upon this planet, all will know the true glory of Chaos.'

*- Epistle of the Fated Speaker
Deshamentus, Bringer of
Enlightenment and Butcher
of the Ellerophosus Hivebelt*

FORCES OF THE IRON WARRIORS

The Iron Warriors wage war with a cold and bitter hatred. On Vigilus, each callous strike was well planned and driven home with the expertise of a master artisan. They broke apart the most heavily defended of the planet's integral sites at Mortwald, allowing the wider forces of Chaos to flood inside.

The Warsmith Kharrack began his campaign upon Vigilus by remotely scrying the fortifications of the Imperial defences. He and his fellow Warsmiths took extensive images from low orbit and amassed data through the use of corrupted servo-skulls released onto the planet below. By the time

Haarken Worldclaimer's challenge rang out, the Iron Warriors were well prepared; thousands of pict-captures had already been relayed back to the bridge of their flagship, the *Portcullis*. However, upon sighting the vibrant heraldic yellow of their long-term enemies – the Imperial Fists – the Iron Warriors

altered their intended campaign. Though their invasion was designed to assail multiple fronts, the better to crack the defences of the planet wide open, it soon turned into a singular assault upon the defences of Mortwald's eastern edge. The stage was set for a clash that would see no quarter asked nor given.

The armoured skull symbol of the Iron Warriors is often a harbinger of a mechanised assault.

The black skull, worn over a field of gunmetal, can denote a specialist close-combat slaughter-team.

The white skull often denotes the masters of heavy firepower.

But for industrial markings that speak of danger, the gunmetal armour of the Iron Warriors is largely unadorned. This is a sign of the pragmatic and efficient style of warfare practiced by the Sons of Perturabo.

THE SHATTERING OF THE SHIELDS

Though the Warmaster of Chaos charged the Iron Warriors with the destruction of Vigilus' defence networks, they greeted the order with indifference, even scorn. The prosecution of sieges was their art, and they would practice it no matter the greater plan. Their first act was to attack an unremarkable fringe of each hivesprawl, aiming for those areas that were too poor or strategically insignificant to be well defended. Their Warpsmiths then polluted the Bastion force field networks that ran around them with a potent machine plague. Were it not for the semi-psychic nature of the Bastion fields, the plague would have struggled against the inbuilt fail-safes installed by the Adeptus Mechanicus, but there was a hostile sentience to the scrapcode entity that was introduced. With the force fields already glitching and damaged due to the coming of the Great Rift, the machine plague thrived – indeed, it multiplied – by feasting on the empyric

component of each node. By leaping through psycho-electric fields from one generator to another, it spread with horrible rapidity. By the second stage of the War of Nightmares, a full two-thirds of the force field generators were functionally useless.

The Imperial defenders were disastrously unprepared for this new development. On the outskirts of Mortwald, those armies that had left the trenches, relying on the Bastion networks to guard their flanks, found out the hard way that the shield generators had been compromised. Lord Deinos' suspicions as to their efficacy had been confirmed, yet even his traditional defences were found wanting. The Iron Warriors, using their preferred vector of mechanised assault, drove home a series of attacks that blitzed through the trench networks with humbling ease. Scores of Iron Warriors kill teams had been despatched to Megaborealis early in the war, their aim to secure the

mighty Tectonic Fragdrills there. These were brought to the trenches whenever a bunker network proved unbreachable, and used to create localised earthquakes that cracked fissures through shell-strewn ground and fortification alike. Into every split in the Imperial defence, the Iron Warriors pushed home another wedge attack that widened hairline breaches into yawning gaps. A fierce, grinding war began between the Space Marines of Dorn's heritage and the traitors of Perturabo's ancient order – in sheer violence, savagery and obstinate refusal to yield, it was reminiscent of the legendary Iron Cage. Ultimately, Captain Fane's loyalist forces, having been battered by the Orks of the Western Scrap City Cluster and then attacked head-on by their most hated nemeses, had not the manpower to hold the line. The Imperial Fists were forced to withdraw to Hyperia, conceding Mortwald to the Iron Warriors and the Flawless Host.

SHATTERING OF THE SHIELDS

Fane's Imperial Fists

Ventrillian Nobles 141

Sonasthi Royal Guard 217

Iron Warriors Mechanised Blitz

Tectonic Fragdrill Deployment Site

Site of Scrapcode Infection

Bastion Field Network [Infected]

Bastion Field Network [Operative]

Disabled Force Field

The Iron Warriors under Warsmith Kharrack saw the Deinos Trench Line not as a hindrance, but a challenge. Rather than risk drawing the fire of the defence lasers that protected the major sites still in Imperial hands, they made planetfall in the wastes outside the false continent, then used scrapcode infection to compromise the already unstable Bastion force field network. In doing so, they took many of the Imperial forces there by surprise, and pushed through to deploy Tectonic Fragdrills they had secured earlier in the war. The resultant earthquakes disrupted the entire front.

RENEGADE FORCES

The Heretic Astartes upon Vigilus numbered in the tens of thousands. Given the fact they were the equal of the Space Marines they once called brothers, that was more than enough to conquer a planet. Much of that number was made up of renegades, each turncoat Chapter a vicious bane in its own right.

The Space Marines that fell to Chaos after the tumultuous time of the Horus Heresy are amongst the most cunning of the Heretic Astartes, and in the business of war each is worth a hundred mortal men. Some are veterans of the unending battle against the False Emperor and his works, heretics that have spent long and blood-soaked centuries tearing down the empire they once strove to protect. Others are more recent converts to the causes of the Dark Gods, their hatred of the Imperium burning bright as they rejoice in the breaking of the bonds that once trammelled every aspect of their existence.

These Renegade Chapters were considered a powerful asset in the warhosts of the Black Crusades, and to the people of Vigilus – and its Astra Militarum defenders – they were feared just as much as their traitor predecessors.

Each Renegade Chapter brought with it its own unique strategic specialities, Chaotic boons and potent materiel – and to underestimate them was to invite a painful death.

Twelve Renegade Chapters fought as part of the Vigilus invasion, each sworn to Abaddon's cause. Whether through notions of fealty,

common cause, or opportunism, each of them took the fight to the hivesprawls with abandon. For the most part, they did so with lightning raids and swift strikes, the doctrines they had practised as loyalist Chapters. Now they brought the very skills imparted to them by the Imperium to bear against their former comrades.

The Red Corsairs are expert raiders. Operating out of the Maelstrom, these piratical killers were the bane of Imperial shipping routes.

The Scourged were cursed by Tzeentch to hear the falsehoods of all Mankind – a trait that leads to madness as often as it does a strange kind of insight.

THE FLAWLESS HOST

The Flawless Host saw the self-important nobility of Mortwald much as a snake sees a warren of mice. They descended from their magnificent starships to parade amongst the preening aristocrats of that false continent, at first arriving with all the pomp of some neighbouring monarchy sent to dispense largesse. As soon as the first shot was fired upon them, they turned into furies, screeching their hatred as they slaughtered household guards and elite Militarum Tempestus escorts by the hundred. When the Iron Warriors finally drove their Imperial Fists nemeses from the trench lines and took control of the hives, they found only corpses in the richest zones. At the heart of each such region they encountered the Flawless Host, availing themselves of Mortwald's finest rejuvenat clinics in an attempt to regain what they saw as the pinnacle of human beauty.

THE BRAZEN BEASTS

The Daemonkin hosts of the Brazen Beasts were instrumental in the destruction of Megaborealis' silo districts. After the refractor field that protected Silo XV had been brought down, Abaddon's punitive bombardment slew the majority of the Brazen Beasts within a three-mile radius. Only those with Daemon taint in their blood rode out the firestorm, the Chaos-touched renegades howling praise to the Blood God as the ash of mortals billowed past them. Khorne cares not from whence the blood flows, and he was pleased with the callous slaughter. The Warmaster subsequently sent a vast horde of Bloodletters to reinforce the Brazen Beasts, who then went on to conquer a significant portion of Megaborealis. The Herald Skulltaker led them, along with a slew of Daemon Engines, in a hunt for the heads of the hivesprawl's Tech-Priests.

THE PURGE

The Purge, devotees of Nurgle in his destroyer aspect, afflicted Dontoria Hivesprawl. They despised life in all its forms, and there the planet's overpopulation was by far the most pronounced. It was an obvious target for their morbid obsession with death and destruction – though in time, the Purge intended to spread their conquests across the planet entire.

In their relentless and efficient killing sprees, the Purge used every weapon and trick they could conceive of – fast-spreading epidemics, airborne poisons, wholesale demolition, and even arson. Provided the populace was slaughtered – and along with them, every other creature, from their grox breeding stock to the bloodlice that infested their bunks – the Purge considered their duty fulfilled. To them, every form of life was hopelessly corrupt.

The warriors of the Purge once swore to defeat Chaos no matter the cost, but in exterminating every living thing to prevent its corruption, they too serve the Dark Gods.

The Flawless Host wear lurid colours and commit acts of unbridled excess at will, for they believe they can do no wrong. Their destructive fits of pique are legendary.

Spreading across eastern Dontoria into the west, the Purge came into conflict with Death Guard elements whose philosophy concerning Nurgle meant they embraced the great cycle of life, death and rebirth. Where one wanted to slay all life, the other wished to propagate it – albeit in its most repugnant form. A religious schism of sorts saw the two opposed forces all but neutralise one another, but the civil conflict was cold comfort to the Vigilus Senate; by that point, Dontoria was already lost.

RED CORSAIRS

The Red Corsairs, firm allies of Abaddon since he found common cause with their master Huron Blackheart, were the scourge of the planet's shipping lanes and spaceports. Arguably the best steersmen in the entire Chaos invasion force, they swiftly moved to establish void superiority above all the major hivesprawls, stymieing the Imperial reinforcements that

might otherwise have bolstered their kindred planetside.

Wherever Imperial forces were sent by the Vigilus Senate to reclaim the spaceports that had fallen into the hands of the Red Corsairs, the renegades would at first fight from on high, unleashing bombardments and making strafing runs as their Heldrakes clawed rival craft out of the skies. Only when they were certain of victory did the Red Corsairs jump out of their drop craft to join the fray and finish off the survivors.

It is said the Red Corsairs fought with a fury and determination that made even the White Scars reconsider their assaults upon the spaceports. The renegades' given duty was to ensure the planet was kept under lockdown, and that no unauthorised ships could make passage in or out. Though they had not the numbers to cover every spaceport, as raiders beyond compare, they were well qualified to fulfil this task.

Only a few spacecraft slipped the cordon of the Red Corsairs over the course of the War of Nightmares, such was its efficacy. Critically, one of the craft to avoid their clutches was the vessel known as *Vaul's Ghost*, the ship that carried the deadly payload of Deathstrike missiles to Abaddon's flagship the *Vengeful Spirit*, with destructive consequences. Were it not for this singular failing, the war for Vigilus would likely have been a total victory for the forces of Chaos.

THE SCOURGED

The Renegade Chapter known as the Scourged have a particular connection with Vigilus, for they hail from the neighbouring death world of Falsehood, where squalls of acid rain are as common as the dawn. They are renegades like no other, for they have the uncanny ability to hear lies whenever they are spoken. Just as a good and faithful statement has the ring of truth about it, a lie can be perceived as hollow by one who knows the signs. On Falsehood, it became common practice to guard against falsity, for the planet itself had been founded on a deception concerning its viability as a home world, and its people had grown to despise untruths ever since. It is a tragic irony – of the type much beloved of the Dark Gods – that the Scourged now have no choice but to hear every foul utterance spoken by Mankind.

Once, long ago, the Scourged were a Chapter of noble Space Marines known as the Seekers of Truth. They did everything in their power to live up to that name. But all too often they were despatched on crusades to kill the innocent alongside the guilty, and that rankled their sensibilities – no more so than with their Chapter Master, Gallus Herodicus.

In a moment of weakness, Herodicus prayed at length to somehow be granted the power to discern the guiltless from the damned, to know truth from deceit, and hear the lies of men for what they were. His wish was granted, but not by the Emperor. It pleased the Architect of Fate to give every member of the Chapter a gift. From that day on, they heard all the lies spoken across the galaxy, a constant susurration of perfidy that robbed them of clear thought. Though they heard those spoken near them loudest of all – and hence were often able to pick out the true agendas of their enemies amongst the background noise of

Mankind's duplicity – they were plagued by so much mental pollution they gradually lost their minds. By turning to Tzeentch's worship in the hope it would lessen their burden, the Scourged became a far deadlier threat to the innocent than they ever were before – and a merciless bane to those who spin lies as a way of life.

During the War of Nightmares, the Scourged descended upon Dirkden in a devastating aerial assault, dropping in to carefully chosen beachheads around the safe houses of the criminal dynasties. They attacked the lairs and subterranean nodes of the Genestealer Cult in a synchronous assault, for the lies and deceptions perpetuated by the cult to keep those strongholds safe made them glow with the energy of falsehood. Their attack did irreparable damage to the xenos war effort but, in the end, the cultists proved too many, and the victory too was proved false.

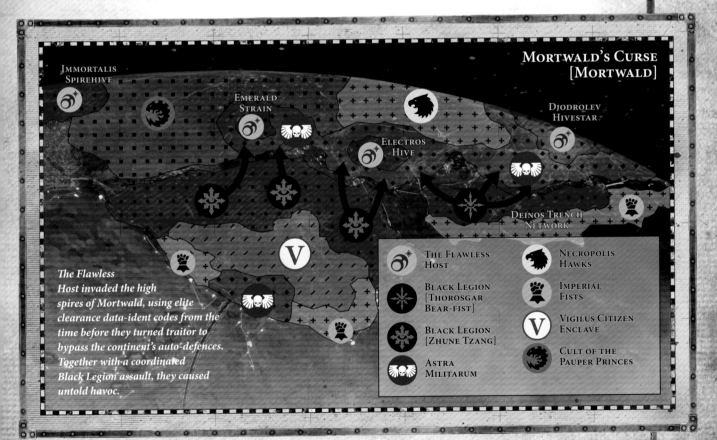

MORTWALD'S CURSE [MORTWALD]

IMMORTALIS SPIREHIVE

EMERALD STRAIN

ELECTROS HIVE

DJODROLEV HIVESTAR

DEINOS TRENCH NETWORK

The Flawless Host invaded the high spires of Mortwald, using elite clearance data-ident codes from the time before they turned traitor to bypass the continent's auto-defences. Together with a coordinated Black Legion assault, they caused untold havoc.

THE FLAWLESS HOST

BLACK LEGION [THOROSGAR BEAR-FIST]

BLACK LEGION [ZHUNE TZANG]

ASTRA MILITARUM

NECROPOLIS HAWKS

IMPERIAL FISTS

VIGILUS CITIZEN ENCLAVE

CULT OF THE PAUPER PRINCES

FORCES OF THE WARP

Over the course of the War of Beasts, the psychic maladies that plagued Vigilus rarely gave rise to daemonic manifestation. That changed as the Chaos invasion took hold, however, and the frequency of these occurrences increased dramatically over the course of the War of Nightmares.

Upon Vigilus, the talons of the Dark Gods had gouged deep. Each Noctilith Crown hammered into its crust increased the amount of empyric energy saturating the planet; to the witch-sighted Astropaths of Neo-vellum, these structures burned brighter than any blazing spire or urban firestorm. Once the blackstone reserves of Megaborealis were shattered, it was as if a dam had broken, and the trickle of daemonic manifestations became a flood. Here was the true legacy of the Great Rift – not just panic and terror, but also another dimension breaching realspace in a catastrophic cascade of warp energy.

Dontoria's slow descent into a plague-racked hellscape had been engineered from below the city

streets since the early stages of the War of Beasts. The Death Guard, content to play the long game, had infected half the populous with a hideous cornucopia of diseases. Fiercest amongst them were Nurgle's Rot and the Gellerpox, supernatural plagues that led to Nurglings and Mutoid Vermin infesting the alleyways and undersumps of the quarantine zones. The privation, drought and hunger inflicted upon the populace, worsened by the Vhulian Anomaly, turned once-teeming hab-zones into landscapes of flyblown corpses.

DAEMONS OF NURGLE

When two Noctilith Crowns were raised in Dontoria, a massive influx of plague Daemons poured through the weakened fabric of realspace to infect the hivesprawl. They were

led by the entity known as Rotigus Rainfather. An endless deluge of filthy rainwater hammered out of the skies as that obese monstrosity lumbered through the streets, chortling as the arid ground greedily absorbed the flood until it became more marsh than desert. Millions of Dontoria's remaining citizens, half-mad with thirst after having their water supplies dwindle to nothing, drank of that foul water – and in doing so, damned themselves. The Astra Militarum, the Munitorum, even the more human elements of the Pauper Princes partook of the gushing fluids that poured from the pregnant skies. Everyone that let that water pass their lips spent their last few days riddled with grey flux, tsepsis and goitre-plague; some even found themselves expelling

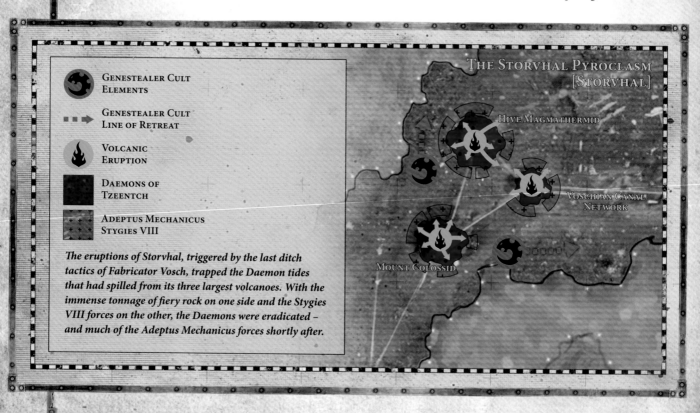

GENESTEALER CULT ELEMENTS

GENESTEALER CULT LINE OF RETREAT

VOLCANIC ERUPTION

DAEMONS OF TZEENTCH

ADEPTUS MECHANICUS STYGIES VIII

The eruptions of Storvhal, triggered by the last ditch tactics of Fabricator Vosch, trapped the Daemon tides that had spilled from its three largest volcanoes. With the immense tonnage of fiery rock on one side and the Stygies VIII forces on the other, the Daemons were eradicated – and much of the Adeptus Mechanicus forces shortly after.

THE STORVHAL PYROCLASM
[STORVHAL]

HIVE MAGMATHERMID

VOSCHIAN CANAL NETWORK

MOUNT COLOSSID

DAEMONS OF CHAOS

The manifestations of Daemons that blighted the War of Nightmares were not confined to its third phase, but escalated dramatically once the Noctilith Crowns had been placed on sites of geomantic import by the Black Legion and the Word Bearers. Around those sites, the malefic energies gathered by the runic devices lent great strength to the daemonic forces fighting nearby.

KHORNATE WAR LEGIONS

The Cruel Blades	6 warbands (infantry)
Harnak's Gauntlet	2 warbands
The Feet of Khorne's Ire	5 warbands (cavalry)
The Steeltalons	8 warbands
The Red Doom	3 warbands (estimate)
The Scarlet Manifestation	8 warbands
The Brazen Shield	2 warbands
Ulxor's Thunder	1 warband (Skull Cannons)
The Furnace-maws	1 warband (Skull Cannons)

SLAANESHI HOSTS OF EXCESS

Vishy's Last Cavalcade	6 warbands (chariots)
Slathslaver's Merciless Sistren	13 warbands
Gluggatach's Obesons	3 warbands (immobile)
Helmynch's Psyrens	8 warbands (psyker-heavy)

TZEENTCHIAN WARP CABALS

The Ritual Scorch	9 warbands (pyrotechnic)
The Flickering Fires	3 warbands
Twisten Helicas	6 warbands (Glossolalian)
The Capering Choir	8 warbands
Brimstone Purgers	3 warbands (toxic air)
Verenastia's Gifted	2 warbands (psykers)

NURGLESQUE PLAGUE HORDES

Olghott's Gifted	2 warbands
The Sepsikh Choir	7 warbands
The Mortwald Tallymen	7 warbands (arboreal)
The Bilegut Guard	4 warbands (armoured)
The Vomitous Deluge	7 warbands (floodborne)
The Hollowed	11 warbands
Foulgyre's Pretties	3 warbands (Nurgling-heavy)

CULTS OF SUMMONATION

Proven incidence of deliberate alliance with Daemons and subsequent warp/realspace breach recorded

The Faithwrought	pyroclastic cult
The Sons of Vannadan	pyroclastic cult
The Clarion Daemonic	demagogue cult (unaligned)
The Rhetormentors	demagogue cult (unaligned)
The Eightfold Blessed	Khornate cult
The Cadian 666th 'Purified'	Khornate cult
The Tattered Veil	Nurglesque cult
Sons of the Silver King	Slaaneshi cult
Children of the Blessed Light	Tzeentchian cult
The Touched	Tzeentchian cult

TITHE OF THE SOUL FORGES

The Dark Bargain	Soul Grinder pack
Rust Incarnate	Soul Grinder pack
The Stalker on the Horizon	Greater Brass Scorpion

INFERNUS-CLASS GOD-MACHINES

End of Hope	Banelord Titan
Nullifact Malignus	Traitor Warlord Titan
Desecrator	Traitor Warlord Titan
Diabolus Rex	Traitor Reaver Titan
Helclaw	Traitor Reaver Titan
God of Hate	Traitor Reaver Titan
Stormstalker	Traitor Warhound Titan
Phantom Abominus	Traitor Warhound Titan
Preytaker	Traitor Warhound Titan
Fleshripper	Traitor Warhound Titan

++CONTINUED IN FILE IMP.VIG/PGS2/1-12

ALL DIABOLUS-CLASS FILES CLASSIFIED BY ORDER OF THE ORDO MALLEUS

Mindwipe Protocol auto-activated for Unknown Biomark Ident Vigilus conflict codified 'War of Nightmares' codified in auxiliary dataslate Imp.Vig/PG2w3/121-125.

---

stomach-grown Nurglings in a vomitous mockery of birth.

By that time the Death Guard and the Purge had begun their self-destructive war for control of the damned false continent; the bloated cadavers of Dontoria outnumbered the living ten times over, and plague Daemons of all kinds capered freely through the sprawl.

DAEMONS OF TZEENTCH

The magma farms of Storvhal had played host to the phenomenon dubbed the Flickering Fires, beings that danced in the flames, since the first phase of the War of Beasts – or so its workers claimed. At first, their overlords and Tech-Priest handlers had put these fanciful tales down to the superstition of heat-addled minds – perhaps to avoid any Inquisitorial scrutiny – so the rumours went unchecked. However, the sudden manifestation of lurid-coloured Daemons, which appeared at around the time of

Silo XV's destruction, proved the workers right.

The volcanoes of each geothermic farm began to overflow, but this was no natural eruption – a kaleidoscopic cascade of warpfire spilled flame-spewing Daemons down the flanks of each mountain. For a while, Skitarii, servitor and slave fought bravely to hold them back, levelling firepower from the Voschian Canals. Then the defenders found their lines attacked from behind by the pyroclastic cults that had long been gaining power in Storvhal. The mortal servants of the Capering Choir cried out in supplication to the feathered Lords of Change soaring in the thermals high above, while the Twisten Helicas rode the lava flow into the Voschian Canal Network, gibbering in foul tongues. As unharmed by the refined magma as sump-swimmers in an underwater river, they headed out into the client continents that were fuelled by Storvhal's exported energy, there

to cause untold havoc amongst the populace.

The Tech-Priests sanctioned protocols for Geothermis Extremis, using their Fragdrill networks to puncture Storvhal's tectonic plates in such a way that the carefully marshalled volcanic currents were goaded into a full-scale eruption. This time it was magma that boiled from the cupolas of each active volcano – not burning away the Daemons so much as burying them under billions of tons of glowing rock-sludge. It was a devastating counterstrike, but one that crippled Vigilus' expertly managed supply of energy forever.

In the hivesprawls furthest from Storvhal, the autocandles and lumens began to go out, and Mankind's most ancient fear rose to the surface across a landscape lit only by the Great Rift. With the demise of Storvhal's industry, Vigilus was consigned to the darkest night of all.

DAEMONS OF KHORNE

The Daemons that assailed Vigilus were attracted by the hot and stinking winds of war, and none more so than the Daemons of Khorne. Some were invited by ritual, others raised from rivers of spilt blood. On Mortwald, they were summoned by anger itself.

Upon the southern outskirts of that once-prosperous false continent, the downtrodden workers of the hab-zones had endured countless generations of hardship in the name of their uncaring aristocratic masters. They worked without complaint amongst the cactus farms and forests of thorned succulents, though their limbs ached and their skin was scarred head-to-toe by poison-festered barb mark, for they knew it was their duty to provide the vegetation so difficult to grow elsewhere on the arid planet to the people of the hivesprawls. When the aristocracy of Mortwald sequestered that

hard-won bounty for themselves, the people of southern Mortwald felt a bone-deep anger that grew fiercer with every day they went hungry. Fiery rhetoric turned to looting, then to riots in the streets. Three days after the Great Tithe, the local Adeptus Arbites – drafted into the fight against the Orks plaguing the eastern trench lines – sent a comms-tube to the Vigilus Senate announcing that they had lost control. At the time, they had no idea how true that was – that region was shortly thereafter to become the site of a full-blown daemonic manifestation.

When the people of Mortwald hammered their fists bloody on the doors of the Equilateral Bastion, stronghold of the Mortwald elite, their rage was goaded to blinding fury by the words of their leaders. Amongst them was a group of Dark Disciples that secretly served a demagogue known as Vodt Redtooth. Only when the

riot turned to a stampede, which became a massacre, did Redtooth bring his dagger-shaped craft in from low orbit. Making landfall south of the Deinos Trench Network with his retinue of Khorne Berzerkers, he bade his pilot blast apart the great gates that led to the upper levels of the bastion. Dozens died as rubble tumbled down, but the rest of the citizens raced into the breach in their thousands, howling for blood. Pillaging their way through the citadel, throttling and thrashing and beating their former masters to death, the furious mob fell upon those that had taken from them for so long. In places, their oppressors were ripped bodily apart.

As the streets ran red with blood, the veil between reality and the warp thinned to the point that it all but disappeared. In a burst of crimson light, the daemonic servants of Khorne stampeded through the shimmering portal

that manifested there, the imposing figure of the head-hunting Daemon Skulltaker at the fore. They paid no mind to the station of those they killed during the ensuing slaughter; scar-skinned agri-peasants lay dying upon the corpses of the most well-dressed men on Vigilus. The south of Mortwald had fallen to the Daemons of Khorne, just as its trench lines fell to the forces of the Iron Warriors, and its inner sanctums to the Flawless Host. Though not one of these Chaos forces had coordinated with another, together they were able to destroy the most heavily defended area of Vigilus outside of Hyperia Hivesprawl.

Megaborealis was also to feel the wrath of Khorne, for where the Daemon Engines of the Brazen Beasts rampaged through the streets, they left a trail of carnage that could be seen in the warp as well as in realspace. The *Cerberite*, that vast semi-sentient spacecraft

with which the renegades had made planetfall upon Vigilus, roared with bloodlust as it felt its Daemon Engine children carve their way across the industrial landscape. From within its roiling guts came horned Bloodletter riders mounted on brazen Juggernauts, thundering down the unfurled ramps of the Daemon barge just as Maulerfiends and Venomcrawlers had done before.

Beating great leathery wings as they manifested fully in realspace, eight of Khorne's mighty Bloodthirsters flew above them, swooping down to hack apart the clades of Onager Dunecrawlers that were stabbing the beams of their neutron lasers towards the great craft. When Fabricator Vosch of Megaborealis saw a noospheric relay of the Greater Daemons hacking apart the Warhound Titans sent to reinforce the Adeptus Mechanicus forces, he immediately engaged consolidation protocols, abandoning the entire

silo district and putting into place a procedure for his own evacuation. To him it was a binary calculation devoid of emotion, but to those that knew the minds of the Tech-Priests of Megaborealis, it was as close to a declaration of utter defeat as his brotherhood ever made.

EQUILATERAL BASTION [MORTWALD]

MORTWALD

REJUVENIS STRONGPORT

TZELLER LINE

MOAT PRIORIS

VIRIDIAN FORESTS

The Astra Militarum trench reserves of the Tzeller Line paid little heed to the mobs of Vigilus citizenry that assailed the Equilateral Bastion and the other strongholds of the Mortwald aristocracy – though whether they chose to turn a blind eye to the vengeful attacks, or simply neglected their duty, will never be known.

MORTWALD REBEL POPULACE

ASTRA MILITARUM TRENCH RESERVES

DAEMONS OF KHORNE ASSAULT

VODT REDTOOTH'S STRIKE CRAFT

REBEL CITIZEN ASSAULT

DESTRUCTION OF THE GREAT GATE

DAEMON WARP RIFT

DAEMONS OF SLAANESH

Wherever an act of dedication or exploration crosses over into dangerous intensity, the gaze of a Slaaneshi Daemon is sure to be drawn. On Vigilus, where the population had been riddled with madness for decades, the Daemons of Slaanesh found their own kinds of paradise amongst the war-torn landscapes.

The forces of Slaanesh were seen in a great many war zones across Vigilus, for each hivesprawl had its own version of excess. In Hyperia, this revolved around gilded splendour, the pride of corrupt leaders seeing them spend the planet's tithes on their own self-aggrandisement. In Mortwald, it was greed, for the aristocracy there had revelled in gluttony and feasting after sequestering the food of an entire continent. In Oteck Hivesprawl, the populace tried desperately to save the water reserves that were being drained by the Vhulian Anomaly, leading to the hoarding of aqua receptacles and the raising of water magnates

to the status of kings. In places, several aqua-besotted urban tribes died not of thirst, but of drinking too much tainted water for their bodies to process – and in doing so, opening the way for daemonic manifestation.

At first, where the veil grew thin, these manifestations would start with a shimmer in the air – bruised purple, fulsome peach, sickly pink and all the colours of flesh swirling into one. Through that portal would step a handmaiden of Slaanesh, then another, then an entire court of Daemonettes, singing, screaming and keening in ecstasy as they cavorted amongst the stunned citizens that had summoned them – whether knowingly or not.

Next would come a Herald, tall and statuesque, a muse of dark desires whose presence hypnotised every soul who saw her with the possibilities of unbound excess. With a sharp clack of the claws, she would give the signal for the killing to begin, and the simmering threat of conflict would boil over into a tide of unbridled savagery.

Those Daemons of excess that lived for the thrill of the chase found Vigilus much to their liking. In the cities, they pursued their prey through the streets upon sinuous, arrow-swift steeds and elegantly sculpted chariots, slashing at the backs of those who fled their sport. In Hyperia, the Vigilant Guard sent beyond the Ring of Nothingness to stop the Daemons rampaging around the capital gunned down a few of the leading charioteers, but were nowhere near fast enough to neutralise the force entire. The vanguard of the Daemon cavalry leapt straight over the Astra Militarum front line, then darted unhindered through the barricades with the ease of bladefish slipping through a coral reef. Trilling with glee, they assassinated officers and Commissars alike. When the main body of the cavalcade hit home, its sickle-wheeled chariots ploughed through the ordered ranks of the Astra Militarum like auto-threshers through a field of scrubgrass. Blood flew in high arcs, glittering in the light of the Great Rift – a darkly beautiful sight that brought the Greater Daemon Leiwa'quasca to

THE PALE STALKER

In the frosted wilderness of Kaelac's Bane, the ascendant Drukhari were to meet a disturbing foe indeed – an avatar of their most feared nemesis, the creature that had once assailed the *Laurels of Victory*. During the war for Vigilus, the Dark Eldar clashed many times with the Rubricae of the Thousand Sons, both Aeldari and Heretic Astartes seeking to use the webway portal concealed on that continent as their base of operations. The Drukhari had the greater claim, for they had used the webway long before the Imperium had ventured forth into the stars – they saw the Thousand Sons as parasites that needed to be slain. But in the Rubricae and their sorcerous masters, they found an intractable foe that was all but immune to their poisons and agony-inducing weapons. The Drukhari were finally able to defeat the Rubricae

by using an ancient terraforming engine they discovered, which lowered the temperature of Kaelac's Bane so severely that its blizzards and snowdrifts froze the slow-moving automatons in place. But the Sorcerers, many of whom rode the skies on daemonic discs that whispered secrets in strange, guttural voices, remained active. Shorn of their footsoldiers, they withdrew from the war zone entirely – but not before enacting a summoning ritual as a parting gift to their Aeldari rivals. That dark spell brought forth not a greater Daemon of Tzeentch but one of Slaanesh – and an extremely powerful one at that.

The Pale Stalker of Kaelac's Bane was a huntress of inhuman skill and patience. Some thirty feet in height, she was strong enough to pierce a darting Raider skiff

with her spear and dash it to pieces upon the icy rock, and she could remain unseen at will, her milk-white skin blending perfectly with the blizzards. She hunted down the Drukhari skimming across the ice continent as an eagle hunts crows, devouring the bodies of the slain by distending her jaws so she could swallow them whole. The many-limbed Daemon queen took to wearing the clawed limbs of any ice mantis beasts foolish enough to attack her, lending her an even stranger and more formidable silhouette. Within three weeks of the Pale Stalker's manifestation, the Drukhari had lost a full third of their number. The remainder were so petrified at the threat of this nigh-invisible stalker they made one last foray into the hivesprawls, captured as many victims as they could, and withdrew from Vigilus entirely.

the fray. It is a matter of record that the Keeper of Secrets' rampage covered a full half of the Van Gollick Macrohighway before the statuesque Daemon was finally brought down by the concerted efforts of Temperance Blaise and her fellow Canonesses.

In the wastelands outside the hivesprawls, the artful chase enjoyed by the Daemons turned into a savage running battle as the mounted warbands of Slaanesh clashed with the Speed Freeks that had claimed the wilderness for their own. The Orks were at first bewildered by this new foe, and goggled in amazement at the slender beasts that were able to keep pace with their hot rods and up-gunned wagons. Then the faces of the Daemons split with wicked smiles, and they darted in to slash and stab at the drivers of the vehicles, which then careened away to crash and burn in the desolate dunes.

Word spread of these Daemon huntresses as fast as the Orks could get their vehicles from one camp to another, and the next time the Slaaneshi riders attacked, they were greeted with a storm of solid shot. A new race began in the wilderness, for an excess of raw speed nourishes the Daemons of the Dark Prince as much as any other kind, and Orks are not ones to turn away from a challenge. Though no formal Imperial records exist of these clashes, rumours and tales of pale cavaliers battling rugged greenskin vehicles circulated throughout the War of Nightmares.

'It is said by the masters of the Ordo Malleus that should even a single Daemon find a way through the gatehouse, the castle is already damned. Vigilus, once a mighty fortress whose every entrance was barred with physical might, faith and arcane technology, is now a broken and ruined shell, its portals left all but unguarded.'

- Inquisitor Thanst Rendars-Mao, Ordo Malleus, Astravigila Delegation

FORCES OF THE IMPERIUM

The Imperium's military machine had been battered and broken down in the first phase of the War of Beasts, only to be shored up and brought back to thunderous, belligerent life by the arrival of the Adeptus Astartes. Over the War of Nightmares, they too were to find themselves sorely pressed.

The War of Beasts had seen Vigilus drained of much of its strength. The uprising of the Pauper Princes, prematurely triggered by the Ork invasion, had a particularly devastating effect on the planet's supply lines and infrastructure, for it bypassed every layer of defence by striking from within.

With the wastelands controlled by the Orks and so many hidden victories already won by the time the Genestealer Cultists engaged the Imperium, the armed forces that sought to hurl the xenos back – be they Astra Militarum, Adepta Sororitas or Adeptus Astartes – found they were on unstable ground.

The coming of the Chaos threat looked to be the grievous blow that would take the planet to its death, for Abaddon's three-stage invasion threatened to tip the destabilised planet into utter disaster. Some of Vigilus' strategos posited the theory that the xenos invasions had been sent by the Warmaster to deliberately exhaust the resources of the Imperium's war machine. To a man, these unfortunates were hung by the neck until dead, for they had committed the crime of Doomsaying in the Face of Catastrophe. Such hated foes as the greenskin and the xenocultist were terrifying enough without word spreading that they ultimately served the unspeakable powers of the Heretic Astartes.

Yet perhaps there was a kernel of truth to these claims. The opening of the Great Rift was a crux point in history; even the most blinkered fool could not deny that. It was from that warp storm's depths that the Orkoid invasion had emerged to threaten Vigilus. Those amongst the Emperor's Holy Inquisition that made a study of the Warmaster had noted that many of the systems targeted by his Black Crusades had since been swallowed by the Cicatrix Maledictum, including the Cadian Gate itself – surely it was no coincidence that he now sought to conquer a sentinel world guarding the Nachmund Gauntlet.

> 'The Great Rift promised us doom, and by the Emperor, it delivered. Some said the planet was lost as soon as the heretic fleet appeared in the sky. But they are weak-spirited fools, and deserve death.'
>
> - Vanguard Operative Dain Fellerus, Kill Team Ebony Gladius

IMPERIUM VIGILANT

Though the vast majority of the Imperial defenders that fought in the War of Beasts still existed in some form to fight back the subsequent Chaos invasion, some were wiped out entirely before they could be reinforced. Others were reduced to tatters, clinging tenaciously to those gains they had made against their xenos foes only to be brought to the brink of annihilation by the Warmaster's incursions.

HYPERIAN GUARDIANS

Ultramarines	7 demi-companies (impromptu)
White Consuls	3 companies
Black Templars	1 demi-company
Praetors of Orpheus	2 companies
Silver Skulls	1 demi-company (prognostic)
Genesis Chapter	1 company (PERDITAS)
Hawk Lords	1 company
Howling Griffons	2 companies
Novamarines	1 company
Void Tridents	1 company
Castellans of the Rift	1 company
Space Wolves (Krom Dragongaze)	1 Great Company
Vigilant Guard	15 regiments
Vigilant Creedsmen	4 regiments
Dragoons Demonstratus	2 echelons
Vyacine Adepts	EXPURGATOS
Adamant Rifles	2 regiments
Dagmar Guard	1 regiment (PERDITAS)
Golohastus XIIth 'Decapitators'	1 demi-regiment
Black Torus Scouts	1 company
Dharan Bloodfists	2 regiments
Anark Zeta Abhuman Auxilla	1 detachment
Kanak Skull-takers	REMNANTS
Cthonol Nineguards	2 regiments
Miasman Redcowls	2 regiments

ADEPTA SORORITAS

Order of the Last Prioress	11 preceptories
Order of the Bloody Rose	4 preceptories
Order of the Ebon Chalice	2 preceptories
Order of the Argent Shroud	2 preceptories
Order of Our Martyred Lady	1 preceptory

OTECK COMBINED DEFENCE GROUP

Space Wolves (Icepelt/Sabrewulf)	1 strike force
Mortifactors	1 company, 1 demi-company
Ultramarines	1 strike force (Primaris)
Vigilant Guard	EXPURGATOS
Vigilant Creedsmen	4 regiments
Utica Pikemen River Guard	2 regiments
Palladion Rifles	EXPURGATOS
Tallarn Raiders	2 cavalier regiments
Miasman Redcowls	3 regiments
Hydroplant Water Hounds	2 castellanries
Vastadt I Expedrines	2 sabot groups
Gharti Volunteers	EXPURGATOS
Tekarn Iron Men	1 iron phalanx
Vresh Grenadiers	EXPURGATOS
Anark Zeta Bullgryn Auxilla	2 brute regiments

ADEPTA SORORITAS

Order of the Last Prioress	2 preceptories
Order of the Argent Shroud	1 preceptory

DIRKDEN REARGUARD

Crimson Fists	3 companies
Vigilant Underhivers	EXPURGATOS

KAELAC'S BANE TASK FORCE

+++WITHDRAWN IN EXTREMIS+++

++CONTINUED IN FILE IMP.VIG/PGS4/14-29

Participants in second and third stages of Vigilus conflict codified 'War of Nightmares' listed in auxiliary dataslate Imp.Vig/PGs3/30-90. Adeptus Mechanicus participants listed in Imp.Vig/AMech4/12-45.

DONTORIAN QUARANTINE CORPS

Iron Hands	4 clan companies
Brazen Claws	3 companies
Necropolis Hawks	3 companies
Silvered Blades	2 companies
Vigilant Guard	4 regiments
Vigilant Creedsmen	EXPURGATOS
Mordian Iron Guard	1 regiment (PERDITAS)
Gantor Rough Riders	3 cavalier regiments
Indigan Praefects	2 regiments
Ezelti Lancers (8th)	3 echelons
Ocanan Rad Waste Troopers	EXPURGATOS

MORTWALD SAVIOUR DETAIL

Imperial Fists	1 demi-company
Mortifactors	1 company
Fire Lords	1 company (PERDITAS)
Necropolis Hawks	3 companies
Cadian Shock Troops	EXPURGATOS
Catachan Jungle Fighters	EXPURGATOS
Vigilant Guard	REMNANTS
Vigilant Creedsmen	EXPURGATOS
Ventrillian Nobles	1 regiment

VIGILUS ARMOURED ELEMENTS

Sondoran Gearheads	PERDITAS
Cadian Heavy Armoured	3 armoured regiments
Ustenoran Gundogs	EXPURGATOS
Kharbys Iron Cavalry	2 armoured regiments

OFFICIO ASSASSINORUM

Imperial Assassins	6 operatives

The Praetors of Orpheus adhere to every facet of Guilliman's revised Codex. They operate as a well-calibrated engine of war.

The Brazen Claws, stoic successors of the Iron Hands, use mechanised warfare and value remorseless assault above all else.

The Howling Griffons are an Ultramarines successor Chapter known for their acts of valour and extreme dedication to duty.

Whatever the truth of the matter, the coming of the Chaos invasion saw the situation on Vigilus grow even more dire for the Imperial forces stationed there. Every new day, the Vigilus Senate rang with raised voices and bellowed oaths as its delegates were forced to make ever more desperate decisions. Their forces were stretched thin, and though they gave everything they had to save the planet, the War of Nightmares fast became an exercise in callous expediency.

Nonetheless, the Imperium, as stubborn and dogged as ever, refused to yield. Urban conflicts raged across every sector of every hivesprawl, the new war against the heretic often blending into the ongoing conflict with the xenos.

The vast majority of the Space Marine Chapters present on Vigilus were assigned to the wider battle-group known as the Hyperian Guardians, for Hyperia was the principal site of governance and strategy, and it could not fall. From there, the Imperium's elite forces met the Chaos assault head-on, pouring ever more resources and manpower into the meat grinder of the wider war.

DIRKDEN

The continent that fell furthest to these manifold threats was the sprawling urban eyesore of Dirkden. This region had been a hive of crime and corruption ever since the disastrous breakdown of relationships between its ruling dynasties and the Aquilarian Council over the Hyperia-Dirkden Fortwall. The false continent was then infiltrated by the Pauper Princes from Megaborealis in the north, and there the xenos had thrived. The Astra Militarum of the Dirkden Reclamation Group and their Crimson Fist allies evacuated vast swathes of its populace to Hyperia, but they could not save them all, especially when it became clear that many of their own regiments had recruited gene-tainted xenocultists into their number.

During the War of Nightmares, the battles between the Night Lords, the Scourged and the Pauper Princes saw much of the continent's central mass consumed in flames, vindicating Calgar's decision to evacuate. Only the Dirkden Rearguard was left behind to cover the Imperial withdrawal, for that hivesprawl was surely lost.

DONTORIA

Dontoria was next to be struck from the Vigilus Senate's list of viable war zones. Over the course of the War of Nightmares, the plagues introduced

The Imperial Fists are paragons of discipline and the stalwart refusal to yield. Expert siege-masters, they excel at the defence of Imperial installations of all kinds.

The Iron Hands are known for their strict, methodical approach to war, their belief that the flesh is weak, and their propensity to use cybernetics and heavy war assets.

there by the Death Guard reached epidemic proportions, and the formal quarantine was extended from the area around Litmus Dock to encompass the entire hivesprawl. As the populace grew ever more desperate, the Dontorian Quarantine Corps – a combination of Space Marine and Astra Militarum elements – stopped fighting with the intention of saving the citizenry, and instead imposed martial law to ensure they could not escape. It was a devastating blow to the people of Vigilus. A great many of the Vigilant Guard hailed from the Big Fug, as Dontoria was colloquially known, and the quarantine effectively doomed their people to death by a panoply of supernatural diseases, or the merciless scouring of the Purge.

All shipping routes around the hivesprawl were closed down, and all convoys leaving the hivesprawl were hunted and neutralised – if not by the Imperial Navy fighter pilots seeking to maintain the integrity of the quarantine zone, then by the Ork Speed Freeks of the wastelands. The Ultramarines, including Calgar himself, had fought against the scions of the Plague God before, and although these actions seemed extreme, they knew there could be no other choice.

MORTWALD

Mortwald fell soon after Dontoria, assailed from within as well as without by the Chaos menace. The Cadian Shock Troops and Ventrillian Nobles stationed at the Deinos Trench Network and the Tzeller Line fought with honour and comportment, earning accolades from the Imperial Fists, Mortifactors and Fire Lords they fought alongside. The sparse but powerful forces of the Catachan Jungle Fighters, very much at home in the hydroponic jungles and fields of poisonous cacti, fought the Ork Kommandos that penetrated the trench networks to a standstill, and the Vigilant Creedsmen burned the spoor of the xenos from the rejuvenat districts with commendable thoroughness.

For a while, Mortwald held. Yet as the upper echelons retreated into seclusion and the abandoned citizens turned to the most diabolical of patrons in order to seek revenge for their mistreatment, the scourge of Chaos began to take hold. The four-pronged assault – the Flawless Host on the citadels and palaces, the Black Legion upon sites of strategic import, the Daemons of Khorne fighting alongside revolutionaries in the streets, and the Iron Warriors siege-masters punching through the eastern trench lines – proved too much for even the Imperial Fists to counter. Captain Fane himself sent the missive to Marneus Calgar that the false continent was lost.

The Space Wolves of Ragnar Blackmane's Great Company are known for their ferocious aerial assaults, usually launched from Drop Pod or Stormwolf gunship.

The Crimson Fists rose from the flames of a long war against the Orks to fight on Vigilus. They have a great many Primaris reinforcements in their ranks.

OTECK

During the War of Nightmares, the skies high above Oteck were criss-crossed by the contrails of warring aircraft as the Combined Defence Group fought hard to retake control of the hivesprawl's vital reservoirs. On the ground, the Adepta Sororitas continued to hunt the xenocultists of the Genestealer Cult. Though the focus of the wider war had shifted upon the Warmaster's arrival – and though the Sisters of Battle stationed on Vigilus fought on every front against a staggering variety of foes – the majority of their orders still battled to defend their home territories against the alien threat.

Towards the end of the war, Oteck Hivesprawl had become all but unrecognisable. The triggering of explosives beneath Greigan Hollow had exposed a honeycomb of tunnels – passageways that the Pauper Princes knew well, for their miners and excavation teams had

created them. The Adepta Sororitas ventured into that underground warren and fought to contain the worst sites, with the Orders of the Last Prioress and the Argent Shroud working in concert to extend incineration protocols across any zones they deemed irrevocably lost. The deeper they ventured inside Oteck's maze-like undercity, however, the more the scale of their task became clear.

The tunnels extended not just beneath Oteck, but out into the wastelands towards Dirkden and Hyperia. When the lumen-lit underworks of the city gave way to innumerable crude shafts dug from the bare rock of the planet's under-strata, the Sisters of Battle uncovered the true extent of the xenos infestation. They were faced with tens of thousands of miles of labyrinthine tunnels that led from one false continent to another, and as they investigated them with torch and bolter, they found many of

them were infested with monstrous aberrations. To purge them clean would take years. With the Chaos scourge raining hell down on the cityscape above, that was time they did not have.

The matter was brought to Temperance Blaise, of the Order of Our Martyred Lady. At first she flew into a rage – but then, as dawn broke, she conceded that Oteck was irredeemable, and recommended the mustering of all Adepta Sororitas forces for a last stand at Hyperia.

THE WASTES

The wastes between the hivesprawls belonged almost wholly to the Orks, for the warlords and Big Meks of the Speedwaaagh! valued the vast tracts of land between the hivesprawls precisely because they were so desolate. Though they had little in the way of resources except those they had recycled from their own invasion craft, the Orks

OTECK

OTECK TUNNEL NETWORKS

AGAMEMNUS HOLLOW

MYSANDREN HOLLOW

OSTAVEER HOLLOW

SPIRE-CONVENT STRONGPOINT OR PRECEPTORY

ORDER OF OUR MARTYRED LADY

ORDER OF THE EBON CHALICE

ORDER OF THE ARGENT SHROUD

GENESTEALER CULT INFESTATION HOLDOUT

XENOCULTIST TUNNEL NETWORK

The Adepta Sororitas uncovered a network of tunnels used by the Pauper Princes. Dug by drill, pick and even claw, they extended hundreds of miles to the east towards Hyperia and Megaborealis.

defended their chosen territory with every bullet they could muster, and fought like enraged bulls in defence of the scrap cities that still blighted the horizon. Despite this threat, the Adepta Sororitas braved these wildernesses to ensure their convoys and mercy missions crossed them safely.

The Order of the Ebon Chalice was to make an invaluable contribution to the war effort when they painstakingly assembled a map of locations where the Orks typically gathered, and the routes their Speedwaaagh! races took around the planet. Once this was distributed via the Orders Dialogus, it proved an indispensable aid for those escorting water convoys and refugee columns from the lost hivesprawls to the nearest zone still in Imperial hands. However, when word spread amongst the greenskins that to approach a column guarded by the Adepta Sororitas was to initiate a fierce and lethal battle, the belligerent xenos went out of their way to hunt the wastes for Imperial convoys that were under the protection of the Sisters of Battle.

The Orks were not the only threat faced by the Adepta Sororitas in their missions of mercy, for over the course of the War of Nightmares, the wastes were raided by Drukhari war parties, xenocultist outriders, giant terrestine molerats and wild grox herds. After the Word Bearers of Abaddon's invasion force had planted the dread structures known as Noctilith Crowns across the planet's surface, these wastes were also haunted by living tempests of empyric energy – supernatural phenomena known to the Adepta Sororitas as warp-gheists – and even Daemon manifestations. Not one part of Vigilus could be called safe.

The Order of the Bloody Rose, though created some 2,500 years after the founding of the Adepta Sororitas, have distinguished themselves in a thousand war zones. They are known for the ferocity of their assaults against the ranks of the heretic and the mutant.

The Order of the Ebon Chalice was the first of the Orders Militant. Its symbol, a flaming grail, represents the burning, white-hot knowledge imparted from the Emperor himself to their founder, Alicia Dominica.

The Sisters of the Order of the Argent Shroud are taciturn and laconic, preferring to let their actions speak on their behalf. They take their symbol from the silvery impression of a death mask left on the funerary shroud of their founder, Saint Silvana.

'With the holy trinity of bolter, flamer and melta we shall blast, burn and annihilate every last traitor on this planet. The omniscient Emperor watches over us, even under these troubled skies. He gives us strength to forge the glorious destiny of Mankind, and with his grace we cannot fail.'

- Sister Superior Verita Gondari, Order of the Ebon Chalice

KAELAC'S BANE

During the War of Nightmares, Kaelac's Bane was forsaken entirely by the Imperial war effort, its armed forces withdrawn to support the vital stronghold of Hyperia while it still stood. The Void Tridents and Castellans of the Rift had fought hard against the Speed Freeks operating out of Mekstop City, working in concert to ensure the glacier quarrymen and their Skitarii overseers could escape from the Drukhari menace of the ice continent and reach safety. Thanks to the valour of these Primaris Chapters, many of the ice-carrying convoys made it to the nearest points of Oteck, Mortwald and Hyperia, continents in as much need of water as they were of manpower.

The pure ice water they carried with them was soon distributed amongst the populace – but not in the manner they had anticipated. Upon reaching civilisation, many of the convoys came under attack from well-organised bands of cut-throat xenocultists and strike forces sent out by the crime lords of the Oteck and Mortwald underworlds. They were opposed by the local Astra Militarum of the Vigilant Guard, the Vigilant Creedsmen and the Utica Pikemen River Guard, but with hostile elements appearing all around them, the Imperial forces were soon overwhelmed. So it was that the aqua glacius the Primaris Chapters had given so much to protect ended up wetting the throats of criminals, madmen and xenos hybrids instead of the citizens and soldiers for which it had been intended.

HYPERIA

The Imperium had yielded one fiercely contested war zone after another as the War of Nightmares ground on, but in doing so, had managed to consolidate its resources at Hyperia. While that once-glorious hivesprawl was still under Imperial control, there was something to fight for, and that war zone was reinforced time and time again at the behest of the Ministorum and the Vigilus Senate alike.

Saint's Haven had withstood punitive Aeldari attacks and Ork assaults throughout the phases of both wars. Its defences included forces from the Ultramarines and eleven other Adeptus Astartes Chapters – including the Black Templars, the Howling Griffons, the Silver Skulls and the Space Wolves of Krom Dragongaze. The hivesprawl was the keep at the heart of the Vigilus fortress; though the ramparts had tumbled, its inner sanctum did not fall. Towards the end of the War of Nightmares, the planet's defenders mustered there to make their last stand.

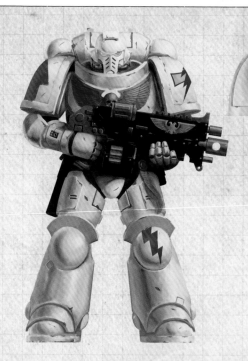

The Dark Angels, known as the First, also have a sinister sobriquet – the Unforgiven. Few indeed know of their secret mission, for outwardly they are duty incarnate.

The White Scars, descendants of the free-willed Primarch Jaghatai Khan, are experts in the art of mounted warfare. They rejoice in the thrill of battle.

A GLIMMER IN THE HEAVENS

When the legendary Gloriana-class battleship, the *Vengeful Spirit*, made its emergency warp translation, it did so with haste rather than safety as its priority. In doing so, it escaped the vortex that was gnawing at its flank, the violent maelstrom that had been created by the detonation of the Deathstrike missiles delivered by *Vaul's Ghost*. Amid the storm of energy with which the vast spacecraft slipped from realspace into the hell dimension of the warp, the vortex was diffused. The *Spirit* would live on to blight the Imperium with the Warmaster still at its helm.

Unfortunately for the Chaos fleet gathered around that vast spaceship, the warp breach brought about by the emergency translation – aggravated by the detonation of the Vortex warheads – spilled out a tremendous amount of raw empyric energy. It consumed several dozen Heretic Astartes warships in quick succession before blending into the Great Rift – for after the destruction of Silo XV and the raising of the Noctilith Crowns, that vast warp storm had encroached upon Vigilus to the point that it threatened every fleet.

In forcing his adversary to turn tail, Calgar had not only robbed the Chaos fleet of its most prized asset, but torn out its heart. He had turned the same energies that had blighted Vigilus against those who sought to amplify them, and sent almost a third of the Chaos fleet screaming into the hellscape of the warp. No small number of Imperial craft were caught in the sucking riptide of that emergency translation; amongst a dozen lesser craft and inbound torpedoes, the *Duke Aareloph* and the *Haraju Monarch* were both snatched away, never to be heard of again. The Vigilus Senate considered the sacrifice more than worthwhile.

As the warp breach faded into the greater mass of the Cicatrix Maledictum, the Imperial Navy redoubled its assault – and, over time, found itself reinforced by ships Calgar had sent out on reconnaissance missions during his initial approach to Vigilus. The battle swung from a last-ditch defence to a long-ranged stalemate, and then, as more Imperial craft joined the fray, a gradual climb towards victory.

By this point, word was reaching the Chaos troops upon Vigilus that their armada was stricken – the Lord Macragge made sure of it. Rigged up to a vox array in the foremost apothecarium of Saint's Haven, Calgar spoke loudly and with great conviction of the inevitable victory of the Imperial troops. That broadcast was relayed through the Ministorum's own laud hailer systems, which were spread far and wide to carry Pontifex Galluck's sermons to the faithful in every hivesprawl. All those who doubted Calgar's assertions had but to look up at the night sky, where a swirling blue-green vortex was surrounded by the pinpricks of light that had once been the Chaos fleet.

The Black Templars are highly unusual in the Adeptus Astartes, for they have a religious faith in the Emperor. They harbour hatred for all witches and mutants.

The Silver Skulls place great stock in omens and prognostications, valuing superstition as others do logic. They fight their wars with an uncanny prescience.

THE WAR UPON THE BRINK

The destruction of the planet Vigilus was all but complete, yet still the Imperium would not yield. Though anarchy reigned in every hivesprawl – even Hyperia – Saint's Haven still stood, and with the breaking of the Chaos armada, a slow trickle of reinforcements began to reach the planet. It was not over yet.

Calgar's widely broadcast speeches reached millions of the citizens that had panicked, gone to ground or turned from the light of the Emperor over the course of the War of Nightmares. They were being addressed directly by Marneus Calgar, the son of the Primarch himself, a figure who had become so legendary over the course of the war that even the shanty tribes had heard tell of his name. This great warrior was exhorting them to fight back, to keep strong in their faith and to ensure that, though Vigilus was sorely wounded, it would not pass into the darkness forever.

At first the message was ignored, for the people of Vigilus had been so traumatised, had seen so much killing, that mere words could not light the flame of defiance in their chests. But here and there, new troops began to join the fight. These were Imperial forces that had been withdrawn from war zones the Vigilus Senate had conceded as lost. From Kaelac's Bane came the Void Tridents and the Castellans of the Rift; from Mortwald came the battle-scarred remnants of Captain Fane's command; and from Oteck came not only a massive influx of Sisters of Battle, but Haldor Icepelt and the heroic Brand Sabrewulf, last of his strike force to survive the xenos insurrections of that troubled sprawl. Cadian Shock Troops and Ventrillian Nobles rubbed shoulders with Munitorum Preacher militia; Mortifactors joined forces with Ogryn Auxilla; and Ultramarines fought alongside native Vigilant Guardsmen.

When the first of the Ministorum ships sent to reinforce Vigilus emerged from the Nachmund Gauntlet and made planetfall, the tiny seed of hope sown by these reinforcements began to bear fruit. With the Vhulian Anomaly banished as a result of the Dark Angels' strike at the Citadel Vigilant, and with the Chaos fleet in disarray, it was possible to send spacecraft to Vigilus' orbit once more – and from there, to make landing at Hyperia.

THE WHEELS OF JUSTICE TURN SLOWLY

The warships of the Ecclesiarchy were not the only ones to make planetfall after the breaking of the Chaos fleet. In the first stage of the War of Beasts, Lucienne Agamemnus had sent an astrotelepathic petition to Terra requesting a specific kind of aid, the message travelling via Neo-vellum and through the Nachmund Gauntlet. The missive had been received by the Adeptus Astra Telepathica, and – after it had been put through a decade of systemic procedures, and been lost entirely for a while – by chance it found its way to the High Lords of Terra. The Governor's request was granted, though she was long dead by the time the results manifested.

The decision of the High Lords resulted in a small raptor-like craft being diverted on its return journey from the Cadian Gate towards Vigilus. Within its cockpit was a trio of Imperial Assassins, and within the stasis chambers of its hold, three more. It is a testament to the strategic value of Vigilus that such a high number of operatives had been spared by the Officio Assassinorum. The three within the stasis chambers of the hold were from the Eversor Temple; they were deployed via Drop Pod to the heartlands of the Ork Western Scrap City Cluster. Within a single week of making planetfall, their combined kill tally included six Ork warlords, fifteen Big Meks, and the destruction of the Great Gargant, *Gorkzilla*.

While the Eversors had been sent to strike at the greenskins, their fellows had been deployed against the Genestealer Cultists. No less than twenty-two of the Pauper Princes' war leaders were taken down by the trio of Callidus Assassins known as the Daughters of Meh'Lindi. These infiltrators had disguised themselves as latter-generation Genestealer Hybrids to get as close as possible to the heart of the cult.

The crowning glory of their covert mission saw the Patriarch Grandsire Wurm slain by phase blade, though none of the Assassins escaped alive. They did not realise that there was more than one Patriarch upon Vigilus – for the planet was populous enough to support several independent gene-sects – and that the latter incarnation of Grandsire Wurm would rise amongst the planet's xenocultists as a saviour reborn.

The Assassins completely ignored the Chaos presence upon Vigilus, for the request from the Governor had been sent before the War of Nightmares had begun, and hence the heretics lay outside of their mission parameters. But their lethal ministrations destabilised, if not halted, the invasions of the xenos species that had battered the Imperial defences for so long. In doing so, they bought the Imperial forces a reprieve in which they could focus on hurling back the renegades and traitors that still stalked the streets. It was another step on the path to victory, and Calgar was glad of it.

More and more Ecclesiarchy ships arrived, summoned by the fervent pleas of Slyne Galluck and the terse demands of Temperance Blaise, and each disgorged another battalion of Sisters of Battle. Block by city block, hab by filthy hab, the Adepta Sororitas began to purge the taint of Chaos and the lingering stench of the xenos invader from the hivesprawl of Hyperia. Calgar adapted his speeches to incorporate the latest intel with each day, weaving inspirational tales designed to resonate with the mentality of a populace that was slowly beginning to believe Vigilus could be saved. Every new dawn, more citizens came out of hiding to sign up to fight alongside the Sisters of Battle; they came first in dribs and drabs, then in mobs, then in crowds, until the frateris militia numbered almost as many as the Adepta Sororitas themselves.

A scattering of warships made it across the Nachmund Gauntlet, for though that great channel had narrowed, and was more dangerous to cross than ever, it had not disappeared entirely. The ships brought a few hundred reinforcements each; a paltry number in the grand scheme of things, and though the propaganda broadcasts made much of their arrival, they contributed little but a boost in morale. For a time, it seemed that only Hyperia could truly be saved. Yet as more Imperial ships began to reach the capital, the troops under Calgar started to push outwards rather than simply to shore up defences. The long road to recovery had begun, but whether that was a fool's errand or a realistic goal, none could say.

Vigilus could not be forsaken, could not be subject to Exterminatus as Imperial doctrine would have it. As Calgar had maintained over and over again, this was a planet the Imperium could not afford to lose. A few still clung to the hope that the crippled world of Vigilus could one day be counted as a functional node in the Imperium once more, but it was not clear whether the Lord Macragge was truly amongst them. Many of the senate saw a darker fate unfolding, though they dared not speak of it openly. Ominous possibilities hung in the air, unvoiced, but powerful nonetheless. The war for the sentinel planet could well become a hungering void into which the forces of Mankind would pour more and more resources, without ever truly defeating the enemies they had faced there.

CAMPAIGN RULES

'Fight fire with fire. Fight fury with fury. But most important of all, fight on, however you can, and do not stop until you have shed every drop of your blood in the name of the Emperor. Only then will you know peace.'

- *Pontifex Slyne Galluck of Hyperia*

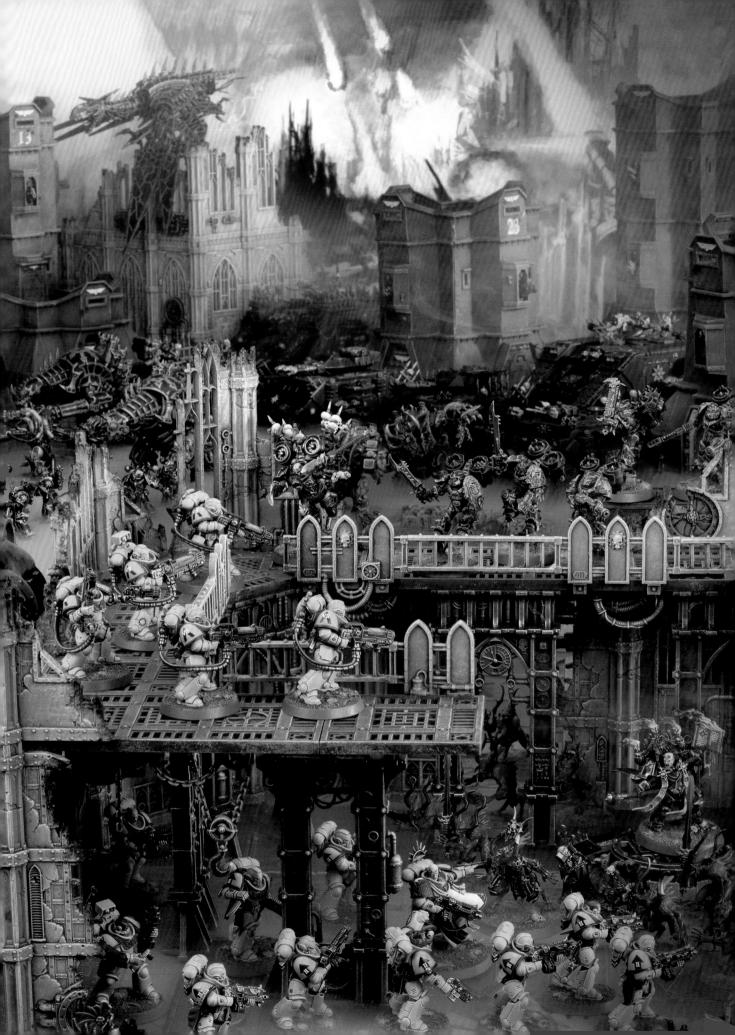

VIGILUS ABLAZE CAMPAIGNS

These Vigilus Ablaze Campaign rules allow you to bring the thrilling narrative presented in this book to life on the tabletop. Battles won and lost take on greater importance as you fight for control of Vigilus, not only reliving the climatic moments in the narrative, but also forging your own tales of glory or crushing defeat. Will your army stand in defiance or seek to tear Vigilus asunder? This is the planet's darkest hour, and its fate is in your hands.

INTRODUCTION

Linking your games together into a campaign can add a whole new dimension to your games of Warhammer 40,000. If the idea of a campaign is daunting, fear not, for on the following pages you will find everything you need to run a thrilling campaign for you and your friends set on war-torn Vigilus.

This section starts by detailing how to organise a campaign, how to group players into teams, how to arrange battles and how campaign glory points (GPs) are awarded. On pages 112-117 you will find rules for the three different phases of the War of Nightmares. It is intended that players will choose the phase of the war that either best matches their collection of Citadel Miniatures, or the phase of the war that they would most like to play. Lastly, on page 118 you will find additional rules for running campaigns set on other worlds within the Imperium Nihilus.

The Vigilus Ablaze Campaign is ideal for new players and veterans alike. Rather than having a rigid structure, it gives players a lot of freedom with regards to the armies they muster and the missions they fight. This allows the narrative to take centre stage in your games. Players will get the most out of a Vigilus Ablaze Campaign if they embrace its narrative spirit, perhaps by basing their Warlord on a general presented in this book, or by inventing a story around their army that ties them into the unfolding chronicle of this war-torn planet.

ORGANISING A CAMPAIGN

The first thing you must do in order to organise a campaign is to find some other players to take part in it. A Vigilus Ablaze Campaign is designed to have between 4-16 players divided into equal-sized teams. If you have an odd number of players, don't worry; we offer advice later on how to accommodate uneven teams.

You will next need to decide how long you want the campaign to last. We have found it is better to choose to fight a short campaign of six to eight weeks (rather than a longer and more sprawling campaign) to keep all the players involved excited – after all, there is nothing stopping you from starting a new campaign immediately after the first has been completed!

CAMPAIGN ROUNDS

A Vigilus Ablaze Campaign is broken into campaign rounds. Each round follows the narrative of the Vigilus war and represents a milestone in the timeline. There are 6 campaign rounds for each phase of the War of Nightmares and thus it is recommended each campaign round lasts for one week in a six-week campaign.

Each campaign round will have special rules that affect the battles played in its duration. It will also state which missions earn additional bonus campaign glory points. You will need to decide how many battles each player can participate in during a campaign round. A limited approach of allowing each player to

play once or twice per campaign round ensures a level playing field; similarly if your players are organised into teams, you can balance out uneven teams by allowing the team with fewer players to participate in more battles each campaign round. Alternatively, you might decide to allow players to participate in as many battles as possible to emulate the desperate nature of war, with each team rallying to earn the most victories. This method can be as frantic as it is fun! Discuss with the players which approach is best suited to your campaign.

FIGHTING BATTLES

Once the campaign is underway the players are free to organise and fight battles as and when they wish. The players can fight any Warhammer 40,000 mission but there are extra incentives for using the missions and battlezones presented in this book. Players are also free to change Army Rosters between battles. After a battle has been fought, the players earn campaign glory points as shown on the table below. It can be a good idea to nominate one player in the campaign to record all the glory points earned by each team, or for each team to

have a captain that records the glory points earned by their teammates.

DECLARING THE WINNER

Once all the campaign rounds have been completed, the campaign glory points earned by each team are tallied up and the winning team is announced. To give the campaign a memorable send-off, all players should be brought together when the winner is announced. You could even schedule the last round of battles to happen immediately before the campaign is concluded to allow for some tense and nail-biting final moments.

Finishing a campaign is a momentous achievement and it shouldn't only be the winners of the campaign who are celebrated. For example, you might want to keep a record of each player's win/loss ratio and announce the individual with the highest. You could also focus on other aspects of the hobby – for example, you could include bonus awards for the 'coolest army', the 'best-painted Warlord' and the 'most sporting opponent', all voted for by the players.

CAMPAIGN GLORY POINTS

CONDITION	CAMPAIGN GPS EARNED
Winning the battle	**10 GPs** to every winning player
Using a Vigilus Ablaze battlezone (pg 146-151)	**2 GPs** to every player
Playing a Vigilus Ablaze Crucible of War mission (pg 122-132)	**1 GPs** to every player
Playing a Vigilus Ablaze Echoes of War mission (pg 134-145)	**3 GPs** to every player
Fulfilling the criteria for bonus glory points in each campaign round	See the following pages

FIRST PHASE OF THE WAR OF NIGHTMARES

ROUND 1

14.989 POST: IMPERIAL COUNTERMEASURES

Galvanised by Haarken Worldclaimer's dread boast, and the news of Abaddon's approach, the Imperial forces led by Marneus Calgar strike back at the armies of Chaos all across the war-torn planet.

15.134 POST: BATTLE IN THE VOID

Marneus Calgar boards the *Laurels of Victory*, intent on intercepting the Despoiler's fleet before it comes within striking distance of Vigilus. However, even as the fleets engage, the bridge of his flagship is assaulted by Slaaneshi Daemons.

SPECIAL RULES

In this campaign round the following special rules apply:

Commanding Position: Battle-forged armies that only include models with the CHAOS keyword have one extra Command Point.

Countermeasures: Add 1 to the Leadership characteristic of IMPERIUM units while there are any enemy CHAOS units on the battlefield.

BONUS GPs

Players earn 5 bonus GPs each time they participate in one of the following missions:

- **On the Bridge** (pg 134)
- **Contact Lost** (*Warhammer 40,000* rulebook)

Players earn 1 bonus GP each time they participate in a mission using the following battlezone:

- **Battlezone: Spaceship** (pg 146)

ROUND 2

15.187 POST: A DARK NEW DAWN

Marneus Calgar coordinates the defence of Vigilus, but the Chaos threat is too great. Abaddon's fleet disgorges forces beyond belief on the beleaguered surface of Vigilus, and some ships even dock with the hive-spires to allow the traitors to disembark directly into combat.

15.301 POST: UNDERGROUND WAR

As battle rages on the surface of Vigilus and tears through the hive cities, another war is fought underground. The Genestealer Cultists find their advances checked by regiments of Astra Militarum, convents of Adepta Sororitas, and the zealous disciples of the Machine God in several great caverns.

SPECIAL RULES

In this campaign round the following special rules apply:

Out of Nowhere: If a unit is set up during a turn, until the end of that turn add 1 to charge rolls made for that unit.

Tremors of War: Roll a D6 at the start of each battle round. On a roll of 1, subtract D3 from all Move characteristics (to a minimum of 0) until the end of the battle round (roll once and apply the result to all models). Models that can FLY are unaffected by this rule.

BONUS GPs

Players earn 5 bonus GPs each time they participate in the following mission:

- **Planetfall** (*Warhammer 40,000* rulebook)

Players earn 1 bonus GP each time they participate in a mission using the following battlezone and/or war zone:

- **Battlezone: Perilous Cavern** (pg 147)
- **Dirkden Hivesprawl** (pg 153)

ROUND 3

15.390 POST: TERROR AND LOATHING

The coming of the forces of Chaos, and the apparent rout of their Imperial defenders, drive millions to seek salvation elsewhere, no matter who might offer it. Chaos cults and the Pauper Princes both receive a massive influx of newly converted devotees.

15.504 POST: STRANGE DELIVERANCE

Abaddon has not anticipated the Genestealer Cult lurking on Vigilus, and when his forces advance deep into the heart of Dirkden Hivesprawl expecting little resistance, they find themselves ambushed by a seemingly endless tide of cultists.

SPECIAL RULES

In this campaign round the following special rule applies:

Stream of Devotees: GENESTEALER CULTS Troops units and Chaos Cultists units can be brought back into play using the rules for Sustained Assault (pg 121), regardless of whether or not their controlling player is the Attacker. However, they only do so on an unmodified roll of 5+, and they must be set up wholly within both their deployment zone and 6" of a battlefield edge. Do not use this rule in missions that use Sustained Assault.

BONUS GPs

Players earn 5 bonus GPs each time they participate in one of the following missions:

- **From an Unexpected Quarter** (pg 122)
- **Cleanse and Capture** (*Warhammer 40,000* rulebook)

Players earn 1 bonus GP each time they participate in a mission using the following war zone:

- **Dirkden Hivesprawl** (pg 153)

16.021 POST: THE SIEGE OF THE HOIST

In Megaborealis, the forces of the Genestealer Cult are engaged in all-out war with the Adeptus Mechanicus and Adeptus Astartes for the Greater Omnissian Hoist. An infiltration force of xenos has found a hidden route to the vital machinery of the space elevator, but the Skitarii defenders are able to purge the infestation.

16.302 POST: WAR IN THE HEAVENS

Even as the forces of the Despoiler spread across the surface of Vigilus like a dark plague, Abaddon's fleet engages Imperial forces across the system, harrying the beleaguered and scattered defenders from all angles.

16.605 POST: TO CAUTERISE THE WOUND

Forced to take drastic action in the face of the Chaos onslaught, Marneus Calgar orders the complete destruction of the infested upper levels of the hive cities, consigning billions to a fiery death.

17.202 POST: WAR FOR THE WEBWAY

A hidden war is fought for control of the webway portal in Kaelac's Bane. The forces of the Thousand Sons clash with the Drukhari defenders of the webway – whoever claims victory will be able to summon almost limitless reinforcements with which to strike at the choicest sites of Vigilus.

18.532 POST: WITHIN THE VHULIAN SWIRL

Abaddon knows something that the defenders of Vigilus do not – the existence of a secret fortress hidden deep within the Vhulian Swirl. The citadel guards the Voidclaw, a mechanism that Abaddon plans to use to unleash a devastating gravitic anomaly upon the planet. Winning the loyalty of the Fallen encamped within the citadel, Abaddon takes control of the cataclysmic weapon for himself.

18.902 POST: FIGHTING BLIND

The Imperium is forced to engage its enemies on a variety of fronts where visibility is low and intel scarce – whether due to dust storms, roiling smog banks, or smoke from the fires of outright war.

SPECIAL RULES

In this campaign round the following special rules apply:

The Cults Show Their Strength: Re-roll hit rolls of 1 for GENESTEALER CULTS units in the Fight phase.

Determined Defenders: Subtract 2 from Morale tests for IMPERIUM units in any mission in which their controlling player is the Defender.

BONUS GPs

Players earn 5 bonus GPs each time they participate in one of the following missions:

- **Siege of the Hoist** (pg 136)
- **Secure and Control** (*Warhammer 40,000* rulebook)

Players earn 1 bonus GP each time they participate in a mission using the following war zone:

- **Greater Omnissian Hoist** (pg 154)

SPECIAL RULES

In this campaign round the following special rules apply:

Desperate Measures: If your army is Battle-forged and includes any Space Marines Detachments (excluding Auxiliary Support Detachments), you can use the Orbital Bombardment Stratagem without spending any Command Points (you cannot use this Stratagem more than once per battle).

Hidden Portal: Add 1 to Reserve rolls for AELDARI and CHAOS units.

BONUS GPs

Players earn 5 bonus GPs each time they participate in one of the following missions:

- **Control the Gate** (pg 128)
- **Patrol** (*Warhammer 40,000* rulebook)

Players earn 1 bonus GP each time they participate in a mission using the following battlezone and/or war zone:

- **Battlezone: Raging Inferno** (pg 148)
- **Kaelac's Bane** (pg 155)

SPECIAL RULES

In this campaign round the following special rules apply:

Hidden Plot: At the start of the battle, each player receives 1 Command Point for each CHAOS Detachment (other than Auxiliary Support Detachments) in their army.

Caught Unawares: At the start of the battle, each player subtracts D3 from their total number of Command Points (to a minimum of 0) if they have one or more IMPERIUM Detachments in their army.

BONUS GPS

Players earn 5 bonus GPs each time they participate in one of the following missions:

- **Bunker Assault** (*Warhammer 40,000* rulebook)

Players earn 1 bonus GP each time they participate in a mission using the following battlezone:

- **Battlezone: Deadly Storm** (pg 149)

SECOND PHASE OF THE WAR OF NIGHTMARES

ROUND 1

19.014 POST: THE VOIDCLAW

Abaddon uses the Voidclaw to open a pinpoint singularity in the space above Vigilus, disrupting not only the Imperial fleet, but the armies on the planet beneath. The resulting cataclysm ushers in tectonic upheaval, toppling spires and causing a wave of panic in a horrific new phase of the war.

19.351 POST: FALSE TIDES

The precious reserves of water on Vigilus are devastated, as the Vhulian Anomaly tears at the surface of the planet. Water begins to flow from reservoirs and underground lakes, rushing in rivers across the planet to be lost forever.

SPECIAL RULES

In this campaign round the following special rules apply:

Drought: Subtract 1" from the Move characteristic of **INFANTRY** models.

Gravitic Anomaly: Add 1" to the Move characteristic of units that can **FLY**, but roll a D6 each time such a unit moves in the Movement phase. On a roll of 1 that unit suffers 1 mortal wound.

BONUS GPs

Players earn 5 bonus GPs each time they participate in the following mission:

- **Retrieval Mission** (*Warhammer 40,000* rulebook)

Players earn 1 bonus GP each time they participate in a mission using the following battlezone:

- **Battlezone: Deadly Storm** (pg 149)

ROUND 2

20.435 POST: BY ANY MEANS NECESSARY

Calgar's Fires have denied Abaddon's forces a quick victory in the hive cities, but the traitors change tack, striking from the wastes. Faced with enemies on all sides, the Imperial leaders wage a campaign of misdirection, luring xenos forces into conflict with the Chaos armies.

20.464 POST: THE IRON FIST CLOSES TIGHT

The Chaos Space Marines attack in ever greater number, but their very ferocity makes them a prime target for the Orks, to whom the anarchy of the War of Nightmares is little more than an invitation to a greater war.

SPECIAL RULES

In this campaign round the following special rules apply:

Confusion Reigns: Subtract 1 from the Leadership characteristic of all models other than **IMPERIUM** models.

Gravitic Anomaly: Add 1" to the Move characteristic of units that can **FLY**, but roll a D6 each time such a unit moves in the Movement phase. On a roll of 1 that unit suffers 1 mortal wound.

BONUS GPs

Players earn 5 bonus GPs each time they participate in one of the following missions:

- **Allies of Convenience** (pg 124)
- **Carnage** (*Warhammer 40,000* rulebook)

Players earn 1 bonus GP each time they participate in a mission using the following battlezone and/or war zone:

- **Battlezone: Speedwaaagh!** (pg 150)
- **Dirkden Hivesprawl** (pg 153)

ROUND 3

20.834 POST: THE HOARD BESET

Abaddon sends the Brazen Beasts to attack Silo XV – where vast stockpiles of blackstone have been amassed – intending to disable its defences before shattering the site with an orbital bombardment.

20.872 POST: INFERNAL MACHINES

The grinding war in the wastes between the Orks and the Chaos worshippers intensifies before undergoing a sudden convulsion. Warboss Krooldakka, intent on proving that he is the mightiest on Vigilus, mobilises his Blitz Brigades into an unstoppable Waaagh! and engages the Daemon Engines attacking Megaborealis.

SPECIAL RULES

In this campaign round the following special rules apply:

Unstoppable Tide: ORK Troops units can be brought back into play using the rules for Sustained Assault (pg 121), regardless of whether or not their controlling player is the Attacker. However, they only do so on an unmodified roll of 5+, and they must be set up wholly within both their deployment zone and 6" of a battlefield edge. Do not use this rule in missions that use Sustained Assault.

BONUS GPs

Players earn 5 bonus GPs each time they participate in one of the following missions:

- **Metal Onslaught** (pg 126)
- **Blitz** (*Warhammer 40,000* rulebook)
- **Spoils of War** (*Warhammer 40,000* rulebook)

Players earn 1 bonus GP each time they participate in a mission using the following battlezone:

- **Battlezone: Speedwaaagh!** (pg 150)

ROUND 4

21.017 POST: CULTS AND CONQUESTS

The doomsday cults of Vigilus perform a series of blood rituals that summon forth Daemons from the Great Rift. A new nightmare begins.

21.351 POST: THE END IS NIGH

Apocalypse cults spring up amongst the aristocracy of Mortwald, giving rise to hedonistic cliques determined to indulge in every excess. Seeing the decadence of their superiors, the deprived populace of Mortwald give in to their growing rage. They slaughter the aristocracy, and then simply kill for killing's sake.

SPECIAL RULES

In this campaign round the following special rules apply:

Nightmare Incursion: Add 1 to Morale tests.

Warp Surge: Add 1 to Psychic tests and Deny the Witch tests. In addition, add 1 to the number of mortal wounds a **PSYKER** suffers from Perils of the Warp when taking a Psychic test.

BONUS GPs

Players earn 5 bonus GPs each time they participate in one of the following missions:

- **Bunker Assault** (*Warhammer 40,000* rulebook)
- **Deadlock** (*Warhammer 40,000* rulebook)

Players earn 1 bonus GP each time they participate in a mission using the following battlezone:

- **Battlezone: Field of Nightmares** (pg 151)

ROUND 5

21.619 POST: THE NOCTILITH CROWNS

Abaddon's campaign begins to take its toll on the Nachmund Gauntlet as the arcane structures called Noctilith Crowns are put into place. Reports of deadly warp-gheists, daemonic incursions and psychic awakenings flood in from every war zone.

22.464 POST: VILE REVELATIONS

The Imperial defenders of Dontoria, already reeling from countless afflictions, face a new assault from the Purge. The Death Guard already encamped in the region engage in an ideological clash with the renegade newcomers. When the dust settles, the collateral damage to the hivesprawl is beyond repair.

SPECIAL RULES

In this campaign round the following special rules apply:

Nightmare Incursion: Add 1 to Morale tests.

Virulent Plague: Subtract 1 from the Toughness characteristic of **INFANTRY** models. **NURGLE** units are unaffected by this rule.

BONUS GPs

Players earn 5 bonus GPs each time they participate in one of the following missions:

- **Schism** (pg 130)
- **The Relic** (*Warhammer 40,000* rulebook)

Players earn 1 bonus GP each time they participate in a mission using the following battlezone and/or war zone:

- **Battlezone: Field of Nightmares** (pg 151)
- **Dontoria Hivesprawl** (pg 156)

ROUND 6

23.012 POST: WAR FOR STORVHAL

The pyroclastic cults of Tzeentch – once slaves of the Adeptus Mechanicus – turn against their masters. The resulting deaths of both cultists and devotees of the Machine God prove to be a powerful sacrifice, and leaping swarms of Flamers and bounding Horrors appear amidst the warp-tainted lava flows, bringing ever greater destruction.

23.128 POST: ERUPTION

The Adeptus Mechanicus of Storvhal trigger a set of volcanic eruptions that destroy the Daemons of Tzeentch attacking them – but in the process, devastate the planet's energy resources and plunge many of the hivesprawls into darkness.

SPECIAL RULES

In this campaign round the following special rules apply:

The Cults Pyroclastic: TZEENTCH Chaos Cultist units have an invulnerable save of 6+.

A World Ablaze: Subtract 1 from the Leadership characteristic of **IMPERIUM** and **GENESTEALER CULTS** models.

BONUS GPs

Players earn 5 bonus GPs each time they participate in the following mission:

- **The Scouring** (*Warhammer 40,000* rulebook)

Players earn 1 bonus GP each time they participate in a mission using any of the following battlezones and/or war zone:

- **Battlezone: Field of Nightmares** (pg 151)
- **Battlezone: Geothermal Eruption** (*Vigilus Defiant*)
- **Storvhal** (pg 157)

THIRD PHASE OF THE WAR OF NIGHTMARES

ROUND 1

23.223 POST: OF MAN AND XENOS

Marneus Calgar knows that Vigilus is lost – unless he can win allies from an unexpected quarter. At the site of an ongoing battle between the defenders of Saint's Haven and the Aeldari raiders bent on settling their grudge against the high-born of Hyperia, Calgar seeks to orchestrate a stalemate and a parley. The battle here has been grinding on for some time, and concealed snipers make movement on the ground perilous.

23.462 POST: THE PENUMBRAL PACT

The Farseer Keltoc agrees to aid the Imperium in dealing a critical blow to the Chaos Warmaster, lending an advanced Asuryani stealth ship to the cause.

SPECIAL RULES

In this campaign round the following special rules apply:

Hidden Hunters: Each time an **INFANTRY** unit finishes a move, roll a D6. On a 6+ that unit suffers 1 mortal wound.

Vendetta: Each player picks one enemy unit at the start of the first battle round. Each player re-rolls hit and wound rolls of 1 for attacks that target the enemy unit they picked.

BONUS GPS

Players earn 5 bonus GPs each time they participate in one of the following missions:

- **Of Man and Xenos** (pg 138)
- **Cloak and Shadows** (*Warhammer 40,000* rulebook)

Players earn 1 bonus GP each time they participate in a mission using the following war zone:

- **Hyperia Hivesprawl** (*Vigilus Defiant*)

ROUND 2

23.464 POST: DISTRACTION TACTICS

Calgar secures a pact with the Asuryani, at great cost, but the results are immediate and effective. The Wild Riders of Saim-Hann cease their raids on Hyperia and instead strike at Warboss Krooldakka's Waaagh!, nipping at the flanks of that great beast until, enraged, it turns to pursue them – exactly as they intend.

23.476 POST: THE CHARGE CRASHES HOME

The Ork Speed Freeks, lured by the Aeldari riders, find themselves careening headlong into the forces of Chaos.

SPECIAL RULES

In this campaign round the following special rules apply:

Uneasy Allies: Subtract 1 from the Leadership characteristic of **IMPERIUM** and **ASURYANI** models.

Misdirected: At the start of the battle, each player subtracts D3 from their total number of Command Points (to a minimum of 0) if they have one or more **CHAOS** and/or **ORK** Detachments in their army.

BONUS GPS

Players earn 5 bonus GPs each time they participate in one of the following missions:

- **The Serpent's Lure** (pg 140)
- **Ambush!** (*Warhammer 40,000* rulebook)

Players earn 1 bonus GP each time they participate in a mission using the following battlezone:

- **Battlezone: Speedwaaagh!** (pg 150)

ROUND 3

23.511 POST: A DEADLY PAYLOAD

With the pact between the Imperium and the Asuryani forces holding, Calgar sets in motion a daring plan to snatch victory from the Despoiler. As quickly and stealthily as possible, he gathers the Deathstrike missiles of Deinos Agamemnus and conveys them to the New Vitae Docks, from whence they will be carried into orbit.

24.601 POST: THE SIEGE INTENSIFIES

The Iron Warriors use a scrapcode virus and captured Tectonic Fragdrills to bring down Mortwald's layered defences, before pushing home a devastating blitz into the hivesprawl's interior.

SPECIAL RULES

In this campaign round the following special rules apply:

Uneasy Allies: Subtract 1 from the Leadership characteristic of **IMPERIUM** and **ASURYANI** models.

Scrapcode Echoes: Re-roll unmodified hit rolls of 6 for attacks made by **VEHICLES**. **CHAOS VEHICLES** are unaffected by this rule.

BONUS GPS

Players earn 5 bonus GPs each time they participate in one of the following missions:

- **Deadly Payload** (pg xx)
- **Big Guns Never Tire** (*Warhammer 40,000* rulebook)

Players earn 1 bonus GP each time they participate in a mission using the following war zone:

- **Hyperia Hivesprawl** (*Vigilus Defiant*)

ROUND 4

24.623 POST: HEROES OF THE VOID

Loyal to the end, the remnants of the Imperial Navy fleet stationed at Vigilus make a concerted attack on their enemies, striking hard at the Chaos fleet. They pay a terrible cost, but succeed in their mission – to create an opening for Calgar's master stroke. The Aeldari stealth craft, *Vaul's Ghost*, now loaded with enough Deathstrike missiles to hole a battleship, makes its way towards the *Vengeful Spirit*.

24.641 POST: FALL OF THE CITADEL

The Dark Angels besiege the Citadel Vigilant and disable the Voidclaw, thus ending the Vhulian Anomaly.

SPECIAL RULES

In this campaign round the following special rule applies:

Brave Sacrifice: Roll a D6 each time a model is slain, before removing that model from play. On a roll of 6, that model can immediately either shoot as if it were the controlling player's Shooting phase or fight as if it were the controlling player's Fight phase. Then remove that model from play.

BONUS GPS

Players earn 5 bonus GPs each time they participate in one of the following missions:

- **Doomsday Device** (pg 132)
- **Tactical Strike** (*Warhammer 40,000* rulebook)
- **Firesweep** (*Warhammer 40,000* rulebook)

Players earn 1 bonus GP each time they participate in a mission using the following battlezone:

- **Battlezone: Deadly Storm** (pg 149)

ROUND 5

24.722 POST: DEMISE OF A LEGEND

Determined to take whatever measures are necessary to ensure his plan will succeed, Marneus Calgar takes the fight to Abaddon in person. The two warlords clash in the upper spires of Saint's Haven as their fleets battle overhead.

24.815 POST: THE HOLE IN SPACE

The Aeldari ship delivers its missile payload and, in doing so, forces the wounded *Vengeful Spirit* to make an emergency warp translation. Abaddon, loath to let his prized flagship out of his control, teleports back to its bridge just as it enters the warp. The hole that is ripped in the fabric of space does incredible damage to the Chaos fleet, giving the Imperials the upper hand.

SPECIAL RULES

In this campaign round the following special rule applies:

Orbital Debris: Each player rolls 3D6 at the start of each of their turns. For each 6, they can pick a different enemy unit, excluding **CHARACTERS**. That unit suffers D3 mortal wounds.

BONUS GPS

Players earn 5 bonus GPs each time they participate in one of the following missions:

- **Demise of a Legend** (pg 144)
- **No Mercy** (*Warhammer 40,000* rulebook)

Players earn 1 bonus GP each time they participate in a mission using the following battlezone and/or war zone:

- **Battlezone: Field of Nightmares** (pg 151)
- **Hyperia Hivesprawl** (*Vigilus Defiant*)

ROUND 6

24.903 POST: DOOM FROM ABOVE

Debris rains from the skies as the wreckage of the cataclysmic battle in space falls to the planet's surface.

25.141 POST: A PLANET IN FLAMES

Vigilus is saved from immediate destruction, and the long and costly journey towards recovery is begun. Yet word arrives of an attack on Sangua Terra – Vigilus' twin planet on the other side of the Nachmund Gauntlet. The report mentions a giant spaceship approaching in low orbit, a craft that fits the description of a dire threat from ages past – the *Planet Killer*.

SPECIAL RULES

In this campaign round the following special rules apply:

Victors of Vigilus: Add 1 to the Leadership characteristic of **IMPERIUM** and **GENESTEALER CULTS** units if there are any enemy **CHAOS** units on the battlefield.

Leaderless: At the start of the battle, each player subtracts D3 from their total number of Command Points (to a minimum of 0) if they have one or more **CHAOS** Detachments in their army.

Orbital Debris: Each player rolls 3D6 at the start of each of their turns. For each 6, they can pick a different enemy unit (other than a **CHARACTER**); that unit suffers D3 mortal wounds.

BONUS GPS

Players earn 5 bonus GPs each time they participate in the following mission:

- **Meat Grinder** (*Warhammer 40,000* rulebook)

CAMPAIGNS IN THE DARK IMPERIUM

At this pivotal moment, worlds across the Imperium Nihilus are beset by threats from without and within as the defenders' worst nightmares manifest to torment and destroy them. There is only a flicker of hope remaining to them, and it will not take much more for it to be forever snuffed out.

INTRODUCTION

In this section you will find an updated Nihilus Events table. This is an extra layer of rules you can add to each campaign round you play in a Vigilus Ablaze Campaign. Alternatively, you can use these rules to create a campaign set on another war-torn planet or sub-system within the Imperium Nihilus during Abaddon's invasion. This type of campaign is known as a Dark Imperium Campaign.

SETTING UP THE CAMPAIGN

When setting up a Dark Imperium Campaign, follow the guidelines on pages 110-111. Rather than choosing a phase of the War of Nightmares on Vigilus to set your campaign within, you can instead use the Nihilus Events table, opposite, to determine the effects of each campaign round. There are three methods to do this, as follows:

THE CHAOTIC FLUX

The first method is for the rules for each campaign round to be generated randomly. To do so, roll a D6 and a D3 and consult the Nihilus Events table to determine the event and special rules that are in effect for that campaign round. It can be exciting to generate this event only when each new campaign round starts, leaving the players guessing as to what course the campaign will take.

THE ARCHITECT OF FATE

For this method, one member of the gaming group is in charge of choosing the event and special rules that take place in each campaign round. This player should be impartial and not choose results only to gain their team an advantage. This method is great if your gaming group is really embracing the narrative of the campaign. The player dictating the events can take cues from the epic tales of heroism and glory that have already unfolded in the battles of the previous rounds, and might write up the story into an ongoing narrative for all the players to read.

SPOILS TO THE VICTOR

The last method is to allow the team that earned the most campaign glory points in the previous campaign round to choose the event that takes place in the next, (randomly generate the event for the first campaign round). This method adds an extra layer of tension to each campaign round as the winning team will be able to choose an event to bolster their forces (or hinder their foes).

You may want to turn this idea on its head and have the team that earned the least campaign glory points choose the event for the next campaign round, or add in a roll-off between the top and bottom team to determine who decides.

NIHILUS EVENTS TABLE

D6	D3	EVENT	SPECIAL RULE
1	**1**	Warp phantoms and fiends swirl and cackle around the combatants, and nightmares are glimpsed through the haze of battle.	**Nightmare Incursion:** Add 1 to Morale tests.
	2	Warp energy sets the skies ablaze as psykers feel the surging tides of the empyrean flowing within them.	**Warp Surge:** Add 1 to Psychic tests and Deny the Witch tests. In addition, add 1 to the number of mortal wounds a **PSYKER** suffers from Perils of the Warp when taking a Psychic test.
	3	Raw power threatens to overwhelm those with even a hint of psychic potential, and random psychic manifestations wreak havoc.	**Psychic Convulsions:** Roll 2D6 for each of your **PSYKER** units on the battlefield at the beginning of your Psychic phase. If the result is higher than their Leadership characteristic, they manifest *Smite* automatically (it cannot be resisted). When they do so, resolve its effects on the closest other visible unit (including friendly units) within 18" of the psyker. The psyker cannot manifest any other powers in that phase.
2	**1**	A cyclonic storm of horrifying power sweeps over the battlefield just as the armies clash.	**Scouring Storms:** All battles must use the Battlezone: Deadly Storm rules (pg 149).
	2	The skies are aflame, making flight a suicidal prospect and forcing all fighting to take place on the world's tortured surface.	**Skies of Fire:** All battles must use the Battlezone: Raging Inferno rules (pg 148).
	3	Psychic phenomena abound, and in their wake flock malicious warp-gheists in droves.	**Nightmare World:** All battles must use the Battlezone: Field of Nightmares rules (pg 151).
3	**1**	Water reserves are running dangerously low, causing troops to flag.	**Drought:** Subtract 1 from the Move characteristic of **INFANTRY** models.
	2	In the grind of the ongoing war, disease runs rampant.	**Virulent Plague:** Subtract 1 from the Toughness characteristic of **INFANTRY** models. **NURGLE** units are unaffected by this rule.
	3	As the war enters the final phase, exhaustion saps the energy and concentration of all.	**Exhaustion:** Subtract 1 from the Attacks characteristic of **INFANTRY** models (to a minimum of 1).
4	**1**	Over the months of battle, innumerable vendettas have been fostered against hated foes.	**Vendetta:** Each player picks one enemy unit at the start of the first battle round. Each player re-rolls hit and wound rolls of 1 for attacks that target the enemy unit they picked.
	2	Supplies are running desperately low, and every army is suffering from a shortage of ammunition and able bodies.	**Shortages:** At the start of the first battle round, each player subtracts D3 from their total number of Command Points (to a minimum of 0).
	3	So much has been sacrificed by this point that retreat – or defeat – are unthinkable to all sides.	**Unwavering Resolve:** Add 1 to the Leadership characteristic of all models.
5	**1**	In the aftermath of a cataclysmic space battle, fractured remnants of sundered craft rain down in a blaze of fire.	**Orbital Debris:** Each player rolls 3D6 at the start of each of their turns. For each 6, they can pick a different enemy unit (other than a **CHARACTER**); that unit suffers D3 mortal wounds.
	2	With communications failing and the chains of command breaking, raiders find ample opportunity to prey on stragglers.	**Vicious Raiders:** You can add 1 to charge rolls for **BIKER** units and **INFANTRY** units that can **FLY**.
	3	Running battles become more and more frequent as the scattered armies hound each other through the ruins of the world.	**Running Battle:** Re-roll hit rolls of 1 for attacks made by models with a Move characteristic of 8" or higher.
6	**1**	Fanatical fervour sweeps the populace, and even hardened veterans are swept up in the zealotry.	**Zealous Fervour:** Add 1 to the Attacks characteristic of models in a turn in which they charged.
	2	In the world's darkest hour, moments of outstanding heroism come from surprising quarters, with the brave sacrifice of individuals determining the fate of millions.	**Brave Sacrifice:** Roll a D6 each time a model is slain, before removing that model from play. On a roll of 6, that model can immediately either shoot as if it were the controlling player's Shooting phase or fight as if it were the controlling player's Fight phase. Then remove that model from play.
	3	Victory must be secured, no matter the losses! Every side in the conflict sends their final reserves into the fray, holding not a single soldier back in case they might make the difference between victory and defeat.	**Final Reserves:** All missions use the Sustained Assault rules (pg 121). In addition, each player that has one or more battlefield edges can use the Sustained Assault rules, even if they are the Defender. If the mission does not specify, units must be set up wholly within 6" of one of the controlling player's battlefield edges.

NARRATIVE PLAY MISSIONS

The missions presented in this book are designed to allow you to play narrative play games based on some of the events that took place during the War of Nightmares on Vigilus. These missions are also ideal for playing games set on any war-ravaged planet of the Imperium Nihilus.

On the following pages you will find twelve new narrative play missions inspired by the events described in this book. The first six Crucible of War missions are designed to represent some of the challenges regularly faced by the warring armies on Vigilus, and indeed in the Imperium Nihilus at large – such as a sudden and overwhelming ambush, or a running battle through a lethal wasteland. The last six Echoes of War missions recreate specific events from the story of Vigilus, from the desperate battle for the Voidclaw, to the devastating charge brought to bear against the forces of Chaos by Warboss Krooldakka, to Marneus Calgar's masterful gambit against the Asuryani. Each mission is designed to be played on a battlefield that measures 6' x 4' (with the exception of the Serpent's Lure). If your battlefield is larger or smaller than this, you may need to tweak elements of the mission accordingly.

These missions can be played individually or as part of a Vigilus Ablaze or Dark Imperium campaign, as described on pages 108-119. To play a mission individually, you can either choose the mission that you most want to play, or roll on one of the tables below.

CRUCIBLE OF WAR

D6	MISSION
1	From an Unexpected Quarter (pg 122)
2	Allies of Convenience (pg 124)
3	Metal Onslaught (pg 126)
4	Control the Gate (pg 128)
5	Schism (pg 130)
6	Doomsday Device (pg 132)

ECHOES OF WAR

D6	MISSION
1	On the Bridge (pg 134)
2	Siege of the Hoist (pg 136)
3	Of Man and Xenos (pg 138)
4	The Serpent's Lure (pg 140)
5	Deadly Payload (pg 142)
6	Demise of a Legend (pg 144)

MISSION SPECIAL RULES

These missions use one or more additional special rules to better represent the different tactics and strategies used by attackers and defenders. Some of the more in-depth mission special rules are collected below and referenced by the missions that appear later in this section.

RANDOM BATTLE LENGTH

War is rarely predictable, and the time available to achieve your objectives is never certain.

If your mission uses Random Battle Length, at the end of battle round 5, the player who had the first turn must roll a D6. On a roll of 3+, the game continues, otherwise the game is over. At the end of battle round 6, the player who had the second turn must roll a D6. This time the game continues on a roll of 4+, otherwise the game is over. The battle automatically ends at the end of battle round 7.

RESERVES

Reserves are forces which are not directly present at the start of an engagement but are available as reinforcements during battle.

If a mission uses Reserves, it will detail which units from your army start the game in Reserve – these units are not deployed with the rest of your army.

The mission will usually state when the units placed in Reserve arrive on the battlefield – this is typically at the end of a particular Movement phase. If the mission does not specify when units arrive, roll for each unit at the end of your second Movement phase (and at the end of each of your Movement phases thereafter) – this is called a Reserve roll. On a 3+, the unit being rolled for arrives from Reserve. Note that if a unit placed into Reserve is embarked within a **Transport**, they will arrive when their transport does, not separately (if rolling, make a single roll for the transport and the units embarked in it).

The mission will explain how and where to set up units when they arrive from Reserve – typically within a short distance of a specified edge of the battlefield.

Sustained Assault

Occasionally, an army will possess overwhelming superiority in numbers, with wave upon wave of its troops hurling themselves forward.

If your mission uses Sustained Assault, any of the Attacker's units that are destroyed can be brought back into play later in the battle, to represent their almost limitless supply of reinforcements. At the end of each of the Attacker's Movement phases, roll a D6 for each of their destroyed units, adding 2 to the result if that unit has the Troops Battlefield Role. On a 4+, immediately set up that unit within 6" of a battlefield edge – the mission will specify which.

The Attacker can also, at the end of any of their turns, remove any of their units from the battlefield that have a quarter or less of their starting number of models (or, in the case of single-model units, a quarter or less of its starting number of wounds). This unit then counts as having been destroyed for all purposes, and so can be brought back into play later as described above.

Objective Markers

Many battles are fought to secure a vital objective, whether it is a piece of rare archeotech, a fortified stronghold, or a person of vital strategic importance.

Many missions use objective markers – these represent sites of strategic import that both sides are attempting to secure. These can be represented by any appropriate markers or models you have available. A player controls an objective marker if they have more models within 3" of it than their opponent does. When measuring distances involving objective markers, always measure to and from the centre of the marker.

'I used to think Hyperia was a sniper's dream. Lots of eyries, plenty of spires, an endless variety of plazas, parks and boulevards stretching to the horizon. Then I learned what was waiting for us at the tips of those spires. "Don't look up," the Vigilites said. But in keeping our eyes on the street, we let the enemy turn the heavens themselves against us.'

- Vandar Tharke, Eliminator Sergeant

CRUCIBLE OF WAR
FROM AN UNEXPECTED QUARTER

Even the most elite armies and most experienced warriors are not proof against the element of surprise. In this battle, just such a group of warriors realise that they have overextended and, as attackers swarm from every direction, they must battle against hordes of enemies in a desperate fight for survival.

THE ARMIES

Each player must first muster an army from their collection. A player can include any models in their army, but if their army is Battle-forged they will also be able to use the appropriate Stratagems included with this mission (see opposite). Once the armies have been chosen, the players must decide who will be the Attacker and who will be the Defender. If the Power Level of one of the armies is a third or more higher than the opposing army's Power Level, then the player whose army has the higher Power Level must be the Defender and their opponent must be the Attacker. Otherwise the players can roll off to decide.

This mission represents a superior force under attack from a horde of enemies, and will work better if the Attacker doesn't take any units with a Power Rating of 11 or more.

THE BATTLEFIELD

Create a battlefield using the deployment map below and then set up terrain. Dense terrain makes this an ideal spot for an ambush, with forgotten machinery and tumbledown ruins providing plenty of hiding places for the attackers.

DEPLOYMENT

After terrain has been set up, the Defender sets up all of their units wholly within their deployment zone. The Attacker's units are all set up in Reserve (pg 120); they will arrive during the battle as described below.

FIRST TURN

The Attacker has the first turn.

ATTACKER'S RESERVES

The Attacker can bring on any of their Reserve units at the end of each of their Movement phases. When a unit arrives from Reserve it must be set up wholly within 6" of any battlefield edge that is not covered, and more than 9" from any enemy models. A battlefield edge is covered if two or more of the Defender's units are within 6" of that edge, and none of the Attacker's units are within 6" of that edge.

SUSTAINED ASSAULT

The Attacker can use the Sustained Assault rules (pg 121). Units brought back to the battlefield using these rules must be set up wholly within 6" of any battlefield edge that is not covered (as described above).

BATTLE LENGTH

Use the Random Battle Length rules (pg 120) to determine how long the battle lasts.

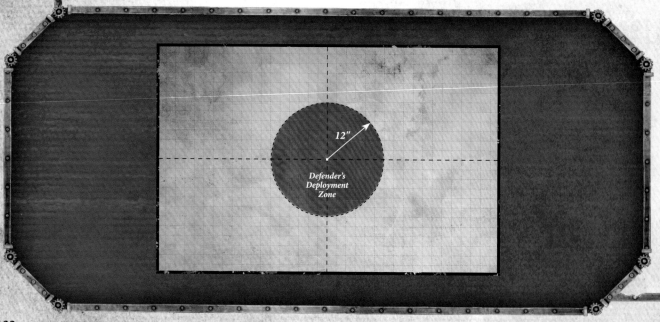

12"

Defender's Deployment Zone

STRATAGEMS

In this mission, the players can use Command Points (CPs) to use the following bonus Stratagems:

1CP — ## PIN THEM DOWN
Attacker Stratagem

Even superior combatants can be brought down by lesser fighters when surrounded.

Use this Stratagem when you pick a unit from your army to fight with in the Fight phase. Until the end of the phase, add 1 to hit rolls for attacks made by models in that unit that target an enemy unit that is within 1" of one or more other units from your army.

2CP — ## BRACE YOURSELVES
Defender Stratagem

As the ambush is sprung, those with the quickest reactions dive for cover and scan for targets.

Use this Stratagem after setting up a unit. Until that unit moves (for any reason) add 1 to saving throws for shooting attacks that target that unit, and add 1 to hit rolls for shooting attacks made by that unit.

2CP — ## OVERWHELMING NUMBERS
Attacker Stratagem

This army seems to be endless, no matter how many of its warriors are slain.

Use this Stratagem at the end of your Movement phase. Add 1 to any rolls you make for Sustained Assault this turn.

2CP — ## AT THE DOUBLE!
Defender Stratagem

The Defending army forges onwards, undeterred by the odds against them.

Use this Stratagem at the start of your Movement phase. Until the end of the phase, you can re-roll Advance rolls for units from your army.

1CP — ## SMOKESCREEN
Attacker Stratagem

The cover of smoke allows soldiers to close with the enemy relatively unscathed.

Use this Stratagem at the start of the first battle round. Until the end of the battle round, both players subtract 1 from hit rolls for shooting attacks.

3CP — ## BRUTAL ASSAULT
Defender Stratagem

These warriors redouble their efforts to cut down the horde before them.

Use this Stratagem when you pick a unit from your army to fight with in the Fight phase. Once that unit has fought, it can immediately fight again.

VICTORY CONDITIONS

At the end of the battle, if one army is totally destroyed, the other army's player wins a major victory. Otherwise, count the number of covered battlefield edges (as described above). If one battlefield edge is covered, the battle is a draw. If no battlefield edges are covered, the Attacker wins a minor victory. If two or more battlefield edges are covered, the Defender wins a minor victory.

CRUCIBLE OF WAR
ALLIES OF CONVENIENCE

Alliances in war are complex and often fleeting, but sometimes the enemy of your enemy can be your friend. However, no matter how aligned your motives appear to be, you were foes of each other once, and will be so again – and your so-called allies could turn on you at any moment.

THE ARMIES

First the players must decide who will be the Attacker and who will be the Defender. If the players cannot agree, they roll off, and the winner decides. The Attacker musters an army from their collection that is divided into two smaller forces each with a combined Power Rating as close a possible to half of their army's Power Level. The mission will work better if these forces are chosen from different factions (e.g. if one is composed of models with the **ORK** keyword and the other is composed of models with the **ADEPTUS ASTARTES** keyword), but this is not necessary. All that matters is that both players are able to tell the forces apart. The Attacker then chooses a Warlord for each of their smaller forces. The player who is the Defender must muster an army from their collection with a Power Level that is equal to or greater than that of the Attacker's army. A player can include any models in their army, but if their army is Battle-forged they will also be able to use the appropriate Stratagems included with this mission (see opposite).

FRACTIOUS ALLIES

In this mission, all units in the Defender's army are referred to as defending units, while all units in the Attacker's army are referred to as attacking units. In addition, the units in each of the Attacker's two forces consider all units from the other Attacker's force as allied units, and the following rules apply:

- Attacking units treat allied units as enemy units;

- When they are set up on the battlefield, attacking units must be set up more than 9" from any allied units;

- If an attacking unit targets a defending unit in the Shooting phase and there are any allied units within 1" of that defending unit, for each attack that hits, the Attacker must randomise which of those units (i.e. the defending unit and any allied units within 1" of that defending unit) is hit;

- If an attacking unit is within 1" of any allied units and no defending units, they do not have to be chosen to fight with in the Fight phase; and models in attacking units do not have to make attacks if the only possible target for those attacks is an allied unit.

THE BATTLEFIELD

Create a battlefield using the deployment map below and then set up terrain. Ruined buildings are dotted around the battlefield to represent the war-torn planet.

DEPLOYMENT

After terrain has been set up, the Defender sets up all of their units wholly within their deployment zone. The Attacker then sets up all of their units wholly within their deployment zones.

FIRST TURN

The Attacker rolls a D6. On a 1, 2 or 3, the Attacker has the first turn; otherwise the Defender has the first turn.

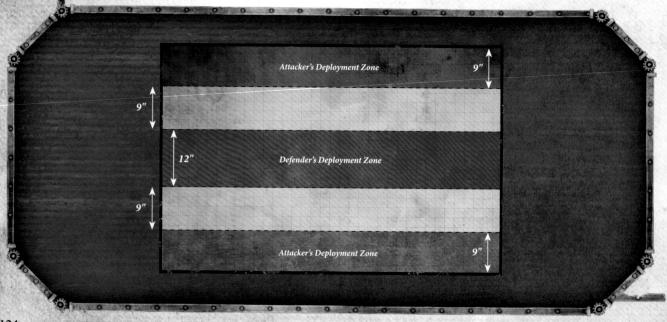

STRATAGEMS

In this mission, the players can use Command Points (CPs) to use the following bonus Stratagems:

KEEP YOUR DISTANCE
1CP

Attacker Stratagem

These troops have strict orders to avoid fraternising or crossing blades with their sometime allies.

Use this Stratagem at the end of the battle round, if an attacking unit is within 1" of one or more allied units and no defending units. Fall Back with that attacking unit as if it were your Movement phase.

USEFUL DISTRACTION
1CP

Attacker Stratagem

It doesn't count as friendly fire if they're not really on your side.

Use this Stratagem when you pick a unit from your army to shoot with in the Shooting phase. Until the end of the phase, add 1 to hit rolls for attacks made by that unit that target a defending unit that is within 1" of one or more allied units.

STRIKE IN CONCERT
1CP

Attacker Stratagem

For now, at least, this alliance will be honoured with the enemy's blood.

Use this Stratagem when you pick a unit from your army to fight with in the Fight phase. Until the end of the phase, add 1 to hit rolls for attacks made by that unit that target a defending unit that is within 1" of one or more allied units.

SOW DOUBT
1CP

Defender Stratagem

A fragile alliance is easily disrupted with misleading and treacherous communications.

Use this Stratagem at the start of the Morale phase. Until the end of the phase, the Attacker adds 1 to Morale tests they take.

MISDIRECTED ATTACK
3CP

Defender Stratagem

One moment of confusion on the battlefield can spell doom for the enemy.

Use this Stratagem in the Attacker's Shooting phase when they pick a unit to shoot with, if that unit is within 12" of one or more allied units. Instead of shooting normally, the shooting unit must target one of those allied units (randomly determine which one) with all of their shooting weapons.

STRENGTH OF UNITY
1CP

Defender Stratagem

Unlike the forces of the enemy, these troops are united under a single banner.

Use this Stratagem at the start of the Morale phase. Until the end of the phase, subtract 1 from Morale tests you take.

BATTLE LENGTH

Use the Random Battle Length rules (pg 120) to determine how long the battle lasts.

VICTORY CONDITIONS

At the end of the battle, if one army is totally destroyed, the other army's player wins a major victory. Otherwise, if one of the Attacker's forces has been totally destroyed, the Defender wins a minor victory. In any other case, compare the total Power Ratings of the surviving units on each side. Whichever side has a greater surviving percentage of the Power Level of their army wins a minor victory. If it is a tie, the Defender wins a minor victory.

MISSION VARIANT

You can play this mission with three players – two Attackers and one Defender. The Attackers choose who will control which force, and share their turns – so they will need to work together to decide how their units move and in what order, which player can pick the next unit to fight with in the Fight phase, and so on. The Attackers will win or lose together.

CRUCIBLE OF WAR
METAL ONSLAUGHT

This world is host to sweeping battles in which god-machines fight Daemon Engines and scrap-built walkers spew oily fumes as they charge clanking into combat. On a field of battle such as this, any infantry caught in the action will have to fight for their lives.

THE ARMIES

Each player must first muster an army from their collection. A player can include any models in their army, but if their army is Battle-forged they will also be able to use the appropriate Stratagems included with this mission (see opposite). Once the armies have been chosen, the players must decide who will be the Attacker and who will be the Defender. If the Power Level of one of the armies is a third or more higher than the opposing army's Power Level, then the player whose army has the higher Power Level must be the Defender and their opponent must be the Attacker. Otherwise the players can roll off to decide.

This mission represents a beleaguered infantry force under attack from a large force of enemy war machines. It works best if the combined Power Rating of the Defender's **Monster** and **Vehicle** units is no more than half of the Power Level of the Defender's army, and if the Attacker includes plenty of **Monster** and/or **Vehicle** units in their army.

THE BATTLEFIELD

Create a battlefield using the deployment map below and then set up terrain. Scattered ruins and the scars of war are all that can be seen in this wasteland.

DEPLOYMENT

After terrain has been set up, the Defender sets up all of their units, other than **Monster** and **Vehicle** units, wholly within their deployment zone. Their **Monster** and **Vehicle** units are set up in Reserve (pg 120). The Attacker then sets up all of their units wholly within their deployment zone.

FIRST TURN

The Attacker has the first turn.

DEFENDER'S RESERVES

When a Defender's unit arrives from Reserve it must be set up wholly within 12" of any battlefield edge and more than 9" from any enemy models.

BATTLE LENGTH

Use the Random Battle Length rules (pg 120) to determine how long the battle lasts. However, if at any point all of one player's **Monster** and **Vehicle** units are destroyed (including those that were set up in Reserve) and the other player has one or more surviving **Monster** or **Vehicle** units, the battle ends immediately.

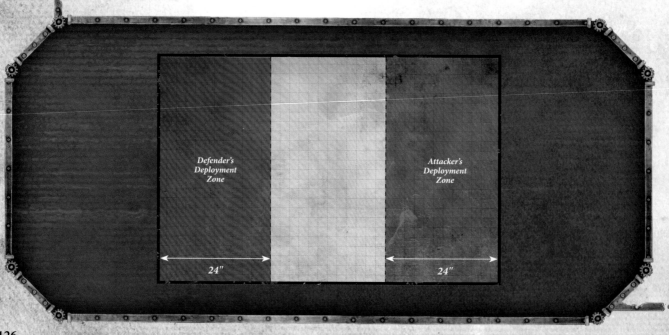

Defender's Deployment Zone

Attacker's Deployment Zone

24"

24"

STRATAGEMS

In this mission, the players can use Command Points (CPs) to use the following bonus Stratagems:

2CP UNSTOPPABLE ASSAULT

Attacker Stratagem

This vehicle's attacks are made all the more lethal by the momentum of its charge.

Use this Stratagem when you pick a **Vehicle** unit from your army that charged this turn to fight with in the Fight phase. Until the end of the phase, add 2 to hit rolls for attacks made by that unit that target units other than **Monster** or **Vehicle** units.

1CP ANTI-TANK ROUNDS

Defender Stratagem

The defending army is equipped with ammunition capable of shredding enemy armour.

Use this Stratagem when you pick a unit from your army (other than a **Monster** or **Vehicle** unit) to shoot with in your Shooting phase. Until the end of the phase, improve the AP characteristic of that unit's weapons by 1 (e.g. AP -1 becomes AP -2).

1CP MONSTROUS MIGHT

Attacker Stratagem

This gargantuan beast tears through the enemy lines.

Use this Stratagem when you pick a **Monster** unit from your army to fight with in the Fight phase. Until the end of the phase you can re-roll wound rolls for attacks made by that unit that target units other than **Monster** or **Vehicle** units.

1CP ARMOURED CLASH

Defender Stratagem

This heavy-hitting unit far outclasses those brought by the enemy.

Use this Stratagem when you pick a **Monster** or **Vehicle** unit from your army that charged this turn to fight with in the Fight phase. Until the end of the phase, you can re-roll hit rolls for attacks made by that unit that target **Monster** or **Vehicle** units.

1CP RAPID ADVANCE

Attacker Stratagem

The attacking army speeds forward, giving the enemy no chance to escape.

Use this Stratagem at the start of your Movement phase. Until the end of the phase, you can re-roll Advance rolls for units from your army.

1CP BEHEMOTH SUPPORT

Defender Stratagem

The arrival of armoured support boosts the morale of nearby troops.

Use this Stratagem in the Morale phase. Until the end of the phase, units from your army do not have to take Morale tests while they are within 6" of a friendly **Monster** or **Vehicle** unit that arrived from Reserve this turn.

VICTORY CONDITIONS

At the end of the battle, if the battle ends because all of one player's **Monster** and **Vehicle** units have been destroyed (note that those in Reserve are not considered to have been destroyed) and the other player has one or more surviving **Monster** or **Vehicle** units, the latter player wins a major victory. Otherwise, add up the Power Ratings of all the destroyed units in the Attacker's army. If more than two-thirds of the Attacker's army was destroyed, the Defender wins a minor victory. Otherwise, the Attacker wins a minor victory.

CRUCIBLE OF WAR
CONTROL THE GATE

One army has control of a way into this war zone that means they are continually reinforced. Their opponent's defeat is all but assured unless they can wrest control of this gateway – and in doing so perhaps even win a safe route for their own support troops to join the battle.

THE ARMIES

Each player must first muster an army from their collection. A player can include any models in their army, but if their army is Battle-forged they will also be able to use the appropriate Stratagems included with this mission (see opposite). Once the armies have been chosen, the players must decide who will be the Attacker and who will be the Defender. If the Power Level of one of the armies is a third or more higher than the opposing army's Power Level, then the player whose army has the higher Power Level must be the Defender and their opponent must be the Attacker. Otherwise the players can roll off to decide.

THE BATTLEFIELD

Create a battlefield using the deployment map below and then set up terrain. A gate dominates the centre of one long edge of the battlefield (see below), and ruined buildings surround it. If either player has a Webway Gate, this model makes a perfect representation of the gate.

DEPLOYMENT

After terrain has been set up, the Defender sets up all of their units wholly within their deployment zone. The Attacker then sets up all of their units wholly within their deployment zone. Both players can place units in Reserve (pg 120); they will arrive during the battle as described below. The combined Power Rating of the units a player sets up in Reserve cannot exceed half of that player's army's total Power Level.

FIRST TURN

The Attacker has the first turn.

CONTROLLING THE GATE

At the start of the game, the Defender controls the gate. If, at the end of a player's Movement phase, there are more models from their army within 3" of the gate than there are models from their opponent's army within 3" of the gate, they gain control of the gate. Otherwise, the player who currently has control of the gate maintains control of the gate.

FROM BEYOND THE GATE

If a player controls the gate at the end of their Movement phase (see above), they can set up any of their units from Reserve wholly within 3" of the gate and more than 9" from any enemy models. Units cannot otherwise be set up from Reserve.

SUSTAINED ASSAULT

Use the Sustained Assault rules (pg 121) in this mission. However, the Attacker only rolls for their destroyed units if they control the gate at the end of their Movement phase (see above) and units brought back into play using the Sustained Assault rules are set up as if they were arriving From Beyond the Gate (see above).

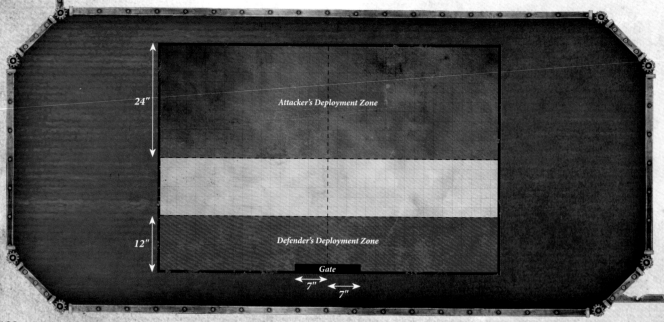

24"

Attacker's Deployment Zone

12"

Defender's Deployment Zone

Gate

7"   7"

STRATAGEMS

In this mission, the players can use Command Points (CPs) to use the following bonus Stratagems:

2CP — RUSH THE GATE
Attacker Stratagem
Capturing the gate is vital for the attacking army's survival.

Use this Stratagem at the start of your Charge phase. Each time a unit from your army attempts to charge this phase, you can re-roll one or both of the dice to determine its charge distance, as long as the targets of the charge are within 3" of the gate.

2CP — FORTIFIED POSITIONS
Defender Stratagem
The defending army digs in, certain of their enemy's intentions.

Use this Stratagem after setting up one of your units. Until that unit moves (for any reason) add 1 to saving throws for attacks made by ranged weapons that target that unit.

1CP — CONSOLIDATE YOUR POSITION
Attacker Stratagem
Once captured, the gate cannot be yielded, no matter the cost.

Use this Stratagem in the Fight phase when a unit from your army consolidates. You can move each model in that unit up to 3" towards the gate instead of towards the nearest enemy model.

1CP — FRESH REINFORCEMENTS
Defender Stratagem
The defending army has held their strongest forces in reserve, waiting for their foe to make a hubristic assault.

Use this Stratagem at the start of your Charge phase. Each time a unit from your army attempts to charge this phase, you can re-roll one or both of the dice to determine its charge distance, as long as that unit was set up from Reserve in this turn.

1CP — BREAKTHROUGH
Attacker Stratagem
The attacking army's reinforcements rush through the gate, turning the tide.

Use this Stratagem at the end of your Movement phase. Add 1 to rolls you make for Sustained Assault in this turn.

2CP — HOLD YOUR GROUND
Defender Stratagem
Forfeiting the gate will mean certain defeat in the ongoing war.

Use this Stratagem at the start of the Morale phase. Until the end of the phase, you can re-roll Morale tests you take.

BATTLE LENGTH
Use the Random Battle Length rules (pg 120) to determine how long the battle lasts.

VICTORY CONDITIONS
At the end of the battle, whichever player controls the gate (see opposite) wins a major victory.

CRUCIBLE OF WAR
SCHISM

In the darkness of a galaxy at war, faith and loyalty are tested as never before, and paranoia and conflict run rife. Sometimes, one faction may decide that it is time to cleanse their ranks of those who do not see eye-to-eye with them, making bitter enemies of those who were once allies.

THE ARMIES

Each player must first muster an army from their collection. A player can include any models in their army, but if their army is Battle-forged they will also be able to use the appropriate Stratagems included with this mission (see opposite). Once the armies have been chosen, the players must decide who will be the Attacker and who will be the Defender. If the Power Level of one of the armies is a third or more higher than the opposing army's Power Level, then the player whose army has the higher Power Level must be the Defender and their opponent must be the Attacker. Otherwise the players can roll off to decide.

This mission works best if both players muster armies in which all models share the same Faction keyword (other than **IMPERIUM**, **CHAOS**, **AELDARI** or **TYRANIDS**) – so, for example, both players could choose armies in which all models have the **HERETIC ASTARTES** keyword.

THE BATTLEFIELD

Create a battlefield using the deployment map below and then set up terrain. There are plenty of fortifications as the armies are not far from the front lines.

DEPLOYMENT

After terrain has been set up, the players alternate setting up their units, one at a time, starting with the Defender. Units can be set up in any of the deployment zones that do not contain any enemy units, and must be set up wholly within that deployment zone. If one player finishes setting up their units, the other player continues to set up units until all units have been set up. Each player can set up units in Reserve (pg 120); they will arrive during the battle as described below. The combined Power Rating of the units a player sets up in Reserve cannot exceed half of that player's army's total Power Level.

FIRST TURN

The Attacker rolls a D6. On a 1, 2 or 3, the Attacker has the first turn, and on a 4, 5 or 6, the Defender has the first turn.

SCRAMBLED RESERVES

Each player can set up any of their Reserve units on the battlefield at the end of each of their Movement phases. When a unit arrives from Reserve it must be set up wholly within 6" of any battlefield edge and more than 9" from any enemy models. The controlling player must then make a Scrambled Reserves roll by rolling a D6 for that unit. On a roll of 1 or 2, that unit cannot use any psychic powers, make any attacks or charge this turn. On any other result they can act normally.

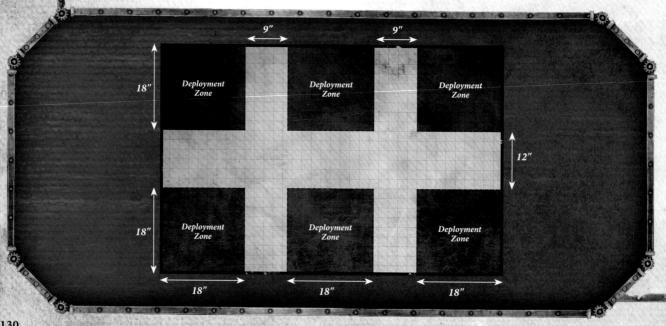

STRATAGEMS

In this mission, the players can use Command Points (CPs) to use the following bonus Stratagems:

PLANNED BETRAYAL
1CP

Attacker Stratagem

This conflict has been a long time coming, and this faction is fully prepared.

Use this Stratagem at the end of your Movement phase, before any Reserve units are set up. You do not need to make a Scrambled Reserves roll for the first unit from your army that arrives from Reserve in this turn.

VENGEFUL HATRED
2CP

Defender Stratagem

Traitorous acts will be avenged with no mercy.

Use this Stratagem when you pick a unit from your army to fight with in the Fight phase. Until the end of the phase, you can re-roll wound rolls for attacks made by that unit.

CRUSH THEIR LEADERS
1CP

Attacker Stratagem

This vile sect will surely wither and die without their leaders.

Use this Stratagem when you pick a unit from your army to shoot with in the Shooting phase or fight with in the Fight phase. Until the end of the phase, add 1 to hit rolls for attacks made by that unit that target an enemy **Character**.

HIGH ALERT
1CP

Defender Stratagem

Any new arrivals not confirmed to be faithful must be met with force.

Use this Stratagem when the Attacker sets up a unit from Reserve. Pick a unit from your army that is within 18" of the Attacker's unit. The unit you picked can shoot as if it were your Shooting phase, but all of their attacks require a 6 for a successful hit roll, irrespective of the firing model's Ballistic Skill or any modifiers, and all of their attacks must target the Attacker's unit that was just set up.

PURGE THE HERETIC
2CP

Stratagem

This force has an opportunity to show the heretics the error of their ways.

Use this Stratagem when you pick a unit to fight with in the Fight phase. Until the end of the phase, you can re-roll hit rolls of 1 for attacks made by that unit.

HOLY WAR
1CP

Stratagem

This cause will live or die today, and the stakes are high for both sides.

Use this Stratagem at the start of the Morale phase. Until the end of the phase, you can subtract 1 from Morale tests you take.

BATTLE LENGTH

Use the Random Battle Length rules (pg 120) to determine how long the battle lasts.

VICTORY CONDITIONS

At the end of the battle, if one player's army is totally destroyed, the other player wins a major victory. Otherwise, compare the total Power Ratings of the surviving units on each side. Whichever side has a greater surviving percentage of the Power Level of their army wins a minor victory. If it is a tie, the Defender wins a minor victory.

CRUCIBLE OF WAR
DOOMSDAY DEVICE

As a war enters its final stages, many commanders will employ desperate last gambits – weapons of unimaginable destruction and devices of untold power. When they do so, their enemies will launch all-out assaults in a bid to shut them down.

THE ARMIES

Each player must first muster an army from their collection. A player can include any models in their army, but if their army is Battle-forged they will also be able to use the appropriate Stratagems included with this mission (see opposite). Once the armies have been chosen, the players must decide who will be the Attacker and who will be the Defender. If the Power Level of one of the armies is a third or more higher than the opposing army's Power Level, then the player whose army has the higher Power Level must be the Defender and their opponent must be the Attacker. Otherwise the players can roll off to decide.

THE BATTLEFIELD

Create a battlefield using the deployment map below and then set up terrain. A doomsday device sits on one side of the battlefield in a fortified position. The device must be represented by a suitable model. The centre of the device must be 18" from one short battlefield edge, and must sit on a line that runs from the centre of one short edge to the centre of the other short edge.

DEPLOYMENT

After terrain has been set up, the Attacker secretly allocates each of the units in their army a different number, and writes these numbers on small pieces of paper. They can also include three 'decoy' pieces of paper, which also have numbers written on them but ones that do not correspond to any units in their army. They then set up each of these pieces of paper wholly within their deployment zone. The Defender then sets up all of their units wholly within their deployment zone. The Attacker then sets up each of their units as close as possible to the piece of paper with the number that corresponds to that unit, wholly within their deployment zone. They then remove all the pieces of paper.

FIRST TURN

The Attacker has the first turn.

ATTACKING THE DEVICE

The Attacker's units treat the doomsday device as an enemy model. When a model fights, any of its attacks that target the doomsday device hit automatically – do not make hit rolls for these attacks. The doomsday device has a Toughness characteristic of 20 and no Save characteristic. It does not have a Wounds characteristic and cannot be destroyed – simply keep a tally of the amount of damage suffered by the device in each battle round (this is called the damage tally). The damage tally is reset to 0 at the start of each battle round. Check the damage tally at the end of each battle round; if it is 5 or more, the doomsday device loses a structure point.

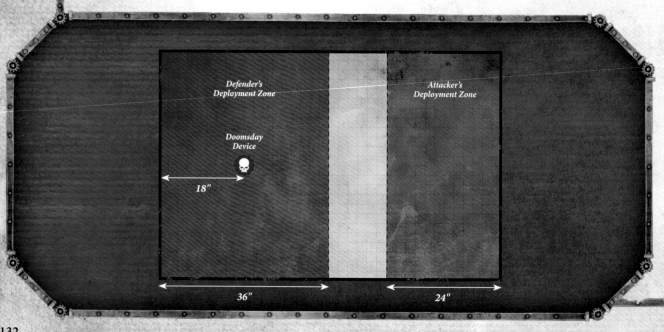

Defender's Deployment Zone

Attacker's Deployment Zone

Doomsday Device

18"

36"

24"

STRATAGEMS

In this mission, the players can use Command Points (CPs) to use the following bonus Stratagems:

1CP — SABOTEUR
Attacker Stratagem
This operative has studied the device's weak points.

Use this Stratagem when you set up a **Character** from your army on the battlefield. Add 1 to wound rolls for attacks made by that **Character** that target the doomsday device in the Fight phase.

1CP — JURY-RIG
Defender Stratagem
Engineers hasten to repair the device.

Use this Stratagem at the end of the battle round, before you make a repair roll for the doomsday device, if any of your models are touching the doomsday device with their base. Add 1 to the repair roll. You can only use this Stratagem once per battle round.

2CP — PRIORITY TARGET
Attacker Stratagem
The device must be destroyed – everything depends upon it.

Use this Stratagem when you pick a unit from your army to shoot with in your Shooting phase. Until the end of that phase, you can add 1 to wound rolls for attacks made by that unit that target the doomsday device.

2CP — DEFEND THE DEVICE
Defender Stratagem
The device must be protected at all costs.

Use this Stratagem when you pick a unit from your army to fight with in the Fight phase, if that unit includes any models that are within 5" of the centre of the doomsday device or that are touching the doomsday device with their base. Until the end of the phase, you can re-roll hit rolls for attacks made by that unit.

2CP — FIGHT TO THE LAST
Attacker Stratagem
The dire circumstances spur the attacking army to ever greater displays of heroism.

Use this Stratagem at the start of the Morale phase. Units from your army that include any models that are within 5" of the centre of the doomsday device or that are touching the doomsday device with their base do not have to take Morale tests.

1CP — IMPROVISED SHIELDS
Defender Stratagem
The device can produce a rudimentary force field, but this will strain the system.

Use this Stratagem at the start of the Attacker's Shooting or Fight phase. Until the end of the phase, the doomsday device has an invulnerable save of 5+. In addition, increase the damage tally by 1.

REPAIRING THE DEVICE

The Defender can attempt to repair the doomsday device at the end of a battle round, before the damage tally is checked, if any of their models is touching the doomsday device with their base. To do so, the Defender makes a repair roll by rolling a D3 and reducing the damage tally by the result, to a minimum of 0.

BATTLE LENGTH

Use the Random Battle Length rules (pg 120) to determine how long the battle lasts. In addition, if the doomsday device has lost 5 structure points, the battle immediately ends.

VICTORY CONDITIONS

If the battle ends because the doomsday device has lost 5 structure points, the Attacker wins a major victory. Otherwise, if the device has lost 4 structure points at the end of the battle, the Attacker wins a minor victory. If the device has lost 3 structure points at the end of the battle, the Defender wins a minor victory, and if the device has lost 2 or fewer structure points at the end of the battle, the Defender wins a major victory.

ECHOES OF WAR
ON THE BRIDGE

The impossible happened on the bridge of the *Laurels of Victory* – reality was rent with an awful scream as Daemons spilled from the warp to assault the crew. Marneus Calgar responded immediately, trusting the ship's commanders to fight the ongoing space battle as he led his elite in their defence.

THE ARMIES

Each player must first muster an army from their collection. The Defender commands the Ultramarines force. The Attacker commands the hordes of attacking Slaaneshi Daemons. A player can include any models in their army, but if their army is Battle-forged they will also be able to use the appropriate Stratagems included with this mission (see opposite).

THE BATTLEFIELD

The Defender creates the battlefield. The battlefield should resemble the interior of a great spaceship, and be fortified in the manner of a ship's bridge. Set up six objective markers as shown on the deployment map to represent essential systems and hardwired servitor crew.

DEPLOYMENT

After terrain has been set up, the Defender sets up their units wholly within their deployment zone. The Attacker then sets up their units wholly within their deployment zone. The Attacker can set up units in Reserve (pg 120); they will arrive during the battle as described below. The combined Power Rating of the units set up in Reserve cannot exceed half of the player's army's total Power Level.

FIRST TURN

The Attacker has the first turn.

SUSTAINED ASSAULT

The Attacker can use the Sustained Assault rules (pg 121). Units brought back to the battlefield using these rules must be set up wholly within 6" of both the Attacker's battlefield edge and the Attacker's deployment zone.

CRIPPLE THE SHIP

The Attacker's units treat objective markers as enemy models. The objective markers have a Toughness characteristic of 4, a Wounds characteristic of 1 and a Save characteristic of 4+. They are also considered to be **CHARACTERS** for the purposes of choosing a target for an attack (but for no other purposes). If an objective marker is destroyed, remove it from the battlefield.

BATTLE LENGTH

Use the Random Battle Length rules (pg 120) to determine how long the battle lasts, though note that the battle may end immediately as described in 'Ship Status'.

VICTORY CONDITIONS

If the battle ends immediately because of the ship status roll (see right), the Attacker wins a major victory. Otherwise, if one army has been entirely destroyed, the other army's player wins a major victory. If neither player has won a major victory, then if there are none of the Defender's **CHARACTERS** on the battlefield, the Attacker wins a minor victory. Any other result is a minor victory for the Defender.

SHIP STATUS

At the start of each of the Defender's turns, they make a ship status roll by rolling a D6 and consulting the following table. They can add 1 to the result for each objective marker on the battlefield.

D6	RESULT
1	**Devastating Hit:** The battle ends immediately.
2-3	**Glancing Hit:** Roll a D6 for each unit (and objective marker) that is within 6" of a battlefield edge. On a roll of 1, that unit (or marker) suffers D3 mortal wounds.
4-5	**Evasive Manoeuvres:** Both players subtract 2 from their units' Move characteristics until the Defender's next turn.
6+	**Steady as She Goes:** No effect.

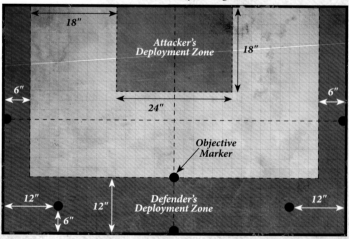

Attacker's Battlefield Edge

18"

Attacker's Deployment Zone

18"

6"   6"

24"

Objective Marker

12"   12"

Defender's Deployment Zone

12"

6"

STRATAGEMS

In this mission, the players can use Command Points (CPs) to use the following bonus Stratagems:

HEEDLESS SLAUGHTER
1CP

Attacker Stratagem

The Daemons that spill onto the bridge are driven by an ecstatic frenzy, uncaring of how many of their number are blasted back to the immaterium.

Use this Stratagem at the start of the Morale phase. Until the end of the phase, you can re-roll Morale tests you take.

INSTANT REPRISAL
2CP

Defender Stratagem

The Ultramarines' exemplary training means they are able to respond rapidly to the daemonic ambush.

Use this Stratagem when a unit from your army fires Overwatch. Until the end of the phase, that unit's attacks require a 5+ for a successful hit roll, irrespective of the firing model's Ballistic Skill or any modifiers.

CAPTIVATE
1CP

Attacker Stratagem

The horrifying allure of the Slaaneshi Daemons proves dangerously distracting for some of the ship's crew.

Use this Stratagem at the start of the Defender's turn, before they make the ship status roll. Pick an objective marker that is within 3" of a unit from your army. For the purposes of the ship status roll in this turn, that objective marker is not considered to be on the battlefield.

PROTECT THE CREW
2CP

Defender Stratagem

The Ultramarines will gladly give their lives to protect the ship's crew.

Use this Stratagem at the start of the Shooting or Fight phase. Until the end of the phase, each time an objective marker suffers a wound, you can roll a D6. If you do, on a 2+ a unit from your army within 2" of that marker suffers 1 mortal wound and the objective marker does not suffer a wound. If you roll a 1 or there is no unit from your army within 2" of that marker, the marker suffers the wound.

THE CALL OF SLAUGHTER
1CP

Attacker Stratagem

The screams of the dying and the delighted howls of their tormentors are a clarion call for the Daemons on the other side of the rift.

Use this Stratagem at the end of your Movement phase, before making any rolls for Sustained Assault, if one or more units from your army destroyed one or more enemy units in the Fight phase of the previous turn. Until the end of the turn, you can add 1 to your rolls for Sustained Assault.

DESPERATE HEROISM
3CP

Defender Stratagem

Though they face almost certain death, and the horrors of the warp are appearing before their very eyes, the crew of the Laurels of Victory *keep to their duties, desperately steering their ship through the battle, no matter the cost.*

Use this Stratagem when you make a ship status roll. You can re-roll the dice. If you do, add 1 to the result.

MISSION VETERANS

In this mission, each player can upgrade one of the units in their army to be a mission veteran. If one player takes a mission veteran but the other does not have a suitable model, the player without the mission veteran gains 1 additional Command Point at the start of the battle.

THE PALE STALKER

Attacker Mission Veteran Stratagem

The daemonic incursion was led by a statuesque Daemon that moved quicker than the eye could follow.

Pick a **KEEPER OF SECRETS** from your army to be the Pale Stalker. Each time you roll a hit roll of 6+ for an attack made by this model in the Fight phase, it can immediately make an extra attack against the same unit using the same weapon. These extra attacks cannot themselves generate any further attacks.

AEGIS SQUAD

Defender Mission Veteran Stratagem

Aegis Squad was assembled with the intention of launching a boarding action. Instead, these Terminators fought to the last to preserve the Laurels of Victory.

Pick a **TERMINATOR ASSAULT SQUAD** from your army to be Aegis Squad. Increase the Attacks characteristic of models in that unit that are armed with a thunder hammer and storm shield by 1.

ECHOES OF WAR
SIEGE OF THE HOIST

As the warriors of the Skitarii fought to hold back the fervent hordes of the Pauper Princes, a clutch of Genestealers slipped past their lines to reach the sanctified control centre of the Greater Omnissian Hoist. A response team was sent in pursuit with orders to eliminate them at any cost.

THE ARMIES

Each player must first muster an army from their collection. The Defender commands the Genestealer Cultists army that has infiltrated behind the Adeptus Mechanicus' lines. The Attacker commands the Adeptus Mechanicus army sent in response. A player can include any models in their army, but if their army is Battle-forged they will also be able to use the appropriate Stratagems included with this mission (see opposite).

THE BATTLEFIELD

Create the battlefield. It should be densely covered with pipes, ducts, machinery and gantries. The Attacker then sets up six objective markers anywhere on the battlefield to represent various entryways. The objective markers must be more than 6" from the edge of the battlefield and from each other. The Defender then sets up four objective markers to represent controls for the hive shutters. Each of these must touch a different battlefield edge and be more than 9" from any other battlefield edge.

DEPLOYMENT

After terrain has been set up, the Defender sets up their units anywhere on the battlefield that is more than 7" from any objective markers. The Attacker sets up their units in Reserve (pg 120); they will arrive during the battle as described below. Do not use the Cult Ambush ability in this mission.

FIRST TURN

The Attacker has the first turn.

RISING FURY

At the end of each of the Attacker's Movement phases, they can set up any units that are in Reserve on the battlefield, following these rules: INFANTRY units must be set up wholly within 6" of any objective marker and more than 1" from any enemy models. All other units must be set up wholly within 6" of any battlefield edge that has an objective marker touching it, and more than 9" from any enemy models. The Attacker must subtract 1 from hit rolls for attacks made by units in their army in the Shooting phase if that unit was set up on the battlefield in the same turn.

LOCKDOWN

At the end of each player's turn, the Defender can remove objective markers from the battlefield. They can only remove an objective marker if there is a model from their army within 3" of that marker, and no enemy models within 6" of that marker.

BATTLE LENGTH

Use the Random Battle Length rules (pg 120) to determine how long the battle lasts. In addition, if all objective markers are removed from the battlefield, the battle ends immediately.

VICTORY CONDITIONS

If the battle ends because all objective markers have been removed from the battlefield, the Defender wins a major victory. Otherwise, if one army has been destroyed, the other army's player wins a major victory. If neither player has won in this way, if there is only one army with any surviving CHARACTERS, that army's player wins a minor victory. Any other result is a draw.

STRATAGEMS

In this mission, the players can use Command Points (CPs) to use the following bonus Stratagems:

1CP — FURY OF THE FAITHFUL
Attacker Stratagem
The forces of the Skitarii burn to avenge the injuries done to their sacred machineries by these xenos aberrations.

Use this Stratagem when you pick a unit from your army to fight with in the Fight phase. Until the end of the phase, re-roll hit rolls of 1 for attacks made by that unit.

1CP — HAUNTED GLOOM
Defender Stratagem
Sections of the battlefield are illuminated only by disquieting half-light.

Use this Stratagem at the start of your opponent's Shooting phase. Pick a unit from your army. Until the end of the phase, your opponent subtracts 1 from hit rolls for attacks that target that unit or any unit wholly within 9" of that unit.

3CP — HIDDEN ENTRANCE
Attacker Stratagem
Familiar with this portion of the hive strata, the Skitarii find hidden routes to the battlefield even as others are closed to them.

Use this Stratagem at the start of your Movement phase if the only objective markers left on the battlefield are touching the edge of the battlefield. You can set up one objective marker more than 6" from the edge of the battlefield and more than 9" from any enemy models. You cannot use this Stratagem after the third battle round.

3CP — COUNTER-AMBUSH
Defender Stratagem
While the Adeptus Mechanicus forces seek to surprise and eliminate the Genestealer threat, the true predators move swiftly to gain the upper hand.

Use this Stratagem when an enemy unit is set up on the battlefield. Pick a unit from your army that is within 3" of that unit and not within 3" of any other enemy units. You can immediately fight with the unit you picked as if it were your Fight phase, with the exception that it must pile in towards the enemy unit that was just set up, and can only target that enemy unit with its attacks.

2CP — SHOCKING ARRIVAL
Attacker Stratagem
The Genestealers are sent skittering away as Skitarii reinforcements suddenly appear.

Use this Stratagem at the start of your Morale phase. Until the end of the phase, your opponent adds 2 to Morale tests they take for units that are within 12" of a **Vehicle** from your army that was set up on the battlefield this turn.

3CP — TERRIFYING SCREAMS
Defender Stratagem
The harrowing sounds of their fellows being slaughtered are enough to test the Skitarii's resolve.

Use this Stratagem at the start of the Morale phase in a turn in which one or more units from your army destroyed one or more enemy units in the Fight phase. Until the end of the phase, your opponent adds 1 to Morale tests they take.

MISSION VETERANS

In this mission, each player can upgrade one of the units in their army to be a mission veteran. If one player takes a mission veteran but the other does not have a suitable model, the player without the mission veteran gains 1 additional Command Point at the start of the battle.

DOMINUS ASCATHRAX VYMM
Attacker Mission Veteran Stratagem
So incensed was Dominus Ascathrax Vymm by this affront to the Machine God that when he fell upon the Genestealer Cultists, he fought with an unseemly fury quite at odds with his usual calculating reserve.

Pick a **Tech-Priest Dominus** from your army to be Ascathrax Vymm. That model's Attacks characteristic is increased to 6.

FIRST MAGUS VELLERON
Defender Mission Veteran Stratagem
Velleron had been entrusted with this mission by the Patriarch, and swore that even death was not enough to keep him from completing it.

Pick a **Magus** from your army to be First Magus Velleron. Each time this model loses a wound, roll a D6; on a 4+, this model does not lose that wound.

ECHOES OF WAR
OF MAN AND XENOS

Forced to take desperate measures to try to ensure the survival of Vigilus, the only recently recovered Marneus Calgar led his army to force a stalemate with the Asuryani raiders. If he could count those skilled warriors as allies, there might still be hope. But there is deep mistrust on both sides.

THE ARMIES

Each player must first muster an army from their collection. The Defender commands the vengeful Asuryani force. The Attacker commands the Ultramarines. A player can include any models in their army, but if their army is Battle-forged they will also be able to use the appropriate Stratagems included with this mission (see opposite).

THE BATTLEFIELD

Create the battlefield and set up terrain. The battlefield should be densely covered by the tangled ruins of a portion of Hyperia Hivesprawl. The players then place three objective markers along the centre line of the battlefield as shown on the deployment map.

DEPLOYMENT

After terrain has been set up, the players take it in turns, starting with the Defender, to set up their units wholly within their deployment zone. If one player finishes setting up their units, the other player continues to set up units until all units have been set up.

FIRST TURN

The Attacker has the first turn.

BATTLE LENGTH

At the end of battle round 5, the Attacker can choose to end the battle. If they do not, at the end of battle round 6, the Attacker can choose to end the battle. If they do not, the battle ends at the end of battle round 7.

VICTORY CONDITIONS

Each player earns victory points throughout the battle as follows:

- 1 victory point each time an enemy unit is destroyed.

- 1 additional victory point if that unit was a **Character**.

- 1 additional victory point if that unit was the army's Warlord.

- 1 victory point for each objective marker that the player controls at the start of their turn.

If, at the end of the battle, the Attacker and Defender have the same number of victory points, the Attacker wins a major victory. If the Defender has more victory points than the Attacker, the Defender wins a major victory. Any other result is a draw.

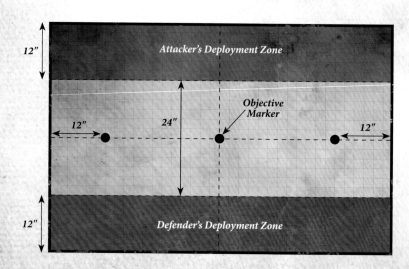

STRATAGEMS

In this mission, the players can use Command Points (CPs) to use the following bonus Stratagems:

1CP — SACRIFICE YOUR ADVANTAGE
Attacker Stratagem
Calgar's aim is to bring this fighting to a standstill and forge an alliance, even if victory is in sight.

Use this Stratagem at the end of your turn. Reduce your victory points by any number.

1CP — DEFENSIVE STANCE
Attacker Stratagem
Calgar orders his warriors to give just as good as they get – but to ensure that is very little.

Use this Stratagem at the start of the Fight phase. Pick a unit from your army. Until the end of the phase, subtract 1 from the Attacks characteristic of models in that unit (to a minimum of 1) and your opponent must subtract 1 from hit rolls for attacks that target that unit.

2CP — SHOW OF FORCE
Attacker Stratagem
The Space Marines demonstrate that they are better allies than enemies.

Use this Stratagem when you pick a unit from your army to shoot with in your Shooting phase. Until the end of the phase, you can re-roll wound rolls for attacks made by that unit.

1CP — PUNISH THEIR ARROGANCE
Defender Stratagem
It is dangerous to underestimate the Asuryani, as they will quickly punish such hubris.

Use this Stratagem when you pick a unit from your army to shoot with in your Shooting phase or fight in the Fight phase. If one or more models from that unit have been destroyed or have fled, until the end of the phase you can re-roll hit rolls of 1 for attacks made by that unit.

1CP — PSYCHIC SUPERIORITY
Defender Stratagem
The Imperial warriors will never be able to match the power and mastery of the Aeldari psykers.

Use this Stratagem at the start of the Psychic phase. Until the end of the phase, you can re-roll any of the dice rolled when you take Psychic tests or Deny the Witch tests for **PSYKERS** from your army.

1CP — SWORN VENGEANCE
Defender Stratagem
The Aeldari warriors are determined to avenge their fallen kin, and will not be easily deterred.

Use this Stratagem at the start of the Morale phase. Until the end of the phase, subtract 1 from Morale tests you take.

MISSION VETERANS

In this mission, each player can upgrade one of the units in their army to be a mission veteran. If one player takes a mission veteran but the other does not have a suitable model, the player without the mission veteran gains 1 additional Command Point at the start of the battle.

HONOURED BROTHER ADEON
Attacker Mission Veteran Stratagem
Honoured Brother Adeon was entrusted with battling the Aeldari war-leader to a standstill.

Pick a **CHAPTER CHAMPION** from your army to be Honoured Brother Adeon. Each time this model loses a wound, roll a D6; on a 5+, the model does not lose that wound. In addition, at the start of each Fight phase, roll a D6 and note the result. Until the end of the phase, unmodified hit rolls for attacks that target this model that match that result fail to hit, regardless of Weapon Skill or modifiers (e.g. if you roll a 3, any unmodified hit rolls of 3 for attacks that target this model in that phase would fail to hit).

BLADES OF KELTOC
Defender Mission Veteran Stratagem
The Blades of Keltoc fell upon the Ultramarines like vengeful spirits, their fury born from unbearable grief.

Pick a unit of **WRAITHBLADES** from your army to be the Blades of Keltoc. When an attack made by this unit destroys an enemy unit, you gain 1 additional victory point.

ECHOES OF WAR
THE SERPENT'S LURE

The riders of Saim-Hann honoured their pact with Marneus Calgar by launching a daring raid on the mighty Speedwaaagh! of Warboss Krooldakka. Successfully goading the Speed Freek, they then led his army in a wild chase that set it on a collision course with the forces of the Black Legion.

THE ARMIES

Each player must first muster an army from their collection. The Defender commands the Saim-Hann Wild Riders. The Attacker commands the Ork hordes of the Speedwaaagh!. A player can include any models in their army, but if their army is Battle-forged they will also be able to use the appropriate Stratagems included with this mission (see opposite).

THE BATTLEFIELD

The Defender creates the battlefield out of two 24" by 24" square tiles placed edge to edge. As the battle continues, the battlefield will change as more 24" by 24" square tiles (referred to simply as tiles) are added and removed. The battlefield should be sparsely covered with ruins, craters and debris.

DEPLOYMENT

After terrain has been set up, each player divides their army into three forces, each with a combined Power Rating as close as possible to a third of their army's Power Level. The Defender then sets up the units from one of those forces wholly within their deployment zone, and sets up the other two forces in Reserve (pg 120). The Attacker then does the same, setting up one of the forces of their army wholly within their deployment zone and the other two in Reserve. Reserves will arrive during the mission as described below.

FIRST TURN

The Attacker has the first turn.

WILD CHASE

At the start of the battle, the tile that contains the Defender's deployment zone is known as the end tile. At the start of each of the Defender's turns, if they have one or more units wholly within the end tile, the battlefield extends. When the battlefield extends, follow these steps:

1. The Attacker secretly chooses a number from 1-6 and notes it down, or hides a dice behind their hand with the number they chose on the dice's uppermost face.

2. The Defender places a new tile adjacent to the end tile, so that the edge of one tile lines up entirely with that of the other. This new tile becomes the end tile.

If the battlefield is then composed of four tiles, the oldest of those tiles is removed (the first tile to be removed in this way will be the tile that contains the Attacker's deployment zone). Any units even partially on that tile are destroyed. Keep a tally of the tiles removed – this is called the chase tally.

3. Determine the direction of travel by drawing a line through the centre of the two previous tiles (see the map). The Attacker then reveals the number they chose. If the number they chose corresponds to the placement of the new end tile relative to the direction of travel, they perform step 4. Otherwise the Defender performs step 4.

4. The player first sets up terrain on the new end tile (following the guidance in 'The Battlefield'), and then, if they have any remaining forces in Reserve, they choose one and set up all the units from that force anywhere wholly within the new end tile and more than 9" from any enemy models (they do not need to make Reserve rolls, and this is the only way that their Reserves can arrive on the battlefield).

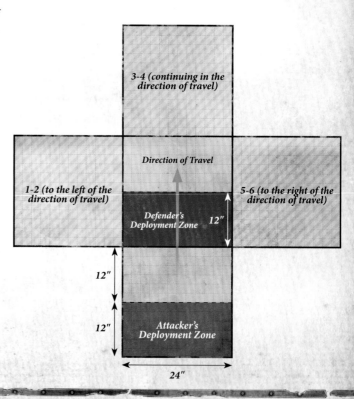

3-4 (continuing in the direction of travel)

Direction of Travel

1-2 (to the left of the direction of travel)

5-6 (to the right of the direction of travel)

Defender's Deployment Zone   12"

12"

Attacker's Deployment Zone   12"

24"

BATTLE LENGTH

Use the Random Battle Length rules (pg 120) to determine how long the battle lasts. In addition, if one army is destroyed (do not count any units still in Reserve) the battle ends immediately.

VICTORY CONDITIONS

At the end of the battle, if the Defender's army has been destroyed (not including any units still in Reserve) the Attacker wins a major victory. If the Defender's army has not been destroyed, and the Attacker's army has been destroyed (not including any units still in Reserve) the result is a draw. If neither army has been destroyed, check the chase tally: if the chase tally is 5 or more, the Defender wins a major victory; if it is 4 the Defender wins a minor victory; and if it is 3 or less the Attacker wins a minor victory.

STRATAGEMS

In this mission, the players can use Command Points (CPs) to use the following bonus Stratagems:

2CP — READY AN' WAITIN'
Attacker Stratagem

To the astonishment and outrage of the Aeldari Wild Riders, the Speedwaaagh! anticipates their movements.

Use this Stratagem when you set up a unit from Reserve. You can immediately shoot with that unit as if it were your Shooting phase.

1CP — THINK YER FAST?
Attacker Stratagem

The confidence of the Saim-Hann host is shaken as the Orks demonstrate themselves masters of the wastes.

Use this Stratagem in your Movement phase when you pick a unit to move. Roll 2D6 and add the highest result to that unit's Move characteristic until the end of the phase.

1CP — GET STUCK IN!
Attacker Stratagem

When the Orks are able to catch or corner their Aeldari tormentors, they vent their frustration in short but extremely violent displays.

Use this Stratagem when you pick a unit to fight with in the Fight phase. Until the end of the phase, you can re-roll hit rolls of 1 for attacks made by that unit.

1CP — PRIDE OF SAIM-HANN
Defender Stratagem

Though the Orks give them good sport, the Saim-Hann Wild Riders ably demonstrate their superior speed and skill.

Use this Stratagem in your Movement phase when you pick a unit to move, if that unit can **FLY**. Until the end of the phase, that unit can Advance even if it Falls Back.

2CP — GOAD THE BRUTES
Defender Stratagem

With whooping calls, dazzling displays of skill, and harrying shots, the Asuryani draw the Orks along their desired path.

Use this Stratagem at the start of the enemy Charge phase. Pick a unit from your army. Enemy units that can declare that unit as a target of a charge in this phase must do so (they can declare other units as targets as well).

3CP — WEAVING SERPENTS
Defender Stratagem

Though they long to give battle, the riders of Saim-Hann know that they must survive to lead the Orks into conflict with the Black Legion.

Use this Stratagem at the start of the enemy Shooting phase. Pick a unit from your army. Until the end of the phase, your opponent must subtract 1 from hit rolls for attacks that target that unit.

ECHOES OF WAR
DEADLY PAYLOAD

Marneus Calgar has committed the allied forces to an all-or-nothing gambit, and each stage of the plan is crucial to its success. The combined forces of the Astra Militarum and Asuryani are entrusted with ensuring that a lethal payload of Deathstrike missiles are safely transported to the fleet.

THE ARMIES

Each player must first muster an army from their collection. The Defender commands an army of two allied forces, one of Astra Militarum and one of Asuryani (choosing a Warlord for each). The Attacker commands the Black Legion. A player can include any models in their army, but if their army is Battle-forged they will also be able to use the appropriate Stratagems included with this mission (see opposite).

THE PAYLOAD AND THE DECOYS

In addition to their allied forces, the Defender will need three units, each made up of a single Valkyrie. One of these three Valkyries represents the vehicle that will carry the payload to the waiting ship, while the other two represent decoy vehicles. The Defender will also need three Skyshield Landing Pads. The Valkyries and Skyshield Landing Pads are not part of any Detachment, do not cost any points and are considered to have a Power Rating of 0 (but they do not prevent the Defender's forces from being Battle-forged).

TRUSTED ALLIES

The units in each of the Defender's forces consider all units from the other force as 'allied units'. Allied units are friendly units, with the following exceptions.

- Abilities on datasheets, psychic powers and Stratagems that refer to friendly units or models do not affect allied units.

- Abilities on datasheets, psychic powers and Stratagems that refer to enemy units or models affect allied units.

THE BATTLEFIELD

The Defender creates the battlefield. They must set up the Skyshield Landing Pads as shown on the map, and the battlefield should be heavily fortified in the Defender's deployment zone and only lightly covered outside of that deployment zone.

DEPLOYMENT

After terrain has been set up, the Defender sets up each of the three Valkyries on a different Skyshield Landing Pad, and then sets up their other units wholly within their deployment zone. They then secretly note down which of the Valkyries has the payload and which are decoys. The Attacker's units are set up in Reserve (pg 120); they will arrive during the battle as described below.

FIRST TURN

The Attacker has the first turn.

RESERVES

In the first battle round, the Attacker can pick units in their army with a combined Power Rating of no more than half of their army's Power Level to arrive at the end of their Movement phase. These units must be set up wholly within 6" of either of the short battlefield edges. The Attacker's remaining units arrive from Reserve as described on page 120, and again must be set up wholly within 6" of either of the short battlefield edges.

SUSTAINED ASSAULT

The Attacker uses the Sustained Assault rules (pg 121). Units brought back to the battlefield using these rules must be set up wholly within 6" of either of the short battlefield edges.

STALLING FOR TIME

The payload Valkyrie and the decoy Valkyries all begin the battle hovering using their Hover Jet ability. The payload Valkyrie cannot stop hovering, and cannot move or attack for any reason. The decoy Valkyries can stop hovering, and can move and/or attack (but this will reveal that they are decoys!).

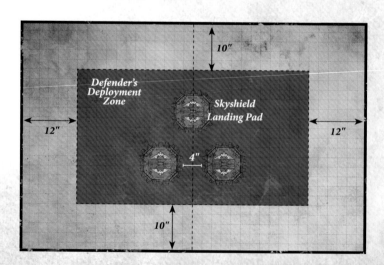

BATTLE LENGTH

Use the Random Battle Length rules (pg 120) to determine how long the battle lasts. However, if the payload Valkyrie or the Skyshield Landing Pad it is set up on is destroyed, the battle ends immediately.

VICTORY CONDITIONS

If, at the end of the battle, the payload Valkyrie or the Skyshield Landing Pad it is set up on has been destroyed, the Attacker wins a major victory. Otherwise, the Defender wins a major victory.

MISSION VARIANT

You can instead play this mission with three players – two Defenders and one Attacker. The Defenders share their turns, so they will need to work together to decide where their units move and in what order, which player can choose the next unit to fight with in the Fight phase and so on. The Defenders will win or lose together.

STRATAGEMS

In this mission, the players can use Command Points (CPs) to use the following bonus Stratagems:

3CP — CHAOTIC INTUITION
Attacker Stratagem

The Imperial lapdogs are playing their part well, but they cannot hide their intent from the intelligences of the warp.

Use this Stratagem at the start of the fourth battle round, if both decoy Valkyries are on the battlefield and neither has been revealed as a decoy. Your opponent must indicate one of the decoys to you.

1CP — EMERGENCY REPAIRS
Defender Stratagem

Even as the Black Legion descends on the landing pads, Tech-Priests and Enginseers frantically tend to the ships that are to carry their hopes.

Use this Stratagem at the start of your turn. Pick the payload Valkyrie, a decoy Valkyrie or a Skyshield Landing Pad to be repaired. That model regains D3 lost wounds. A model can only be repaired once per turn.

2CP — NO QUARTER
Attacker Stratagem

The Despoiler has had quite enough of the resistance of this planet's defenders. It is time to obliterate them.

Use this Stratagem at the start of the Fight phase. Until the end of the phase, each time you roll a hit roll of 6+ for an attack made by a model from your army (or 5+ if the attack targets an **IMPERIUM** unit), that model can immediately make 1 additional attack against the same unit using the same weapon. This is not cumulative with the extra attack granted by the Death to the False Emperor ability. These extra attacks cannot themselves generate any further attacks.

2CP — SUDDEN STRIKE
Defender Stratagem

Pushed to the limit by the approach of the Black Legion, the crew of one of the decoys decides to go out all guns blazing.

Use this Stratagem when you pick a decoy Valkyrie to shoot with in the Shooting phase. Until the end of the phase, double the number of attacks made by that model's weapons (in the case of weapons that make a random number of attacks, instead double the number of dice rolled e.g. Heavy D6 is doubled to Heavy 2D6).

1CP — GRIM DETERMINATION
Defender Stratagem

The men and women of the Astra Militarum defend the landing pads with their guns, their blades and their lives.

Use this Stratagem at the start of the Morale phase. Until the end of the phase, you do not have to take Morale tests for units from your army that are wholly within 3" of one or more Skyshield Landing Pads.

1CP — TERRIFYING DISPLAY
Attacker Stratagem

The Black Legion quickly target the enemy's commanders, slaying them in grisly displays designed to shatter the morale of their foes.

Use this Stratagem at the start of the Morale phase. Pick a unit from your army that destroyed one or more enemy **CHARACTERS** in the previous Fight phase. Until the end of the phase, your opponent must add 1 to Morale tests they take for units from their army within 6" of that unit.

ECHOES OF WAR
DEMISE OF A LEGEND

From the moment that Marneus Calgar heard the hated name of the Despoiler broadcast from the spires of Vigilus, he had known it would come to this. Locking eyes with his foe as their fleets battled above them, he armed his mighty gauntlets and prepared to mete out justice once and for all to this traitor.

THE ARMIES

Each player must first muster an army from their collection. The Defender commands the Black Legion force led by Abaddon the Despoiler. The Attacker commands the strike force of Ultramarines led by Marneus Calgar. A player can include any models in their army, but if their army is Battle-forged they will also be able to use the appropriate Stratagems included with this mission (see opposite). In addition, each player must pick a **Character** to be their Warlord.

THE BATTLEFIELD

Create the battlefield. It should resemble a fortified shrine complex that has been attacked, with defences, ruins, statues and craters. Then place six objective markers as shown on the deployment map. Number these objective markers 1-6 as shown.

DEPLOYMENT

After terrain has been set up, the players place their Warlords in the centre of the battlefield, in the area marked 'Duel Zone' on the map, within 1" of each other. The players then take it in turns, starting with the Defender, to set up their units wholly within their deployment zone. If one player finishes setting up their units, the other player continues to set up units until all units have been set up.

FIRST TURN

The players roll off. The winner decides which player has the first turn.

THE DUEL ZONE

Units outside the Duel Zone cannot move even partially into the Duel Zone, and units within the Duel Zone must remain wholly within the Duel Zone. Units outside the Duel Zone cannot target units inside the Duel Zone, and vice versa. Finally, the Duel Zone blocks visibility for units outside the Duel Zone as if it were a solid column of infinite height. The Duel Zone ceases to exist if one or both of the Warlords are destroyed.

THE DUELLISTS

The Warlords each have a Wounds characteristic of 25 in this mission.

BATTLE LENGTH

Use the Random Battle Length rules (pg 120) to determine how long the battle lasts.

VICTORY CONDITIONS

At the end of the battle, compare the total Power Ratings of the surviving units in each army. Whichever side has a greater surviving percentage of the Power Level of their army wins a minor victory, unless their Warlord is on the battlefield, in which case they win a major victory. If it is a tie, the result is a draw, unless only one player's Warlord is on the battlefield – in that case, that player wins a minor victory.

RAIN OF DEVASTATION

At the start of each battle round after the first, the Attacker rolls a D6 and consults the following table:

D6	RESULT
1	**A Moment of Stillness:** Nothing happens.
2-3	**Rain of Debris:** Roll a D6 for each objective marker. On a roll of 1, each unit within D6" of that objective marker suffers D3 mortal wounds.
4-5	**Stray Ordnance:** Roll a D6. Each unit within 3" of the objective marker corresponding to the result suffers D3 mortal wounds.
6	**Cataclysmic Descent:** Every unit on the battlefield (except the Warlords) suffers D3 mortal wounds.

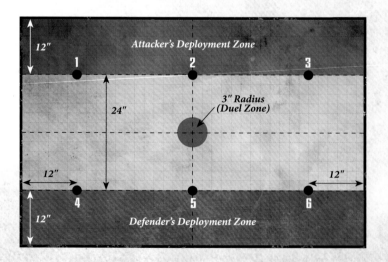

Attacker's Deployment Zone

12"

24"

12"

3" Radius (Duel Zone)

12"

12"

Defender's Deployment Zone

STRATAGEMS

In this mission, the players can use Command Points (CPs) to use the following bonus Stratagems:

POINT-BLANK BURST
1CP

Attacker Stratagem

Calgar unleashes a burst of bolt shells at point-blank range in an attempt to break through Abaddon's defences.

Use this Stratagem at the start of your Shooting phase. Until the end of the phase, your Warlord's ranged weapons have the Pistol type, instead of their normal type (e.g. Rapid Fire 2 would become Pistol 2). In addition, until the end of the phase your Warlord can only target the enemy Warlord with their attacks.

TEN THOUSAND YEARS OF HATRED
3CP

Defender Stratagem

Abaddon faces the Emperor's loyal hound with a snarl on his face. This has been his war for millennia, and this cur will not match him.

Use this Stratagem when you pick your Warlord to fight with in the Fight phase. Until the end of the phase, you can re-roll wound rolls for attacks made by your Warlord that target the enemy Warlord.

RIGHTEOUS FURY
3CP

Attacker Stratagem

Face-to-face with one of the original traitors of the Imperium, Calgar finds reserves of righteous fury of which even he was unaware.

Use this Stratagem when you pick your Warlord to fight with in the Fight phase. Until the end of the phase, you can re-roll wound rolls for attacks made by your Warlord that target the enemy Warlord.

TAMING DRACH'NYEN
2CP

Defender Stratagem

The Daemon bound in his blade writhes and struggles, but in this conflict Abaddon brooks no disobedience, lashing the entity to his will.

Use this Stratagem when you pick your Warlord to fight with in the Fight phase. Roll a D3 and add the result to your Warlord's Attacks characteristic until the end of the phase. In addition, if the result is a 1, your Warlord suffers 1 mortal wound.

POWERED GUARD
2CP

Attacker Stratagem

Wary of his enemy's warp-infused weaponry, Calgar keeps his guard up, batting his enemy's swings away with his invincible gauntlets.

Use this Stratagem at the start of the Fight phase. The players roll off. If you win the roll-off, your opponent must re-roll successful hit rolls for attacks made by their Warlord that target your Warlord.

DARK RESURRECTION
3CP

Defender Stratagem

Calgar's triumphant cry dies in his throat as Abaddon surges back to his feet, dark energy crackling around his impossibly unbroken form.

Use this Stratagem when your Warlord is slain. Do not remove your Warlord from play. Instead, the players roll off. If you win the roll-off, your Warlord regains wounds until their remaining wounds are equal to the number you rolled in the roll-off. The enemy Warlord cannot make any further attacks in this phase. If you lose the roll-off, your Warlord is removed from play as normal.

MISSION VETERANS

In this mission, each player can upgrade one of the units in their army to be a mission veteran. If one player takes a mission veteran but the other does not have a suitable model, the player without the mission veteran gains 1 additional Command Point at the start of the battle.

LIEUTENANT EOTHRUS

Attacker Mission Veteran Stratagem

As his commander surged ahead to confront the hated Despoiler, Lieutenant Eothrus smoothly took command of the strike force, directing them in the elimination of the traitors.

Pick a **Primaris Lieutenant** from your army to be Lieutenant Eothrus. The range of this model's Tactical Precision ability is 12" rather than 6".

VANDRETH, THE BLACK SEER

Defender Mission Veteran Stratagem

Vandreth smiled with satisfaction as Abaddon duelled the leader of the Ultramarines. Surely the gods would be watching and bestow their favour.

Pick a **Terminator Sorcerer** from your army to be Vandreth, the Black Seer. You can re-roll one or both dice each time you take a Psychic test for that model.

BATTLEZONES

The War of Nightmares on Vigilus set aflame a world already racked by war. The very landscape was transformed so that even experienced commanders found they had to adapt constantly to survive. As the planet groaned, the armies fighting there had more to contend with than simply their foes.

In this section you will find six exciting new battlezones to use in your games of Warhammer 40,000. From the whirling maelstrom of the Vhulian Swirl to the sterile confines of a spaceship bridge, each battlezone offers new tactical challenges to enrich your games, and introduces new rules to represent many varied battle environments. Some modify the core rules, for example by affecting how you use weapons. Some provide new rules for phenomena like cyclones and warp-gheists. Some grant additional abilities and Stratagems to certain units.

These rules are designed to reflect some of the environments fought in on Vigilus during the War of Nightmares, but they are entirely optional and, so long as you and your opponent agree, they can be used in any Warhammer 40,000 game, set anywhere.

Agree which, if any, battlezone rules will be used when you are setting up the battlefield, before deployment.

BATTLEZONE: SPACESHIP

The battle that took place on the bridge of the *Laurels of Victory* was extremely perilous. Even aboard such a robust vessel, the chance of stray shots causing catastrophic damage or hull breaches was high. On top of that, the claustrophobic confines meant that retreat was all but impossible.

Enclosed Space: Players cannot use any units with the Flyer Battlefield Role in this battlezone. In addition, models cannot be set up in locations such as high altitude transports, low orbit, clinging to an airborne Harridan, or any other location that suggests that unit would descend from the skies or burrow from underground. Locations such as teleportarium chambers, alternate dimensions or similar locations from which a unit could gain access to a moving, space-bound vessel are permitted. Players should agree before setting up their units if they are unsure if a location is appropriate.

Low Ceilings: Players cannot use ranged weapons to target a unit that is not visible to the bearer (though weapons with such an ability can still be used if the target is visible to the bearer). In addition, each time a unit with the **FLY** keyword moves in the Movement phase, roll a D6 for that unit. On a roll of 1, that unit suffers 1 mortal wound.

Stray Shots: Each time a player rolls an unmodified 1 for a hit roll for an attack made with a ranged weapon with a Strength of 7 or more, draw a straight line 1mm wide that starts from the centre of the firing model's base and runs through the centre of the base of the closest model in the target unit. Continue to draw that line until it comes into contact with a piece of terrain or the edge of the battlefield (whichever happens first). Then roll a D6. On a roll of 1-3, all units within 3" of the end of the line suffer D3 mortal wounds.

BATTLEZONE: PERILOUS CAVERN

There were many caverns under the surface of Vigilus, most the result of mining, some containing resources valuable enough that the armies fighting for the planet were prepared to risk battle to control them. However, such battles were fraught with danger from darkness, chasms and rockfalls.

Cave Network: Players cannot use any units with the Flyer Battlefield Role in this battlezone. In addition, models cannot be set up in locations such as high altitude transports, low orbit, clinging to an airborne Harridan, or any other location that suggests that unit would descend from the skies. Locations such as underground, teleportarium chambers, alternate dimensions or similar locations from which a unit could gain access to an underground chamber are permitted. Players should agree before setting up their units if they are unsure if a location is appropriate.

Death in the Darkness: At the start of each player's turn, they roll a D6 and consult the following table:

D6	RESULT
1	**Unseen Chasm:** Each time a unit moves in your Movement phase or charges in your Charge phase, roll a D6. On a roll of 1, one model of your choice from that unit is destroyed. **CHARACTERS**, **MONSTERS** and **VEHICLES** are unaffected by this rule.
2	**Uneven Ground:** Subtract 1 from the Move characteristic of models from your army for this turn.
3	**Impenetrable Gloom:** When making shooting attacks in this turn, your units can only target enemy units that are within 12".
4	**Flickering Darkness:** Subtract 1 from hit rolls for shooting attacks made by units from your army this turn.
5	**Scratching in the Shadows:** Add 1 to Morale tests you take this turn.
6	**Easy Going:** Nothing happens.

STRATAGEMS

When using this battlezone, the players can use Command Points (CPs) to use the following Stratagem:

2CP

ROCKFALL
Stratagem

Sometimes it's more efficient to take out the ceiling and bury your enemies under a few tonnes of rock.

Use this Stratagem when you pick a unit from your army to shoot with in your Shooting phase. Instead of shooting normally, pick an enemy unit that is within 12" of the unit you picked. Roll a number of D6 equal to the number of ranged weapons in the shooting unit with a Range of 12" or higher and a Strength of 7 or higher (e.g. if a unit has a plasma pistol (S 7-8), a plasma gun (S 7-8), a lascannon (S 9), and seven boltguns (each S 4), you would roll three dice). For each roll of 5+, the enemy unit suffers 1 mortal wound.

BATTLEZONE: RAGING INFERNO

When Marneus Calgar commanded the cauterisation of the hive-spires of Vigilus, the subsequent inferno consumed the tops of the hives, engulfing the Chaos invaders and the last, desperate defenders in flame. In any such scenario, outrunning the firestorm becomes just as important as destroying the enemy.

Levels of Battle: A mission played in a Battlezone: Raging Inferno will generally be better the more terrain there is! After you have created the battlefield, divide it vertically into three levels: the top level, the middle level and the bottom level. For example, the battlefield surface and any low-standing terrain, such as access hatches, can be the bottom level; medium-height terrain, such as the first storey of a two-storey ruin, can be the middle level, and high-standing terrain, such as the top floor of a three-storey ruin, can be the top level. What you designate as bottom, middle and top will depend upon what terrain you have set up on the battlefield. For example, the landing area of a Skyshield Landing Pad might be designated as being in the middle or top level, depending on the height of the other terrain pieces you have set up. Discuss with your opponent before designating levels to ensure you agree on how the battlefield is divided up, and so you both know at what point a unit moves from one level to another.

Descending Inferno: At the start of the second battle round, the top level of the battlefield catches fire. Units with the Flyer Battlefield Role, and any units even partially within the top level suffer D3 mortal wounds.

At the start of the third battle round, the middle level of the battlefield catches fire. Units with the Flyer Battlefield Role, and any units even partially within the top level suffer D6 mortal wounds. Any units even partially within the middle level suffer D3 mortal wounds (unless they have already suffered mortal wounds from being at least partially in the top level this turn).

At the start of the fourth battle round, the bottom level of the battlefield catches fire. Units with the Flyer Battlefield Role, and any units even partially within the top level suffer 2D6 mortal wounds. Any units even partially within the middle level suffer D6 mortal wounds (unless they have already suffered mortal wounds from being at least partially in the top level this turn). Any units at least partially within 1" of any terrain suffer D3 mortal wounds (unless they have already suffered mortal wounds from being at least partially in the top or middle levels this turn).

At the beginning of each subsequent battle round, apply the effects described for the fourth battle round.

Smoking Ruins: A model is not visible to another model if a straight line drawn from the centre of its base to the centre of the other model's base passes across any terrain, unless both models are at least partially within or on that terrain.

Top Level

Middle Level

Bottom Level

BATTLEZONE: DEADLY STORM

Battles that took place on the outskirts of the Vhulian Swirl ran the risk of being caught up in one of the many smaller storms generated by the colossal maelstrom. Although these lost some of their potency as they moved away from the Swirl, they still retained much of their parent's ferocity.

Swirling Cyclone: After players have chosen deployment zones, the player that is setting up the first unit must number the sections of the battlefield 1-6 as shown in diagram *A*, and then roll a D6. The section of the battlefield with the number corresponding to the result is affected by the deadly storm.

Flying Particulate: Models cannot pick an enemy unit as the target of a shooting attack if a line drawn from any part of the attacking model's base to any part of the base of the closest model from the enemy unit they wish to target passes over a battlefield section affected by the deadly storm.

In addition, at the end of each battle round, each unit even partially within the battlefield section affected by the deadly storm suffers D3 mortal wounds.

Roaming Maelstrom: At the start of each battle round after the first, the deadly storm moves into a different section of the battlefield. If the deadly storm is in a corner section of the battlefield, roll a D6 and consult diagram *B* to see which section the deadly storm moves into.

If the deadly storm is in one of the middle sections of the battlefield, roll a D6, re-rolling results of 6, and consult diagram *C* to see which section the deadly storm moves into.

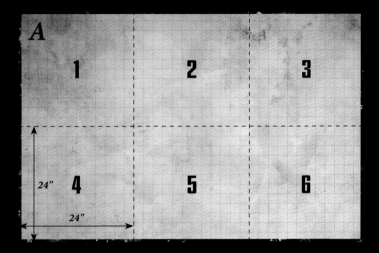

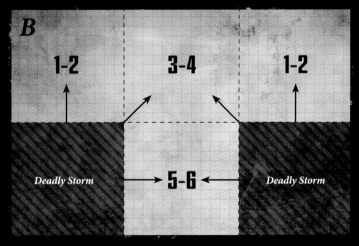

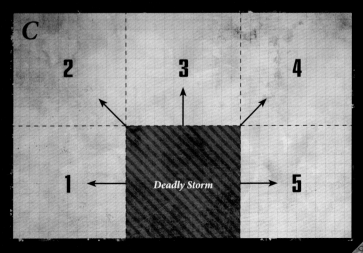

BATTLEZONE: SPEEDWAAAGH!

Krooldakka's Speedwaaagh! was a phenomenon that could be likened to a natural disaster, albeit one that was drawn unerringly to sites of conflict. The tide of roaring, clanking, smoke-spewing vehicles and their speed-maddened drivers and passengers were every bit as unstoppable and devastating as a tsunami.

Until the battle is spotted by the Speedwaaagh! use the following rule only.

Spotted by the Speedwaaagh!: Keep a tally of the number of units destroyed in each battle round. At the end of the battle round, roll a D6. If the result is lower than the number of units destroyed in that battle round, the battle has been spotted by the Speedwaaagh!.

Starting from the battle round after the battle has been spotted by the Speedwaaagh! use the following rules only.

Circling Riders: At the start of the battle round, roll a D6 for each unit that is within 3" of the edge of the battlefield. On a roll of 5+ that unit suffers D3 mortal wounds.

Smog-screen: Subtract 1 from hit rolls for attacks made in the Shooting phase.

Soopa Highway: At the end of the battle round, roll a number of dice equal to the number of the battle round (e.g. roll three dice at the end of battle round 3). If the combined total is 12 or more, the battle has become the site of a soopa highway. If that happens, the players roll off. The winner chooses a long battlefield edge, and the other player chooses a short battlefield edge.

The winner then rolls 12D6 and measures the result in inches along the battlefield edge they chose, starting from the corner furthest from the battlefield edge their opponent chose. They mark that spot with a counter.

The other player then rolls 8D6 and measures the result in inches along the battlefield edge they chose, starting from the corner furthest from the battlefield edge their opponent chose. They mark that spot with a counter.

Draw a straight line 1mm wide through the centres of the two counters. Any model that is even partially within 3" of that line is destroyed. This includes models with the Fortifications Battlefield Role, **Transports** and any units embarked within them. It also includes terrain features that can be removed from the battlefield. Units with the **Fly** keyword and units embarked within a **Transport** that has the **Fly** keyword are unaffected. If a terrain feature with any models standing on it is even partially within 3" of the line, and those models are not destroyed by the soopa highway, the controlling player places those models on the battlefield as close as possible to the terrain feature and in unit coherency. The controlling player then rolls a D6 for each of those models – on a 1, 2 or 3, one model from that model's unit (controlling player's choice) is slain. If possible, the terrain feature is then removed from the battlefield. Once this is resolved, the soopa highway disappears.

Winner's chosen battlefield edge

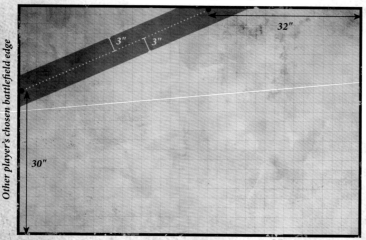

In the example shown here, the winner of the roll-off rolls a total of 32 and the other player rolls a total of 30. After they place their counters as described above, they draw a line between the two and measure 3" each side of that line. Any models even partially in the shaded area are destroyed.

BATTLEZONE: FIELD OF NIGHTMARES

The warring armies on Vigilus occasionally found themselves fighting within highly localised ripples in reality. As well as the terror caused by these phenomena, warriors also had to contend with attacks from malevolent entities and deadly warp-storms that struck without warning.

Living Tempest: At the end of each Psychic phase, each unit that lost one or more wounds in that phase suffers one additional mortal wound.

Warp-gheists: At the beginning of each battle round, roll a D6 and consult the following table to see what effect the warp-gheists have in that battle round:

D6	RESULT
1	**Preventing Escape: INFANTRY** units that have the **FLY** keyword are not considered to have that keyword.
2	**Preying on Stragglers:** At the end of each player's Movement phase, each of that player's units that did not move and is not within 1" of any enemy units suffers D3 mortal wounds.
3	**Haunting the Witches:** In each player's Psychic phase, **PSYKERS** attempting to manifest psychic powers will suffer Perils of the Warp on any double result rolled for the Psychic test, rather than only double 1 or double 6.
4	**Finding Their Way In:** At the end of each player's Shooting phase, any unit that lost one or more wounds during that phase suffers D3 mortal wounds.
5	**Joining the Slaughter:** At the end of each player's Fight phase, each unit that is within 1" of an enemy unit suffers 1 mortal wound.
6	**Sapping Will:** Add D3 to each Morale test taken (roll for each test taken).

STRATAGEMS

When using this battlezone, the players can use Command Points (CPs) to use the following Stratagems:

1CP

SUMMON GHEISTS
Stratagem

Throwing caution to the wind, this psyker attempts to attract even more warp-gheists to the battle.

Use this Stratagem at the beginning of any turn, if there is a **PSYKER** from your army on the battlefield. Make another roll on the Warp-gheists table and apply the result for the rest of the battle round, in addition to the current result. If you roll a result that is already in effect, re-roll until you get a different result.

1CP

COMMAND GHEISTS
Stratagem

Unwilling to become prey to these warp denizens, this psyker engages in a battle of wills with their ephemeral foes.

Use this Stratagem after a player makes a roll on the Warp-gheists table, if there is a **PSYKER** from your army on the battlefield. You can add 1 to or subtract 1 from the result (to a minimum of 1 and a maximum of 6). This Stratagem can only be used once for each roll – if both players wish to use this Stratagem they must roll off: the winner can use this Stratagem. The loser does not spend any Command Points for attempting to use this Stratagem.

WAR ZONE RULES

From the ice-wastes of Kaelac's Bane to the decrepit buildings of Dirkden Hivesprawl, from the systems of the Greater Omnissian Hoist to the volcanic regions of Storvhal, the landscapes and war zones of Vigilus were exotic and varied. This section provides rules to help bring these locations to life on the tabletop.

By the time the War of Nightmares came to Vigilus, there was no landscape that was spared the horrors of war. This section provides rules for how to populate a battlefield with terrain features so as to best represent the different war zones on the planet. It also offers suggestions on the types of missions and battlezones that work particularly well with these terrain features, and some ideas for generating your own narrative play games.

These rules are designed to be totally flexible; you can choose to use as many or as few as you wish in your games. As well as representing the various war zones on Vigilus, these rules can be used to represent any of the varied battlescapes of the Dark Imperium. You can either select a particular set to represent part of the story told in this book, or you can use them to reflect a setting of your own invention or from another story.

SCENERY TABLES

Each war zone presented here has its own scenery table. To use a scenery table, roll a D6 for each 2' by 2' section of the battlefield and consult the table to see which terrain features should be set up. It is a good idea to alternate setting up each section with your opponent (or opponents). If you do not have suitable terrain features, you can either re-roll the dice until you find a result that matches your scenery collection or adjust the table to reflect your collection.

DIRKDEN HIVESPRAWL

Dirkden Hivesprawl was a nightmare tangle of makeshift constructions and ramshackle buildings even before war came to Vigilus. The cramped and chaotic environs made bringing force to bear at any one point fiendishly difficult, forcing small defence teams to engage much larger invading armies.

You can play any battle you like using this set of rules, with any army in your collection. Below we suggest missions and battlezones from this book that work especially well with these rules. We have also included some further ideas – some of which are drawn from the events depicted in this book – to spark your imagination; you can use any of these as the basis for your games, or as inspiration for your own narratives.

MISSIONS AND BATTLEZONES

- Crucible of War: From an Unexpected Quarter (pg 122)
- Crucible of War: Allies of Convenience (pg 124)
- Crucible of War: Control the Gate (pg 128)
- Battlezone: Perilous Cavern (pg 149)

NARRATIVE IDEAS

- An army has overextended perilously, suffering ambush after ambush before finding a defensible position. Their tormentors gather to crush the survivors in one final onslaught.
- Two small forces stalk each other through the tangled warren of Dirkden Hivesprawl, seeking the upper hand before they strike.
- The buildings are so densely packed that the battle may as well be taking place inside – the combatants dare not bring their biggest guns to bear for fear of being caught in the explosion or bringing the dilapidated edifice down on their heads.

OPTIONAL RULE

If both players agree, the following optional rule can be used in any areas of the battlefield designated a Clearing (see right):

UNEVEN FOOTING

The tangled rubble makes for treacherous footing for infantry, who must move carefully.

INFANTRY units that are even partially in this section at the start of the Movement phase cannot move more than 8" in that phase. In addition, an **INFANTRY** unit even partially in this section cannot have a charge distance of more than 8" – if it is more, reduce it to 8". Units that can **FLY** are unaffected by this rule.

DIRKDEN HIVESPRAWL SCENERY TABLE

D6	RESULT
1	**Clearing:** *Collapsed buildings and walkways have created a relatively clear area here.* This 2' square contains scattered ruins and battlefield debris, but is relatively clear. **Optional Rule – Uneven Footing:** This section of the battlefield is subject to the Uneven Footing optional rule (see left).
2-3	**Motley Buildings:** *A common sight in Dirkden Hivesprawl, this area is full of mismatched and tumbledown buildings.* This 2' square contains 3 or more ruins or buildings, which can be a mix of STC Ryza-Pattern, Sector Imperialis and Sector Fronteris pieces.
4	**Illicit Facility:** *An abandoned facility lies here, doubtless constructed in some criminal enterprise.* This 2' square contains 1 Sector Mechanicus building and some Galvanic Servohaulers and Munitorum Armoured Containers.
5	**Industrial Slum:** *The haphazard industries of Dirkden Hivesprawl have been thrown together seemingly at random.* This 2' square has 1 or 2 Sector Mechanicus buildings which are surrounded by other ruins or buildings, which can be a mix of STC Ryza-Pattern, Sector Imperialis and Sector Fronteris pieces.
6	**Walkways:** *A network of walkways provide a level above the battlefield, ideal for scouts and snipers.* This 2' square contains any 3 buildings chosen from the following: Sector Mechanicus Ferratonic Incinerator, Galvanic Magnavent, Promethium Forge.

GREATER OMNISSIAN HOIST

The heavily defended planetside station of the Greater Omnissian Hoist was vital to the Adeptus Mechanicus' water production operations. This made it a priority target for xenos saboteurs, and its loss was a terrible blow to the planet's defenders.

You can play any battle you like using this set of rules, with any army in your collection. Below we suggest missions and battlezones from this book that work especially well with these rules. We have also included some further ideas – some of which are drawn from the events depicted in this book – to spark your imagination; you can use any of these as the basis for your games, or as inspiration for your own narratives.

MISSIONS AND BATTLEZONES

- Echoes of War: Siege of the Hoist (pg 136)
- Echoes of War: Deadly Payload (pg 142)
- Crucible of War: From an Unexpected Quarter (pg 122)
- Crucible of War: Doomsday Device (pg 132)
- Battlezone: Perilous Cavern (pg 147)
- Battlezone: Genestealer Infestation (see *Vigilus Defiant*)

NARRATIVE IDEAS

- *Their defences have been overrun, but the warriors of the Adeptus Mechanicus are unperturbed. They will man their posts and fight with mechanical efficiency to ensure their machines function for as long as they can.*
- *A xenos raiding party strikes just as the Greater Omnissian Hoist delivers its precious cargo from orbit. Will they be able to seize their prize and escape?*
- *While conducting a routine patrol, a unit spots an infiltration force. They must now hold them at bay while they await hastily summoned reinforcements.*

OPTIONAL RULE

If both players agree, the following optional rule can be used in any areas of the battlefield designated as Conduits and Cables (see right):

PLASMA VENTS

Taking cover in this area is a dicey prospect, as so much of the machinery is prone to venting plasma in lethal bursts.

At the end of each Shooting phase, roll a D6 for each unit that is even partially within this section of the battlefield and within 1" of any terrain in this section of the battlefield, if that unit was the target of one or more attacks in this phase. On a 6 that unit suffers 1 mortal wound.

D6	RESULT
	GREATER OMNISSIAN HOIST SCENERY TABLE
1	**Conduits and Cables:** *The workings of the station are laid bare here, so that all may glory in the majesty of the Omnissiah.* This 2' square contains Thermic Plasma Conduits and Thermic Plasma Regulators. **Optional Rule – Plasma Vents:** This section of the battlefield is subject to the Plasma Vents optional rule (see left).
2-3	**Hallowed Machinery:** *This area was a centre of industry, where valuable materials were harvested.* This 2' square contains 2 Sector Mechanicus buildings, and can also include some Munitorum Armoured Containers or Sector Mechanicus Galvanic Servohaulers.
4	**Defended Position:** *The vital machinery here is well protected.* This 2' square has a Sector Mechanicus building at its centre. Arranged around the building are Aegis Defence Lines and weapon emplacements.
5	**Station Shield Generator:** *The station's void shields were designed to defend against assault – or mishap – from space.* This 2' square has a Void Shield Generator at its centre, with a couple of Sector Mechanicus buildings flanking it.
6	**Fortified Entrance:** *The routes that lead to the sensitive innards of the Greater Omnissian Hoist are heavily defended.* This 2' square contains defences that make approach from elsewhere on the battlefield a dangerous prospect, including Wall of Martyrs buildings and Aegis Defence Lines.

KAELAC'S BANE

The arctic wasteland of Kaelac's Bane was once a source of fresh water, but as more and more miners fell prey to unseen hunters, the ice quarries were abandoned. None of those who disappeared survived to tell the tale of arcane structures hidden far from prying eyes.

You can play any battle you like using this set of rules, with any army in your collection. Below we suggest missions and battlezones from this book that work especially well with these rules. We have also included some further ideas – some of which are drawn from the events depicted in this book – to spark your imagination; you can use any of these as the basis for your games, or as inspiration for your own narratives.

MISSIONS AND BATTLEZONES

- Echoes of War: The Serpent's Lure (pg 140)
- Crucible of War: Metal Onslaught (pg 126)
- Crucible of War: Allies of Convenience (pg 124)
- Crucible of War: Control the Gate (pg 128)
- Battlezone: Field of Nightmares (pg 151)
- Battlezone: Tundric Blizzard (see *Vigilus Defiant*)

NARRATIVE IDEAS

- *A lone garrison represents the last of the Imperium's fighting strength in the area – and they are being stalked by Aeldari raiders.*
- *A small group of Aeldari uses the freezing conditions of Kaelac's Bane against their foes, leading them deep into the frozen wastes.*
- *An Adeptus Mechanicus crusade launches an all-out assault on the area, determined to eliminate any threat and recover their sacred machinery at any cost.*
- *A Sorcerer begins an arcane ritual, drawing on some hidden power within the ice. Should they be left undisturbed, it could spell the planet's doom.*

OPTIONAL RULE

If both players agree, the following optional rule can be used in any areas of the battlefield designated as Barren Ice (see right):

BALEFUL GLARE

The Cicatrix Maledictum is clearly visible even by day here, and its malevolent light reflects off the ice, making even the most disciplined warriors flinch.

Each time you take a Morale test for a unit even partially in this section of the battlefield, add 1 to the result.

KAELAC'S BANE SCENERY TABLE

D6	RESULT
1	**Barren Ice:** *Nothing stands in this wasteland, and the glare of the Cicatrix Maledictum is almost blinding.* This 2' square is barren wasteland. **Optional Rule – Baleful Glare:** This section of the battlefield is subject to the Baleful Glare optional rule (see left).
2	**Ruined Structures:** *Neglected to the ravages of the elements and the war, unidentifiable ruins give this area a haunted feel.* This 2' square contains nothing but scattered STC Ryza-Pattern Ruins.
3	**Workers' Shelters:** *When the ice quarries were still in use, the workers sheltered between shifts in STC buildings.* This 2' square contains a number of Sector Fronteris buildings – some whole, some in ruins – arranged in a small settlement.
4	**Loading Area:** *This section of the battlefield was once a loading area where huge ice blocks were stacked for transportation.* This 2' square contains a number of Munitorum Armoured Containers stacked in an orderly fashion, and some Sector Mechanicus Galvanic Servohaulers.
5	**Adeptus Mechanicus Outpost:** *A collection of abandoned structures recall the industry that once served Vigilus here.* This 2' square contains a few Sector Mechanicus buildings, arranged to provide those on the gantries a commanding view of the area.
6	**Eldritch Secrets:** *The secrets hidden in Kaelac's Bane were a mystery to most on Vigilus.* This 2' square contains a Webway Gate surrounded by a few Eldritch Ruins.

DONTORIA HIVESPRAWL

Once the most populous of all Vigilus' hivesprawls, Dontoria was ravaged by disease and torn by constant battle. By the time the War of Nightmares hit Vigilus, Dontoria was home only to the dying and the dead, its people fallen to plague, and the taint of Chaos seeping through the deserted streets.

You can play any battle you like using this set of rules, with any army in your collection. Below we suggest missions and battlezones from this book that work especially well with these rules. We have also included some further ideas – some of which are drawn from the events depicted in this book – to spark your imagination; you can use any of these as the basis for your games, or as inspiration for your own narratives.

MISSIONS AND BATTLEZONES

- Crucible of War: Allies of Convenience (pg 124)
- Crucible of War: Schism (pg 130)
- Battlezone: Deadly Storm (pg 149)
- Battlezone: Field of Nightmares (pg 151)

NARRATIVE IDEAS

- *A regiment of Astra Militarum have contracted a vile plague. Knowing that they are already doomed, they resolve to sell their lives as dearly as possible.*
- *It has been decided that the only way to deal with the infection in Dontoria is to cauterise it. Forces armed with incendiary weapons are despatched to burn the diseased ruins to the ground.*
- *A grinding stalemate between two exhausted armies is disrupted when fresh reinforcements arrive for one side. Are they enough to win the day, or can their determined enemies hold on?*
- *Two battling armies have taken to fighting from their vehicles in a bid to avoid airborne contagions. Tanks battle it out in the cramped streets.*

OPTIONAL RULE

If both players agree, the following optional rule can be used in any areas of the battlefield designated an Empty Plaza (see right):

DRIFTING DISEASE

Deadly contagions drift on the air in this sector, and with one unguarded breath an unwary warrior can doom themselves to a ghastly death.

Each time an **INFANTRY** unit finishes a move even partially in this section of the battlefield, roll a D6. On a 6 that unit suffers D3 mortal wounds. **NURGLE** units are unaffected by this rule.

D6	RESULT
	DONTORIA HIVESPRAWL SCENERY TABLE
1	**Empty Plaza:** *This square is empty and entirely devoid of life.* This 2' square contains no buildings. **Optional Rule – Drifting Disease:** This section of the battlefield is subject to the Drifting Disease optional rule (see left).
2	**War-torn Buildings:** *Though countless thousands once lived in this sector, it is now an abandoned ruin.* This 2' square contains 2 Sector Imperialis Ruins.
3-4	**Cramped Streets:** *The dense population in Dontoria Hivesprawl made it easy for the plagues to spread.* This 2' square contains 4 or more Sector Imperialis Ruins grouped closely together.
5	**Rot at the Heart of the Hive:** *As Nurgle's followers made their presence known, Dontoria saw an awful new form of life blossom from the bodies of the dead.* This 2' square contains scattered Sector Imperialis Ruins, but at the centre of the square are clustered 2 or more Feculent Gnarlmaws.
6	**Chaos Strongpoint:** *The Chaos Space Marines constructed numerous strongpoints during the battle for Dontoria, erecting at the centre of each site a loathsome Noctilith Crown.* This 2' square has a Noctilith Crown in its centre and some scattered Sector Imperialis Ruins or Feculent Gnarlmaws around the edges.

STORVHAL

Storvhal was a continent racked with geothermal activity, experiencing tremors and volcanic eruptions regularly. The Adeptus Mechanicus constructed ingenious machines in robust outposts to siphon off this energy, and the battles of Storvhal were almost entirely fought on and around these facilities.

You can play any battle you like using this set of rules, with any army in your collection. Below we suggest missions and battlezones from this book that work especially well with these rules. We have also included some further ideas – some of which are drawn from the events depicted in this book – to spark your imagination; you can use any of these as the basis for your games, or as inspiration for your own narratives.

MISSIONS AND BATTLEZONES

- Echoes of War: The Serpent's Lure (pg 140)
- Crucible of War: Metal Onslaught (pg 126)
- Crucible of War: Doomsday Device (pg 132)
- Battlezone: Speedwaaagh! (pg 150)
- Battlezone: Geothermal Eruption (see *Vigilus Defiant*)

NARRATIVE IDEAS

- *A Chaos cult triggers a daemonic incursion. Those that survive the Daemons' arrival follow joyfully in their wake as they attack an Imperial stronghold.*
- *An abandoned facility offers rich pickings to the Genestealer Cultists – however, it looks like they will have to contend with some Ork Lootas for the prize.*
- *A convoy is attempting to cross Storvhal when their engines overheat. While their engineers race to get the vehicles moving, an enemy force rapidly approaches.*
- *Two forces battle over a facility, but the fighting grows too fierce, damaging the machinery. As explosions rock the battlefield, survival becomes the priority.*

OPTIONAL RULE

If both players agree, the following optional rule can be used in any areas of the battlefield designated a Volcanic Landscape (see right):

SCALDING ROCK

Some rocks in this area are superheated by the geothermal currents under the surface. Undetectable to the naked eye, they can cause terrible damage to the unwary.

Each time a unit finishes a move even partially within this section of the battlefield, roll a D6. On a 6 that unit suffers 1 mortal wound. Units that can **FLY** are unaffected by this rule.

D6	RESULT
	STORVHAL SCENERY TABLE
1	**Volcanic Landscape:** *This area is a blasted volcanic plain.* This 2' square contains no terrain. **Optional Rule – Scalding Rock:** This section of the battlefield is subject to the Scalding Rock optional rule (see left).
2-3	**Isolated Machinery:** *A few lonely spires are the only signs of the industry taking place below the tortured surface.* This 2' square contains a Sector Mechanicus Galvanic Magnavent or a Sector Mechanicus Alchomite Stack.
4-5	**Drilling Station:** *A massive drill stands ready to bleed pressure from the earth.* This 2' square contains a Tectonic Fragdrill and some Sector Fronteris buildings or ruins.
6	**Major Facility:** *A phenomenal investment of material and manpower has maintained a permanent facility in this volatile landscape.* This 2' square contains 3 or more Sector Mechanicus buildings.

FACTION RULES

'Look upon your devoted
servants, Dark Ones, and see
the carnage we have wrought in
your name! Are we not worthy
of reward? Have we not earned
a divine transformation in
your service?'

- *Dark Apostle Tharaggan*
Twice-Crowned

ARMIES OF CHAOS

This section contains new and updated datasheets for the forces of Chaos, as well as a range of Specialist Detachments that allow you to represent the many battle formations fielded by Abaddon's legions on Vigilus in your games of Warhammer 40,000.

NEW AND UPDATED RULES

This section (pg 162-177) includes new and updated datasheets for a host of Daemon and Chaos Space Marine units, as well as a new suite of prayers that can be chanted by priests, and powerful new fortifications to despoil the battlefield.

The datasheets, wargear and points values presented in this section update those found in the 2017 edition of *Codex: Chaos Space Marines* or the 2018 edition of *Codex: Chaos Daemons*, and should be used in your games of Warhammer 40,000.

SPECIALIST DETACHMENTS

This section (pg 180-187) introduces Specialist Detachments for the forces of Chaos. These rules portray the many unique fighting styles of the various troops that formed the armies dedicated to the Dark Gods on Vigilus.

If your army is Battle-forged, you have access to the Specialist Detachment Stratagems presented in this section. A Specialist Detachment Stratagem is a unique type of Stratagem used when choosing your army. This Stratagem will assign a <SPECIALIST DETACHMENT> keyword to certain units in that Detachment and will unlock Warlord Traits, Relics, Stratagems and psychic powers that those units can take. Each Specialist Detachment Stratagem can only be used once per battle.

Any Detachment from your army (except for Auxiliary Support Detachments) can be upgraded to a Specialist Detachment by using an appropriate Specialist

Detachment Stratagem. A Detachment from your army can only be upgraded to a Specialist Detachment once and thus cannot have multiple Specialist Detachment Stratagems applied to it, even if they affect different units in the Detachment.

WARLORD TRAITS

If your Warlord is a **CHARACTER** and has the relevant <SPECIALIST DETACHMENT> keyword, you can give them a Warlord Trait from the appropriate section in this book instead of one from the *Warhammer 40,000* rulebook or a codex. Named characters such as Abaddon have associated Warlord Traits in their codex and must still take that Warlord Trait if they are your Warlord.

In addition, if your army is Battle-forged, you can use the Stratagem below:

1CP

FIELD COMMANDER
Stratagem

This warrior's specialist expertise is second to none and in battle they lead those under their command with sophisticated tactics.

Use this Stratagem before the battle if you used any Specialist Detachment Stratagems when choosing your army. Choose one **CHARACTER** from your army that has gained a keyword from a Specialist Detachment Stratagem that is not your Warlord and is not a named character. You can give that character the Warlord Trait of the Specialist Detachment they are part of (note that this character is only regarded as your Warlord for the purpose of that Warlord Trait). This Stratagem can be used once for each Specialist Detachment Stratagem you have used (spend 1CP each time you use it). No two characters from your army can have the same Warlord Trait.

RELICS

Before the battle you may give a relic from this section to a **CHARACTER** from your army with the relevant **<SPECIALIST DETACHMENT>** keyword instead of a relic from a codex or *Chapter Approved*. Named characters such as Abaddon the Despoiler cannot be given relics.

Note that some relics replace one of the character's existing weapons. Where this is the case, if you are playing a matched play game or are otherwise using points values, you must still pay the cost of the weapon that is being replaced. Write down any relics your characters have on your army roster.

For example, a **BLACK LEGION** *Detachment can be upgraded to a Bringers of Despair Specialist Detachment using the Specialist Detachment Stratagem found on page 180. Doing so gives the* **BLACK LEGION TERMINATOR** *units in that Detachment the* **BRINGERS OF DESPAIR** *keyword.*

This then allows you to give a **BRINGERS OF DESPAIR CHARACTER** *the Chosen of the Warmaster Warlord Trait and to equip a* **BRINGERS OF DESPAIR CHARACTER** *with the Foecleaver relic. You can also use Command Points to use the Brutal Subjugation and Chosen Enforcers Stratagems in your games.*

CHAOS SPACE MARINES WARGEAR LISTS

Many of the units you will find on the following pages reference one or more of the following wargear lists (e.g. Special Weapons). When this is the case, the unit may take any item from the appropriate list below. The profiles for the weapons in these lists can be found in the Armouries of Chaos section (pg 176).

CHAMPION EQUIPMENT

The champion can take up to two weapons chosen from the following list:

- Bolt pistol
- Chainaxe
- Chainsword
- Lightning claw
- Plasma pistol
- Power axe
- Power fist
- Power maul
- Power sword

One of the champion's weapons can be chosen from the following list:

- Boltgun
- Combi-bolter
- Combi-flamer
- Combi-melta
- Combi-plasma

COMBI-WEAPONS

- Combi-bolter
- Combi-flamer
- Combi-melta
- Combi-plasma

PISTOLS

- Bolt pistol
- Plasma pistol

HEAVY WEAPONS

- Autocannon
- Heavy bolter
- Lascannon
- Missile launcher
- Reaper chaincannon*

*Cannot be taken by Fallen.

SPECIAL WEAPONS

- Flamer
- Meltagun
- Plasma gun

MELEE WEAPONS

- Chainaxe
- Chainsword
- Lightning claw
- Power axe
- Power fist
- Power maul
- Power sword
- Thunder hammer

TERMINATOR MELEE WEAPONS

- Chainaxe
- Chainfist
- Lightning claw
- Power axe
- Power fist
- Power maul
- Power sword

ABADDON THE DESPOILER

WARMASTER OF CHAOS, LORD OF THE BLACK CRUSADES

Striding onto the battlefield like a demigod of war, the Despoiler scowls at the mortal chattel before him. He is an ender of worlds, a destroyer of hope, a bane unto the galaxy itself. Yet he is not beyond the siren call of battle, and leads his Black Legion to acts of pitiless slaughter whenever a worthy foe is near.

The name of Abaddon, Warmaster of Chaos, has become a bitter curse across Mankind's realm. Since the Fall of Cadia and the cataclysmic formation of the Great Rift, his infamy has spread to such an extent that he is counted as the foremost enemy of the Imperium by the High Lords of Terra, the Inquisition and the Chapter Masters of the Adeptus Astartes.

During the Great Crusade, Abaddon rose to Captain of the First Company of the Luna Wolves Legion. Such was his tactical skill and physical prowess, it was rumoured that he may have been a clone-son of Horus. When the Heresy came to a head, it was clear that Abaddon's loyalty lay with his Primarch, rather than with the Emperor. He led the Terminators of the Sons of Horus across Isstvan, Yarant, and Terra itself. Abaddon's anguish at his master's death drove him deeper into madness and

hatred than any mortal should ever sink. Before retreating, Abaddon took up the Warmaster's body and fought his way out of the quickly deteriorating battle. With their cadaverous prize, the Legion fled before the Emperor's armies.

When Abaddon returned, it was at the head of a diabolic horde ravaging star systems around the Eye of Terror. His Chaos Space Marines, now the Black Legion, were at the forefront of the attack, destroying all in their path. During this first Black Crusade, Abaddon formed many bloody pacts with the Chaos Gods. Below the Tower of Silence, he recovered a Daemon sword of prodigious power, making him nigh unstoppable. Since then, Abaddon has dreamed of forging an empire of Chaos upon the ruins of the Imperium. More Black Crusades have followed, each achieving some dark purpose that even the

mightiest sages of the Imperium cannot discern. It is said that he alone has the power to unite the Traitor Legions and finish the treachery begun ten thousand years ago.

Now, as Abaddon's Thirteenth Black Crusade conquers its way out of the Eye of Terror, Cadia has finally been overrun. Though the planet itself has fallen, possession of the Cadian Gate – the only stable path from the Eye of Terror – hangs in the balance. Some say it is too late, for the Great Rift has already split the galaxy, and Abaddon intends for nothing less than to turn the Imperium Nihilus into his own personal fiefdom with which to threaten the heartlands of Mankind's realm. Should Abaddon triumph, the dark tide of Chaos will pour from the Eye of Terror along the length of the Crimson Path to strike at the most prized world of all – Holy Terra itself.

ABADDON THE DESPOILER

12 POWER

NAME	M	WS	BS	S	T	W	A	Ld	Sv
Abaddon the Despoiler	6"	2+	2+	5	5	8	6	10	2+

Abaddon the Despoiler is a single model armed with Drach'nyen and the Talon of Horus. Only one of this model may be included in your army.

WEAPON	RANGE	TYPE	S	AP	D	ABILITIES
Talon of Horus (shooting)	24"	Rapid Fire 2	4	-1	D3	-
Drach'nyen	Melee	Melee	+1	-3	3	Roll a D6 each time the bearer fights. On a 1 they suffer 1 mortal wound and cannot use this weapon further during this phase. On a 2+ they can make that many additional attacks with this weapon.
Talon of Horus (melee)	Melee	Melee	x2	-4	D3	-

ABILITIES	**Death to the False Emperor** (pg 176)	**Mark of Chaos Ascendant:** Friendly **HERETIC ASTARTES** units automatically pass Morale tests while they are within 12" of Abaddon the Despoiler.

The Warmaster: If your army is Battle-forged and Abaddon the Despoiler is your Warlord, you receive 2 additional Command Points.

Dark Destiny: Abaddon the Despoiler has a 4+ invulnerable save. In addition, all damage suffered by Abaddon the Despoiler is halved (rounding up).

Lord of the Black Legion: You can re-roll hit rolls for friendly **BLACK LEGION** units while they are within 6" of Abaddon the Despoiler.

Mark of Chaos Ascendant: Friendly **HERETIC ASTARTES** units automatically pass Morale tests while they are within 12" of Abaddon the Despoiler.

Teleport Strike: During deployment, you can set up Abaddon the Despoiler in a teleportarium chamber instead of placing him on the battlefield. At the end of any of your Movement phases he can use a teleport strike to arrive on the battlefield – set him up anywhere on the battlefield that is more than 9" away from any enemy models.

FACTION KEYWORDS	**CHAOS, KHORNE, NURGLE, SLAANESH, TZEENTCH, HERETIC ASTARTES, BLACK LEGION**
KEYWORDS	**CHARACTER, INFANTRY, CHAOS LORD, TERMINATOR, ABADDON THE DESPOILER**

Warmaster Abaddon wields not only the Talon of Horus, bane of Primarchs, but also the ancient Daemon sword Drach'nyen.

LORDS DISCORDANT
BANE OF MACHINES, BRINGERS OF ANARCHY

To a Lord Discordant, the showers of sparks and coiling of loose wiring from an injured war machine are as pleasing as the jets of blood that gush from an open wound. These machine-obsessed heretics stalk across the battlefield atop Helstalker mounts, a palpable aura of anarchy exuding from their very being.

A Lord Discordant is able to cut his way swiftly through the infantry on the front line, roasting them alive or riddling them with hails of shot, while his metallic steed crushes them to bloody paste beneath its blade-like limbs. But this rent flesh is merely an appetiser for the feast of suffering to come. He continues to spur his Helstalker onwards until he has reached the foe's tanks and towering walkers. As he charges, he bellows profane litanies in a tongue that is vile and incomprehensible to mortal ears, and causes comm systems, vox-grilles and laud hailers to crackle as though screaming in agony. His mere presence causes machinery not riddled with daemonic entities to short-circuit – actuators and servos whir erratically, and targeting augurs cease to function. Once in range, the Lord's Helstalker pounces upon the nearest enemy vehicle, its massive forelimbs stabbing into the hull of its machine prey,

piercing through ablative plating and tearing at gun turrets. Some Helstalkers use magma cutters to slice open the vehicle they have pinned, while others have enormous hypo-armour syringes that – after piercing the outer shell of their prey – inject scrapcode and daemonic dataphages directly into the machine's circuitry.

The Lord Discordant himself lunges forward with his impaler chainglaive, its whirring blade gouging into metal and exposing the vehicle's internal workings, while his mechatendrils rip at its panelling. He hears the machine's pain, he feels it struggle to reroute vital functions to maintain system

integrity, and his Helstalker feeds on this suffering. The Daemon Engine parasitically devours the motive force that powers its prey, be it a machine spirit or some other esoteric data-sentience employed in xenos technology. As it does so, its own metallic frame swells with ingested code and subroutines, while rents in its casing crackle with warp energy and seal closed. The Lord Discordant siphons off the pained spirit of the dying vehicle, his mechatendrils lapping up the spasmodic electrical discharges and corrupting their information signatures. This harvested energy is then used to reinvigorate other Daemon Engines, or is released as a screaming beam to infect the systems of other enemy vehicles.

LORD DISCORDANT
ON HELSTALKER

NAME	M	WS	BS	S	T	W	A	Ld	Sv
Lord Discordant on Helstalker	*	2+	2+	4	6	12	4	9	2+

DAMAGE
Some of this model's characteristics change as it suffers damage, as shown below:

REMAINING W	M	ADDITIONAL ATTACKS
7-12+	12"	5
4-6	9"	4
1-3	6"	3

A Lord Discordant on Helstalker is a single model armed with an autocannon, bolt pistol, impaler chainglaive, mechatendrils, frag grenades and krak grenades. His Helstalker is armed with bladed limbs and tail and a techno-virus injector.

WEAPON	RANGE	TYPE	S	AP	D	ABILITIES
Lord Discordant						
Autocannon	48"	Heavy 2	7	-1	2	-
Baleflamer	18"	Assault D6	6	-2	2	This weapon automatically hits its target.
Bolt pistol	12"	Pistol 1	4	0	1	-
Impaler chainglaive	Melee	Melee	+2	-2	2	If the bearer made a charge move or performed a Heroic Intervention this turn, attacks with this weapon are made with a Strength characteristic of x2 instead of +2.
Mechatendrils	Melee	Melee	User	0	1	Each time the bearer fights, it can make 2 additional attacks with this weapon.
Frag grenade	6"	Grenade D6	3	0	1	-
Krak grenade	6"	Grenade 1	6	-1	D3	-
Helstalker						
Magma cutter	6"	Pistol 1	8	-4	3	-
Bladed limbs and tail	Melee	Melee	+3	-2	D3	After the Lord Discordant makes his close combat attacks, you can attack with his Helstalker. Make a number of additional attacks as shown in the damage table above, using this weapon profile.
Techno-virus injector	Melee	Melee	+4	-4	D3	After the Lord Discordant makes his close combat attacks, you can attack with his Helstalker. Make a single attack using this weapon profile in addition to the Helstalker's bladed limbs and tail. Each time a wound roll for an attack made with this weapon is successful when targeting a **VEHICLE** unit, that unit suffers D3 mortal wounds in addition to any normal damage.

WARGEAR OPTIONS	• The Lord Discordant can replace his autocannon with a baleflamer. • The Helstalker can replace its techno-virus injector with a magma cutter.

ABILITIES	**Death to the False Emperor** (pg 176) **Daemonic:** This model has a 5+ invulnerable save. **Infernal Regeneration:** At the beginning of your turn, this model regains 1 lost wound. **Aura of Discord:** Subtract 1 from hit rolls for attacks made by **VEHICLE** units while they are within 6" of any enemy models with this ability. In addition, add 1 to hit rolls for attacks made by <**LEGION**> **DAEMON ENGINE** units while they are within 6" of any friendly <**LEGION**> models with this ability.	**Spirit Thief:** Each time this model destroys an enemy **VEHICLE** unit in the Fight phase, this model can either repair a friendly Daemon Engine or release a beam of energy. If you choose to repair a friendly Daemon Engine, pick a friendly <**LEGION**> **DAEMON ENGINE** (other than models that can **FLY**) within 3" of this model. That **DAEMON ENGINE** regains D3 lost wounds. If you choose to release a beam of energy, pick an enemy **VEHICLE** within 12" of this model and roll a D6. On a 2+ that **VEHICLE** suffers D3 mortal wounds.

FACTION KEYWORDS	**CHAOS, <MARK OF CHAOS>, HERETIC ASTARTES, <LEGION>**

KEYWORDS	**CHARACTER, VEHICLE, DAEMON, DAEMON ENGINE, WARPSMITH, HELSTALKER, LORD DISCORDANT**

MASTERS OF EXECUTIONS

WARP-SIGHTED HEADSMEN OF THE CHAOTIC HOSTS

Amidst the thunderous tumult of battle, a Master of Executions strides unflinchingly forward, his mind focused on the gruesome decapitations he will soon administer. His existence is driven by an unquenchable desire to take as trophies the heads of mighty champions and charismatic leaders.

As the Master of Executions draws closer to the enemy's champions, he bellows his fatal decree, proclaiming the warrior's life forfeited to the Dark Gods. With a terrifying burst of speed, he closes upon his declared victim, crushing whatever defence they offer with blow after sweeping blow. A final unerring swing sees the energy-wreathed axe blade carve through armour, flesh and spine without slowing. As he watches the opponent's severed flesh spinning through the air and the torrents of arterial blood that jet from their toppling corpse, the executioner feels the gaze of the Chaos Gods fall upon him. A jolt of exaltation runs through his body, his veins crackle with empyric power and his hunger for death grows even stronger.

Through sorcerous rituals, Masters of Executions attune their murderous senses to the currents of the warp, granting them the ability to see the souls of their foes. Some even go so far as to gouge out one of their eyes to allow empyric currents

to coalesce in the raw and empty socket. Even on the most anarchic battlefields an executioner can pick out his targets, looking through the clouds of choking smoke and ranks of lesser foes towards the bright burning spirits of the mightiest enemies, marking them for death.

The deadly expertise of each Master of Executions is evident in their gruesome array of trophies, their collection of heads speaking to the manifold enemies they have slaughtered. The most impressive trophies are given places of

prominence, while from lesser foes sometimes only a tooth or fragment of jawbone is added to the panoply. He might string the eyes, ears and tongue of a powerful mystic around his neck, fuse the shattered bones of a previously undefeated warrior to his wargear or drape the peeled skin of a charismatic leader over his armour.

Within a warband, a Master of Executions is often used to mete out punishment to those who seek to usurp the rule of a Chaos Lord. The wayward Heretic Astartes is corralled by their brethren into a gore-stained arena and forced to face the executioner in a duel to the death. Such contests are brutally swift, and serve to sate the murder-lust of both the warband and the Master of Executions. But a Chaos Lord must be ever wary, for while this practice helps thin out those warriors who have delusions of grandeur, the Master of Executions' axe may also come for him one day, if there are no more enemy champions to slaughter.

MASTER OF EXECUTIONS

4 POWER

NAME	M	WS	BS	S	T	W	A	Ld	Sv
Master of Executions	6"	2+	3+	4	4	4	5	9	3+

A Master of Executions is a single model armed with an axe of dismemberment, bolt pistol, frag grenades and krak grenades.

WEAPON	RANGE	TYPE	S	AP	D	ABILITIES
Bolt pistol	12"	Pistol 1	4	0	1	-
Axe of dismemberment	Melee	Melee	x2	-3	D3	Each time you make a wound roll of 6+ for this weapon, the target unit suffers 1 mortal wound in addition to any other damage.
Frag grenade	6"	Grenade D6	3	0	1	-
Krak grenade	6"	Grenade 1	6	-1	D3	-

ABILITIES	**Death to the False Emperor** (pg 176) **Trophy-taker:** Once per Fight phase, you can re-roll one hit roll, wound roll or damage roll for an attack made by this model that targets a **Character**.	**Warp-sighted Butcher:** After the enemy has completed all of their charge moves, this model can perform a Heroic Intervention if it is within 3" of any enemy models, or 6" of any enemy **Characters**. If this model is within 6" of any enemy **Characters**, it can move up to 6" when performing a Heroic Intervention instead of 3", as long as it finishes this move within 1" of the nearest enemy **Character**.
FACTION KEYWORDS	CHAOS, <MARK OF CHAOS>, HERETIC ASTARTES, <LEGION>	
KEYWORDS	INFANTRY, CHARACTER, MASTER OF EXECUTIONS	

The Master of Executions scans the battlefield, his warp-sight picking out the next head he intends to claim as a trophy.

DARK APOSTLE

5 POWER

NAME	M	WS	BS	S	T	W	A	Ld	Sv
Dark Apostle	6"	2+	3+	4	4	4	3	9	3+

A Dark Apostle is a single model armed with an accursed crozius, bolt pistol, frag grenades and krak grenades.

WEAPON	RANGE	TYPE	S	AP	D	ABILITIES
Bolt pistol	12"	Pistol 1	4	0	1	-
Accursed crozius	Melee	Melee	+1	-1	2	-
Frag grenade	6"	Grenade D6	3	0	1	-
Krak grenade	6"	Grenade 1	6	-1	D3	-

ABILITIES	**Death to the False Emperor** (pg 176)	**Sigil of Corruption:** This model has a 4+ invulnerable save.
	Demagogue: Friendly <Legion> units within 6" of this model in the Morale phase can use this model's Leadership instead of their own.	

| PRIEST | This model can chant prayers. It knows the Dark Zealotry prayer (below) and one prayer from the Prayers to the Dark Gods (opposite). At the start of each battle round, you can pick one of the prayers this model knows and roll a D6. On a 3+, the prayer is heard. That prayer takes effect until the end of that battle round. The same prayer cannot be chanted more than once per battle round by any model in your army, whether it is heard or not.

Dark Zealotry: If this prayer is heard, you can re-roll hit rolls in the Fight phase for attacks made by friendly <Legion> units while they are within 6" of this priest. |
|--------|---|

FACTION KEYWORDS	CHAOS, <MARK OF CHAOS>, HERETIC ASTARTES, <LEGION>
KEYWORDS	CHARACTER, INFANTRY, PRIEST, DARK APOSTLE

DARK DISCIPLES

1 POWER

NAME	M	WS	BS	S	T	W	A	Ld	Sv
Dark Disciple	6"	4+	5+	3	3	1	1	6	5+

This unit contains 2 Dark Disciples. Each model is armed with a close combat weapon.

WEAPON	RANGE	TYPE	S	AP	D	ABILITIES
Close combat weapon	Melee	Melee	User	0	1	-

ABILITIES	**Followers:** Only one unit of Dark Disciples can be included in your army for each Dark Apostle in your army. <Legion> Dark Disciples units do not take up slots in a Detachment that includes any <Legion> Dark Apostles. While this unit is within 2" of any friendly <Legion> Dark Apostles, enemy models can only shoot this unit if it is the closest enemy unit (ignore **Characters** with a Wounds characteristic of less than 10 when determining if this unit is the closest enemy unit to the firing model).	**Relic of Corruption:** While any <Legion> Dark Disciples units are within 2" of a friendly <Legion> Dark Apostle, add 1 to dice rolls to see if a prayer chanted by that Dark Apostle is heard.

FACTION KEYWORDS	CHAOS, <MARK OF CHAOS>, HERETIC ASTARTES, <LEGION>
KEYWORDS	INFANTRY, DARK DISCIPLES

PRAYERS TO THE DARK GODS

The Dark Apostles of Chaos have a singular connection with their deities. It is not for warrior glory nor for self-aggrandisement they fight, but for the furtherance of their patron god's cause – as such they can call upon the favour of the Ruinous Powers to lend them strength at a critical moment.

Before the battle, generate the prayers for **PRIESTS** that can chant prayers from Prayers to the Dark Gods using the table below. You can either roll a D6 to generate their prayers randomly (re-roll duplicates), or you can select the prayers you wish them to have.

MARK OF CHAOS PRAYERS

A **<MARK OF CHAOS> PRIEST** that can chant prayers from the Prayers to the Dark Gods also knows the appropriate **<MARK OF CHAOS>** prayer on the right.

D6 PRAYER

1 BENEDICTION OF DARKNESS

As their words grow louder, inky blackness pours from the priest's eyes, forming a swirling mist around their allies.

If this prayer is heard, pick one friendly <LEGION> unit within 6" of this priest. Subtract 1 from hit rolls made for attacks with ranged weapons that target that unit.

2 LITANY OF DESPAIR

The priest calls upon the Dark Gods to offer his foes all manner of whispered temptations, sapping their will to fight.

If this prayer is heard, your opponent rolls two D6, discarding the lowest result, each time they take a Morale test for a unit within 6" of this priest.

3 OMEN OF POTENCY

The priest begins to glow with the unbridled power of the warp.

If this prayer is heard, add 3 to this priest's Attacks characteristic. In addition, if this prayer is heard, this priest's melee weapons have an Armour Penetration characteristic of -4.

4 WARP-SIGHT PLEA

The priest entreats his dark masters to guide his followers' aim, granting their shots unerring accuracy.

If this prayer is heard, pick one friendly <LEGION> unit within 6" of this priest. Add 1 to hit rolls for attacks made with ranged weapons by models in that unit.

5 SOULTEARER PORTENT

The priest's flock strike at their victim's very souls, the better to release them from their mortal bonds as an offering to the Dark Gods.

If this prayer is heard, pick one friendly <LEGION> unit within 6" of this priest. Add 1 to wound rolls for attacks made with melee weapons by models in that unit.

6 ILLUSORY SUPPLICATION

Chanting words which would drive most mortals mad, the priest alters the very fabric of reality, creating shadowy doppelgängers of nearby allies.

If this prayer is heard, friendly <LEGION> models have a 5+ invulnerable save while they are within 6" of this priest.

WRATHFUL ENTREATY

Drawing blood from his palm, the priest requests Khorne impart a measure of his godly strength to him.

KHORNE PRIEST only. If this prayer is heard, add 2 to this priest's Strength characteristic.

MUTATING INVOCATION

Speaking riddles, the priest bargains with the Master of Fate to make his flesh flow like liquid, absorbing enemy blows.

TZEENTCH PRIEST only. If this prayer is heard, this priest regains D3 lost wounds. Note that unlike other prayers, whose effects last only until the end of the battle round, wounds regained from this prayer are not lost again at the end of the battle round.

FECULENT BESEECHMENT

Belching a cloud of flies, the priest begs Grandfather Nurgle to bless his form with wondrous diseases.

NURGLE PRIEST only. If this prayer is heard, add 2 to this priest's Toughness characteristic.

BLISSFUL DEVOTION

The priest asks Slaanesh to grant him the unnatural swiftness of the Dark Prince's daemonic children.

SLAANESH PRIEST only. If this prayer is heard, this priest can Advance and charge in their turn in this battle round.

CHAOS SPACE MARINES

NAME	M	WS	BS	S	T	W	A	Ld	Sv
Chaos Space Marine	6"	3+	3+	4	4	1	1	7	3+
Aspiring Champion	6"	3+	3+	4	4	1	2	8	3+

This unit contains 1 Aspiring Champion and 4 Chaos Space Marines. It can include up to 5 additional Chaos Space Marines (**Power Rating +4**), up to 10 additional Chaos Space Marines (**Power Rating +7**) or up to 15 additional Chaos Space Marines (**Power Rating +10**). Each model is armed with a boltgun, bolt pistol, frag grenades and krak grenades.

WEAPON	RANGE	TYPE	S	AP	D	ABILITIES
Bolt pistol	12"	Pistol 1	4	0	1	-
Boltgun	24"	Rapid Fire 1	4	0	1	-
Plasma pistol	When attacking with this weapon, choose one of the profiles below.					
- Standard	12"	Pistol 1	7	-3	1	-
- Supercharge	12"	Pistol 1	8	-3	2	On a hit roll of 1, the bearer is slain.
Chainsword	Melee	Melee	User	0	1	Each time the bearer fights, it can make 1 additional attack with this weapon.
Frag grenade	6"	Grenade D6	3	0	1	-
Krak grenade	6"	Grenade 1	6	-1	D3	-

WARGEAR OPTIONS	• The Aspiring Champion may replace his bolt pistol and boltgun with items from the *Champion Equipment* list. • Any Chaos Space Marine may replace his boltgun with a chainsword. • One Chaos Space Marine may replace his bolt pistol with a plasma pistol, or replace his boltgun with one item from the *Special Weapons* or *Heavy Weapons* lists. • If the unit numbers ten or more models, an additional Chaos Space Marine may replace his boltgun with one item from the *Special Weapons* or *Heavy Weapons* lists. • One model may take a Chaos Icon (see *Codex: Chaos Space Marines*).
ABILITIES	**Death to the False Emperor** (pg 176)
FACTION KEYWORDS	**CHAOS, <MARK OF CHAOS>, HERETIC ASTARTES, <LEGION>**
KEYWORDS	**INFANTRY, CHAOS SPACE MARINES**

Chaos Space Marines seek only to tear down the Imperium they left behind, and fight with merciless cruelty to do so.

TERMINATORS

NAME	M	WS	BS	S	T	W	A	Ld	Sv
Terminator	5"	3+	3+	4	4	2	2	8	2+
Terminator Champion	5"	3+	3+	4	4	2	3	9	2+

This unit contains 1 Terminator Champion and 4 Terminators. It can include up to 5 additional Terminators (**Power Rating +14**). Each model is armed with a combi-bolter and chainaxe.

WEAPON	RANGE	TYPE	S	AP	D	ABILITIES
Combi-bolter	24"	Rapid Fire 2	4	0	1	-
Heavy flamer	8"	Heavy D6	5	-1	1	This weapon automatically hits its target.
Reaper autocannon	36"	Heavy 4	7	-1	1	-
Chainaxe	Melee	Melee	+1	-1	1	-
Lightning claw	Melee	Melee	User	-2	1	You can re-roll wound rolls for this weapon. If a model is armed with two lightning claws, each time it fights it can make 1 additional attack with them.

WARGEAR OPTIONS	
	• Any model may replace its combi-bolter with one item from the *Combi-weapons* list.
	• Any model may replace its chainaxe with one item from the *Terminator Melee Weapons* list.
	• Any model may replace its combi-bolter and chainaxe with a pair of lightning claws.
	• For every five models in the unit, one Terminator may replace his combi-bolter with a heavy flamer or reaper autocannon.
	• One model may take a Chaos Icon (see *Codex: Chaos Space Marines*).

ABILITIES	
	Death to the False Emperor (pg 176)
	Terminator Armour: Models in this unit have a 5+ invulnerable save.
	Teleport Strike: During deployment, you can set up this unit in a teleportarium chamber instead of placing it on the battlefield. At the end of any of your Movement phases the unit can use a teleport strike to arrive on the battlefield – set it up anywhere on the battlefield that is more than 9" away from any enemy models.

FACTION KEYWORDS	CHAOS, <MARK OF CHAOS>, HERETIC ASTARTES, <LEGION>
KEYWORDS	INFANTRY, TERMINATORS

Veterans of the Long War, Terminators are living tanks that are almost impossible to stop.

HAVOCS

NAME	M	WS	BS	S	T	W	A	Ld	Sv
Havoc	6"	3+	3+	4	5	1	1	7	3+
Aspiring Champion	6"	3+	3+	4	5	1	2	8	3+

This unit contains 1 Aspiring Champion and 4 Havocs. The Aspiring Champion is armed with a flamer, chainsword, frag grenades and krak grenades. Each Havoc is armed with a heavy bolter or lascannon, and frag grenades and krak grenades.

WEAPON	RANGE	TYPE	S	AP	D	ABILITIES
Flamer	8"	Assault D6	4	0	1	This weapon automatically hits its target.
Heavy bolter	36"	Heavy 3	5	-1	1	-
Lascannon	48"	Heavy 1	9	-3	D6	-
Chainsword	Melee	Melee	User	0	1	Each time the bearer fights, it can make 1 additional attack with this weapon.
Frag grenade	6"	Grenade D6	3	0	1	-
Krak grenade	6"	Grenade 1	6	-1	D3	-

WARGEAR OPTIONS	• Any Havoc may replace their heavy bolter or lascannon with a weapon from the *Heavy Weapons* list. • The Aspiring Champion may replace his flamer with an item from the *Champion Equipment* or *Special Weapons* list. • The Aspiring Champion may replace his chainsword with an item from the *Champion Equipment* list.
ABILITIES	**Death to the False Emperor** (pg 176) **Stabilisation Talons:** This unit can move and fire Heavy weapons without suffering the penalty to their hit rolls.
FACTION KEYWORDS	**CHAOS, <MARK OF CHAOS>, HERETIC ASTARTES, <LEGION>**
KEYWORDS	**INFANTRY, HAVOCS**

Havocs are Heretic Astartes so obsessed with wielding heavy firepower they have become one with their weapons.

NOCTILITH CROWN

NAME	M	WS	BS	S	T	W	A	Ld	Sv
Noctilith Crown	-	-	4+	-	8	14	-	-	3+

A Noctilith Crown is a single model equipped with lashing warp energies.

WEAPON	RANGE	TYPE	S	AP	D	ABILITIES
Lashing warp energies	6"	Pistol D6	7	-2	2	-

ABILITIES	
	Malevolent Locus: PSYKERS attempting to manifest powers within 24" of this model will suffer Perils of the Warp on any double result rolled for the Psychic test, rather than only double 1 or double 6. **CHAOS PSYKERS** are not affected by this ability. **Loathsome Aura:** CHAOS units have a 5+ invulnerable save while they are wholly within 6" of this model. In addition, you can re-roll Psychic tests for **CHAOS PSYKERS** while they are within 6" of this model. At the start of the second and third battle rounds, the range of both these aura abilities is increased by 3" (i.e. it is 9" in the second battle round, and 12" in the third and subsequent battle rounds).	**Immobile:** This model cannot move for any reason, nor can it fight in the Fight phase. Enemy models automatically hit this model in the Fight phase – do not make hit rolls. However, friendly units can still target enemy units that are within 1" of this model in the Shooting phase. **Unstable Energies:** If this model is reduced to 0 wounds, roll a D6 before removing it from the battlefield. On a 6, each unit within D6" of this model suffers D6 mortal wounds.

FACTION KEYWORDS	CHAOS
KEYWORDS	BUILDING, VEHICLE, NOCTILITH CROWN

Noctilith Crowns form vital strongpoints, for these arcane devices can draw in the raw energy of Chaos itself.

SKULLTAKER

5 POWER

NAME	M	WS	BS	S	T	W	A	Ld	Sv
Skulltaker	7"	2+	2+	5	4	4	4	8	3+

Skulltaker is a single model armed with the Slayer Sword. Only one of this model may be included in your army.

WEAPON	RANGE	TYPE	S	AP	D	ABILITIES
The Slayer Sword	Melee	Melee	User	-3	3	Each time you make a wound roll of 6+ for this weapon, that hit is resolved with a Damage of D3+3.

ABILITIES	**Daemonic, Unstoppable Ferocity, Daemonic Ritual** (pg 176) **Skulls for Khorne:** You can re-roll hit and wound rolls for attacks made by Skulltaker that target a **Character**.	**Locus of Decapitation:** You can add 1 to hit rolls made for friendly **Bloodletter** units that are within 8" of Skulltaker in the Fight phase.
FACTION KEYWORDS	**Chaos, Khorne, Daemon**	
KEYWORDS	**Character, Infantry, Bloodletter, Herald of Khorne, Skulltaker**	

The daemonic Herald known as Skulltaker is exceptionally skilled with a blade; few warriors have duelled him and lived to tell of it.

BLOODMASTER

3 POWER

NAME	M	WS	BS	S	T	W	A	Ld	Sv
Bloodmaster	6"	2+	2+	5	4	4	3	8	6+

A Bloodmaster is a single model armed with a blade of blood.

WEAPON	RANGE	TYPE	S	AP	D	ABILITIES
Blade of blood	Melee	Melee	User	-3	D3	Each time you make a wound roll of 6+ for this weapon, that hit is resolved with a Damage of 3.

ABILITIES	**Daemonic, Unstoppable Ferocity, Daemonic Ritual** (pg 176) **Locus of Khorne:** Add 1 to the Strength characteristic of **Khorne Daemon** units within 6" of one or more friendly models with this ability.
FACTION KEYWORDS	**Chaos, Khorne, Daemon**
KEYWORDS	**Character, Infantry, Bloodletter, Herald of Khorne, Bloodmaster**

SKULL ALTAR

A Skull Altar is a single model.

ABILITIES	
	Monument to Slaughter: After it is set up, a Skull Altar is treated as a terrain feature. It cannot move for any reason, is not treated as a friendly or enemy model, and cannot be targeted or affected by attacks or abilities. If a Skull Altar is summoned using a Daemonic Ritual and set up with its base touching the base of a **KHORNE DAEMON INFANTRY CHARACTER** that performed that ritual, you can immediately place that character on the Skull Altar's platform – the level area at the top of the stairs. A Skull Altar cannot be set up on an objective marker, and must be set up more than 1" from any other terrain. **Nexus of Dark Glory:** A model's Locus of Rage ability (see *Codex: Chaos Daemons*) has a range of 12" instead of 6" while they are within 8" of any Skull Altars. **Witchbane:** Subtract 1 from Psychic tests taken for **PSYKERS** within 8" of any Skull Altars.	**Conduit to Khorne's Domain:** You can re-roll any of the dice rolled when you make a summoning roll for a **CHAOS CHARACTER** from your army that is within 8" of any Skull Altars when it attempts to summon a **KHORNE DAEMON** unit to the battlefield using a Daemonic Ritual. **Champion of Murder:** If a **KHORNE DAEMON INFANTRY CHARACTER**'s base is on a Skull Altar's platform (the level area at the top of the stairs), the Skull Altar is said to be occupied by that character. Improve that character's invulnerable save by 1, to a maximum of 3+ (so an invulnerable save of 5+ becomes 4+). In addition, while a **KHORNE DAEMON** unit is wholly within 16" of any occupied Skull Altars, add 1 to the Attacks characteristic of all models in that unit.
FACTION KEYWORDS	**CHAOS, KHORNE, DAEMON**
KEYWORDS	**SKULL ALTAR**

A Skull Altar is a nexus of the Blood God's devotion. Those who fight in its shadow are driven to great acts of bloodshed.

ABILITIES

The following abilities are common to many of the Chaos units presented in this section, as referenced on their datasheets.

DEATH TO THE FALSE EMPEROR

Each time you roll a hit roll of 6+ for a model with this ability in the Fight phase, it can, if it was targeting an IMPERIUM unit, immediately make an extra attack against the same unit using the same weapon. These extra attacks cannot themselves generate any further attacks.

DAEMONIC

Units with this ability have a 5+ invulnerable save.

UNSTOPPABLE FEROCITY

If this unit makes a charge move, is charged, or performs a Heroic Intervention, then until the end of the turn add 1 to the Attacks characteristic of all its models and add 1 to the Strength characteristic of all the melee weapons the unit is armed with.

DAEMONIC RITUAL

Instead of moving in their Movement phase, any CHAOS CHARACTER can, at the end of their Movement phase, attempt to summon a unit with this ability by performing a Daemonic Ritual (the character cannot do so if they arrived as reinforcements this turn, or if they were themselves summoned to the battlefield this turn).

If they do so, first choose one of the four Chaos Gods – KHORNE, TZEENTCH, NURGLE or SLAANESH. A CHARACTER who owes allegiance to one of the Dark Gods can only attempt to summon the units of their patron – for example, a KHORNE CHARACTER could only attempt to summon a KHORNE unit.

Roll up to three D6 – this is your summoning roll. You can summon one new unit with the Daemonic Ritual ability to the battlefield that has a Power Rating equal to or less than the total result so long as it has the same Chaos God keyword you chose at the start (in the case of units that have a choice of allegiance, such as Furies, the unit when summoned will have this keyword). This unit is treated as reinforcements for your army and can be placed anywhere on the battlefield that is wholly within 12" of the character and more than 9" from any enemy model. If the total rolled is insufficient to summon any unit, the ritual fails and no new unit is summoned.

If your summoning roll included any doubles, your character then suffers 1 mortal wound. If it contained any triples, it instead suffers D3 mortal wounds.

THE ARMOURIES OF CHAOS

The blood-soaked weapons wielded by the forces of Chaos are an array of dread tools of torture and execution, designed to inspire absolute terror amongst their foes. The following tables provide new and updated weapon profiles for the units included in this book, to be used in conjunction with the weapon tables in *Codex: Chaos Space Marines* and *Codex: Chaos Daemons*.

RANGED WEAPONS						
WEAPON	RANGE	TYPE	S	AP	D	ABILITIES
Lashing warp energies	6"	Pistol D6	7	-2	2	-
Reaper chaincannon	24"	Heavy 8	5	-1	1	-

MELEE WEAPONS						
WEAPON	RANGE	TYPE	S	AP	D	ABILITIES
Accursed crozius	Melee	Melee	+1	-1	2	-
Axe of dismemberment	Melee	Melee	x2	-3	D3	Each time you make a wound roll of 6+ for this weapon, the target unit suffers 1 mortal wound in addition to any other damage.
Bladed limbs and tail	Melee	Melee	+3	-2	D3	After the Lord Discordant makes his close combat attacks, you can attack with his Helstalker. Make a number of additional attacks as shown in the damage chart, using this weapon profile.
Drach'nyen	Melee	Melee	+1	-3	3	Roll a D6 each time the bearer fights. On a 1 they suffer 1 mortal wound and cannot use this weapon further during this phase. On a 2+ they can make that many additional attacks with this weapon.
Impaler chainglaive	Melee	Melee	+2	-2	2	If the bearer made a charge move or performed a Heroic Intervention this turn, attacks with this weapon are made with a Strength characteristic of x2 instead of +2.
Talon of Horus (melee)	Melee	Melee	x2	-4	D3	-
Techno-virus injector	Melee	Melee	+4	-4	D3	After the Lord Discordant makes his close combat attacks, you can attack with his Helstalker. Make a single attack using this weapon profile in addition to the Helstalker's bladed limbs and tail. Each time a wound roll for an attack made with this weapon is successful when targeting a VEHICLE unit, that unit suffers D3 mortal wounds in addition to any normal damage.
Thunder hammer	Melee	Melee	x2	-3	3	When attacking with this weapon, you must subtract 1 from the hit roll.

POINTS VALUES

If you are playing a matched play game, or a game that uses a points limit, you can use the following lists to determine the total points cost of your army. Simply add together the points values of all your models, as well as the weapons and wargear they are equipped with, to determine your army's total points value.

CHAOS SPACE MARINES

UNIT	MODELS PER UNIT	POINTS PER MODEL
Abaddon the Despoiler	1	240*
Chaos Space Marines	5-20	13**
Dark Apostle	1	100**
Dark Disciples	2	5**
Havocs	5	14**
Lord Discordant on Helstalker	1	150**
Master of Executions	1	70**
Noctilith Crown	1	100**
Terminators	5-10	26**

*Includes wargear
**Does not include wargear

CHAOS SPACE MARINES MELEE WEAPONS

ITEM	POINTS PER ITEM
Accursed crozius	0
Axe of dismemberment	0
Bladed limbs and tail	0
Chainaxe	1
Chainfist	11
Chainsword	0
Impaler chainglaive	0
Lightning claws (single/pair)	8/12
Mechatendrils	0
Power axe	5
Power fist	9
Power maul	4
Power sword	4
Techno-virus injector	0
Thunder hammer (CHARACTERS)	21
Thunder hammer (other models)	16

CHAOS DAEMONS

UNIT	MODELS PER UNIT	POINTS PER MODEL (including wargear)
Bloodmaster	1	56
Skull Altar	1	100
Skulltaker	1	84

CHAOS SPACE MARINES RANGED WEAPONS

ITEM	POINTS PER ITEM
Autocannon	10
Baleflamer	30
Bolt pistol	0
Boltgun	0
Combi-bolter	2
Combi-flamer	8
Combi-melta	15
Combi-plasma	11
Flamer	6
Heavy bolter	10
Heavy flamer	14
Lascannon	25
Lashing warp energies	0
Magma cutter	16
Meltagun	14
Missile launcher	20
Plasma gun	11
Plasma pistol	5
Reaper autocannon	10
Reaper chaincannon	20

CHAOS SPACE MARINES OTHER WEAPONS

ITEM	POINTS PER ITEM
Frag grenade	0
Krak grenade	0

CHAOS ICONS

ICON	POINTS PER ICON
Icon of Despair	10
Icon of Excess	10
Icon of Flame	5
Icon of Vengeance	5
Icon of Wrath	10

BRINGERS OF DESPAIR

The Bringers of Despair march across the battlefield like a walking, spike-studded fortress. Abaddon's elite guard are utterly devoted to their master, body and soul. They excel in the art of brutal subjugation, and the acts they have committed in his name ensure they are feared far and wide.

SPECIALIST DETACHMENT

If your army is Battle-forged, you can use the Specialist Detachment Stratagem below:

1CP

BRINGERS OF DESPAIR
Specialist Detachment Stratagem

The elite warbands of the Black Legion are known as Bringers of Despair, and they strike a sledgehammer blow into the heart of the enemy.

Use this Stratagem when choosing your army. Pick a **BLACK LEGION** Detachment from your army to be a Bringers of Despair Specialist Detachment. **BLACK LEGION TERMINATOR** units in that Detachment gain the **BRINGERS OF DESPAIR** keyword.

STRATAGEMS

If your army includes any Bringers of Despair Specialist Detachments, you can use Command Points (CPs) to use the following Stratagems:

1CP

BRUTAL SUBJUGATION
Black Legion Stratagem

These warriors are terrifying killers without compare, tearing through the foes with contemptuous ease.

Use this Stratagem at the start of the Fight phase. Pick a **BRINGERS OF DESPAIR** unit from your army. Each enemy model slain by this unit in this phase counts as two models in the subsequent Morale phase.

1CP

CHOSEN ENFORCERS
Black Legion Stratagem

Abaddon's Terminator bodyguard are a visual reminder of his power over those who serve him.

Use this Stratagem when a friendly **HERETIC ASTARTES** unit that is within 18" of a **BRINGERS OF DESPAIR** unit from your army is required to take a Morale test. That unit automatically passes that Morale test.

WARLORD TRAIT

If a **BRINGERS OF DESPAIR CHARACTER** is your Warlord, you can give them the following Warlord Trait.

CHOSEN OF THE WARMASTER

When the Warmaster himself is not present, this warrior has the strength to lead the forces of the legion in his stead.

Re-roll hit rolls of 1 for attacks made by friendly **BRINGERS OF DESPAIR** units while they are within 6" of your Warlord. If your Warlord has the Lord of Chaos ability, you can instead re-roll hit rolls for attacks made by friendly **BRINGERS OF DESPAIR** units while they are within 6" of your Warlord.

RELICS OF THE LEGION

If your army includes any Bringers of Despair Specialist Detachments, you can give the following relic to a **BRINGERS OF DESPAIR CHARACTER** from your army.

FOECLEAVER

This brutal axe has been carried by members of the legion since the early days of the Great Crusade.

Model with power axe only. Foecleaver replaces the model's power axe and has the following profile:

WEAPON	RANGE	TYPE	S	AP	D
Foecleaver	Melee	Melee	+3	-2	D3

Abilities: Add 1 to hit rolls for attacks made with this weapon that target **IMPERIUM** units.

DEVASTATION BATTERY

A devastation battery is assembled whenever a Chaos Lord's prey locks themselves away within a seemingly impregnable fortification. In a furious storm of heavy weapons fire, the fools are disabused of that notion, their prized defences laid open and the Chaos marksmen moving in for the kill.

SPECIALIST DETACHMENT

If your army is Battle-forged, you can use the Specialist Detachment Stratagem below:

1CP
DEVASTATION BATTERY
Specialist Detachment Stratagem
When enemy fortifications or armoured forces must be brought low, many Chaos Lords will gather their most destructive followers together to focus their tremendous firepower.

Use this Stratagem when choosing your army. Pick a Chaos Space Marine Detachment from your army to be a Devastation Battery Specialist Detachment. **<Legion> Chaos Lords, Warpsmiths, Havocs** and **Obliterators** in that Detachment gain the **Devastation Battery** keyword.

WARLORD TRAIT

If a **Devastation Battery Character** is your Warlord, you can give them the following Warlord Trait.

ARMOUR BANE

Adept at meeting and stopping enemy sallies, this warrior instinctively knows how to blunt an armoured counter-attack.

Re-roll wound rolls of 1 for attacks made by friendly **Devastation Battery** units that are within 6" of your Warlord if the target is a **Vehicle**.

RELICS OF CHAOS

If your army includes any Devastation Battery Specialist Detachments, you can give the following relic to a **Devastation Battery Character** from your army.

THE DAEMON'S EYE

Used by the greatest battery commanders to augment their forces, this multi-lensed scanner unit is bound with the spirit of a Daemon who excelled at spotting mortal weaknesses. The scanner digests and distributes advanced targeting information to nearby units with supernatural speed.

At the start of your Shooting phase, pick a friendly **Devastation Battery** unit within 6" of the bearer. Enemy units do not receive the benefit of cover against that unit's weapons this phase.

STRATAGEMS

If your army includes any Devastation Battery Specialist Detachments, you can use Command Points (CPs) to use the following Stratagems:

1CP
WALL-BREAKERS
Chaos Space Marines Stratagem
No fortress can stand before the massed guns of the Heretic Astartes legions, especially when controlled by those with an affinity for heavy weapons.

Use this Stratagem at the start of your Shooting phase. Pick a **Devastation Battery** unit from your army. You can re-roll damage rolls for attacks made with ranged weapons by that unit that target **Buildings** until the end of the phase.

1CP
PUNISHING VOLLEY
Chaos Space Marines Stratagem
When up against a Heretic Astartes weapons battery, even the most cunning enemies find their every avenue of advance met with heavy volleys of fire.

Use this Stratagem at the end of your opponent's first Movement phase, if you did not have the first turn. Pick a **Devastation Battery** unit from your army. That unit can shoot as if it were the Shooting phase.

CULT OF THE DAMNED

The existence of the Dark Gods is a closely kept secret, but those who have seen the blasphemous power they can offer will often give their lives to sample it for themselves. Led into battle by devout warlords and Dark Apostles that preach the word of Chaos, such devotees fight in a state of religious frenzy.

SPECIALIST DETACHMENT

If your army is Battle-forged, you can use the Specialist Detachment Stratagem below:

1CP — CULT OF THE DAMNED
Specialist Detachment Stratagem

Dark Apostles gather large groups of mortal followers, damning their souls with promises of power.

Use this Stratagem when choosing your army. Pick a Chaos Space Marine Detachment from your army to be a Cult of the Damned Specialist Detachment. **DARK APOSTLES**, **DARK DISCIPLES** and **CHAOS CULTISTS** in that Detachment gain the **CULT OF THE DAMNED** keyword.

WARLORD TRAIT

If a **CULT OF THE DAMNED CHARACTER** is your Warlord, you can give them the following Warlord Trait.

EXULTANT PREACHER

Screaming praise to the Dark Gods, this leader drives his troops forward with hysterical fervour.

You can re-roll charge rolls for friendly **CULT OF THE DAMNED** units while they are within 6" of your Warlord.

RELICS OF CHAOS

If your army includes any Cult of the Damned Specialist Detachments, you can give the following relic to a **CULT OF THE DAMNED CHARACTER** from your army.

THE INFERNO TOME

Flames lick at the pages of this ancient book, but the parchment never burns. With the correctly spoken words, these flames blast forth, incinerating the foe.

The bearer is armed with a ranged weapon with the following profile in addition to any other ranged weapons it is armed with:

WEAPON	RANGE	TYPE	S	AP	D
Inferno Tome	8"	Assault D6	5	-1	D3

Abilities: This weapon automatically hits its target.

STRATAGEMS

If your army includes any Cult of the Damned Specialist Detachments, you can use Command Points (CPs) to use the following Stratagems:

1CP — RITUAL OFFERINGS
Chaos Space Marines Stratagem

Those unfortunate enough to be taken alive by Chaos Cultists only serve as fuel for their fanatical devotions.

Use this Stratagem when an enemy model is destroyed by an attack made by a **CULT OF THE DAMNED CHAOS CULTISTS** unit from your army in the Fight phase. That Chaos Cultist unit automatically passes Morale tests for the rest of the battle.

1CP — CHORUS OF THE TRUE FAITH
Chaos Space Marines Stratagem

The rhythmic chanting of underlings lends power to prayers in times of great need.

Use this Stratagem when a **CULT OF THE DAMNED DARK APOSTLE** from your army chants a prayer. If there are any friendly **CULT OF THE DAMNED CHAOS CULTISTS** units within 6" of that Dark Apostle, add 1 to the dice roll to see if that prayer is heard.

DAEMONKIN RITUALISTS

Those who consort with warp entities – or act as hosts for a malign being – are sometimes known as Daemonkin. When they gather together, they wage war as if it were a religious experience, working grim rituals with the flesh and blood of the foe to call down the favour of the Dark Gods.

SPECIALIST DETACHMENT

If your army is Battle-forged, you can use the Specialist Detachment Stratagem below:

DAEMONKIN RITUALISTS

1CP

Specialist Detachment Stratagem

When gathered together in large groups, the powers of those who have given their bodies to a Daemon from the warp are amplified.

Use this Stratagem when choosing your army. Pick a Chaos Space Marine Detachment from your army to be a Daemonkin Ritualists Specialist Detachment. **DARK APOSTLES**, **DARK DISCIPLES**, **MASTERS OF POSSESSION**, **POSSESSED** and **GREATER POSSESSED** units in that Detachment gain the **DAEMONKIN RITUALISTS** keyword.

WARLORD TRAIT

If a **DAEMONKIN RITUALISTS CHARACTER** is your Warlord, you can give them the following Warlord Trait.

SHEPHERD OF THE TRUE FAITH

This skilled firebrand drives his followers to ever greater acts of violence.

Each time you roll an unmodified wound roll of 6 for an attack made with a melee weapon by a friendly **DAEMONKIN RITUALISTS** unit within 6" of your Warlord, that attack inflicts 1 mortal wound on the target in addition to the normal damage.

RELICS OF CHAOS

If your army includes any Daemonkin Ritualists Specialist Detachments, you can give the following relic to a **DAEMONKIN RITUALISTS CHARACTER** from your army.

THE BURNING ROD

This daemonic stave whispers forbidden secrets, searing the ears of nearby unbelievers.

Model with force stave only. The Burning Rod replaces the bearer's force stave and has the following profile:

WEAPON	RANGE	TYPE	S	AP	D
The Burning Rod	Melee	Melee	+3	-1	D3

Abilities: At the end of each Fight phase, you can pick a unit within 1" of the bearer. That unit suffers 1 mortal wound.

STRATAGEMS

If your army includes any Daemonkin Ritualists Specialist Detachments, you can use Command Points (CPs) to use the following Stratagems:

VESSELS FOR THE NEVERBORN

Chaos Space Marines Stratagem

The proximity of a Master of Possession allows Daemon and mortal to bond more closely, allowing even greater power to be unleashed.

Use this Stratagem at the start of the Fight phase. Pick a **DAEMONKIN RITUALISTS DAEMON** unit from your army that is within 6" of a friendly **DAEMONKIN RITUALISTS MASTER OF POSSESSION**. Add 1 to the Strength and Attacks characteristics of models in the unit you picked until the end of the phase.

SOULS OF THE DEVOTED

Chaos Space Marines Stratagem

The most unscrupulous amongst the Traitor Legions will think nothing of sacrificing the souls of their followers for personal glory.

Use this Stratagem at the start of your Movement phase. Pick a **DAEMONKIN RITUALISTS POSSESSED** unit from your army and a friendly **DAEMONKIN RITUALISTS CHARACTER** that is within 6" of that unit and roll a D3. The **POSSESSED** unit suffers a number of mortal wounds equal to the result. The **CHARACTER** then regains a number of lost wounds equal to the result.

SOULFORGED PACK

The demented creations of Heretic Astartes Warpsmiths are often goaded to war by their creators. Those twisted engineers of war find great satisfaction in seeing their mechanical menageries drive home one thunderous charge after another, each infernal engine covered in splatters of gore by battle's end.

SPECIALIST DETACHMENT

If your army is Battle-forged, you can use the Specialist Detachment Stratagem below:

SOULFORGED PACK
Specialist Detachment Stratagem
Warpsmiths and Lords Discordant often gather their deranged creations together into packs before sending them forth to strike the enemy lines like a thunderbolt.

Use this Stratagem when choosing your army. Pick a Chaos Space Marine Detachment from your army to be a Soulforged Pack Specialist Detachment. **WARPSMITH** and **DAEMON ENGINE** units in that Detachment gain the **SOULFORGED PACK** keyword.

WARLORD TRAIT

If a **SOULFORGED PACK CHARACTER** is your Warlord, you can give them the following Warlord Trait.

MASTER OF THE SOULFORGES

Barking scrapcode and lashing with mechatendrils, this warrior drives his deranged creations forward into the foe.

Add 2" to the Move characteristic of friendly **SOULFORGED PACK DAEMON ENGINES** while they are within 6" of your Warlord.

RELICS OF CHAOS

If your army includes any Soulforged Pack Specialist Detachments, you can give the following relic to a **SOULFORGED PACK CHARACTER** from your army.

MECHA-SERPENTS

Imbued with a daemonic sentience of their own, these parasitic tendrils lash out viciously at anything within reach.

Model with mechatendrils only. The Mecha-serpents replace the bearer's mechatendrils and have the following profile:

WEAPON	RANGE	TYPE	S	AP	D
Mecha-serpents	Melee	Melee	+1	-1	2

Abilities: Each time the bearer fights, it can make 1 (and only 1) attack with this weapon for each enemy model within 1" of the bearer.

STRATAGEMS

If your army includes any Soulforged Pack Specialist Detachments, you can use Command Points (CPs) to use the following Stratagems:

DAEMONFORGE OVERDRIVE
Chaos Space Marines Stratagem
By channelling the energies of the warp into its metal frame, even a badly damaged Daemon Engine can still be a significant threat.

Use this Stratagem at the start of the Fight phase. Pick a **SOULFORGED PACK DAEMON ENGINE** from your army. Double the number of wounds that model has remaining for the purposes of determining what characteristics to use on its damage table until the end of the phase, or until this model is reduced to 0 wounds, whichever occurs first.

INFERNAL ENGINES
Chaos Space Marines Stratagem
When they catch the scent of their foe, Daemon Engines push their piston-driven limbs to the limit in order to close with their prey.

Use this Stratagem at the start of your Charge phase. Pick a **SOULFORGED PACK DAEMON ENGINE** from your army. That model can charge in this phase even if it Advanced earlier in the turn.

HOST RAPTORIAL

Those of the Chaos hordes that have become obsessed with the power of flight will form together into formations of airborne killers known as Hosts Raptorial. Comprised largely of Raptors and Warp Talons, they scream down from on high to launch close-quarters attacks on their earthbound foes.

SPECIALIST DETACHMENT

If your army is Battle-forged, you can use the Specialist Detachment Stratagem below:

HOST RAPTORIAL
1CP

Specialist Detachment Stratagem

When large numbers of Raptors and Warp Talons convene, they form screeching packs of airborne killers, plunging down from the skies to strike the weakest points in the foe's lines.

Use this Stratagem when choosing your army. Pick a Chaos Space Marine Detachment from your army to be a Host Raptorial Specialist Detachment. **<Legion> Jump Pack** units in that Detachment gain the **Host Raptorial** keyword.

STRATAGEMS

If your army includes any Host Raptorial Specialist Detachments, you can use Command Points (CPs) to use the following Stratagems:

VICIOUS DESCENT
1CP

Chaos Space Marines Stratagem

Hosts Raptorial strike without warning or mercy, catching the enemy unaware and decimating their formations before they can coordinate a counter-attack.

Use this Stratagem when a **Host Raptorial** unit from your army is set up on the battlefield at the end of the Movement phase. You can re-roll hit rolls for attacks made by that unit until the end of the turn.

TERROR STRIKE
1CP

Chaos Space Marines Stratagem

To see one's comrades brutally torn asunder is often more than most soldiers can take.

Use this Stratagem when an enemy unit is destroyed by a **Host Raptorial** unit from your army. Subtract 1 from the Leadership characteristic of enemy units while they are within 6" of any **Host Raptorial** units from your army until the end of the turn.

WARLORD TRAIT

If a **Host Raptorial Character** is your Warlord, you can give them the following Warlord Trait.

THE TIP OF THE CLAW

This warlord insists on leading his assault troops from the front, always seeking to be the first to draw the blood of the foe.

Add 2 to charge rolls made for friendly **Host Raptorial** units while they are within 6" of your Warlord.

RELICS OF CHAOS

If your army includes any Host Raptorial Specialist Detachments, you can give the following relic to a **Host Raptorial Character** from your army.

CHIROPTERAN WINGS

The wearer of this viciously bladed jump pack is able to swoop low over the enemy, slicing off limbs and opening veins as he passes.

Roll a D6 for each enemy unit that was moved across by the bearer in the Movement or Charge phase. On a 4+, that unit suffers D3 mortal wounds.

FALLEN ANGELS

The Fallen hail from the time when a vast swathe of the First Legion went renegade – and they have been a deadly bane to the Imperium ever since. The Dark Angels consider them the worst of all possible foes, for not only do they conceal an empire-shattering secret, they are next to impossible to catch.

SPECIALIST DETACHMENT

If your army is Battle-forged, you can use the Specialist Detachment Stratagem below:

FALLEN ANGELS
1CP

Specialist Detachment Stratagem

When the Fallen gather in numbers, the machinations of Cypher gain incredible momentum.

Use this Stratagem when choosing your army. You can include Sorcerers and Chaos Rhinos in a Vanguard Detachment that includes only FALLEN units. If you do so, they replace their <MARK OF CHAOS>, HERETIC ASTARTES and <LEGION> keywords with the IMPERIUM and FALLEN keywords. FALLEN Sorcerers also replace their Death to the False Emperor ability with the Fallen Angels ability from the Fallen datasheet. Pick a FALLEN Detachment from your army to be a Fallen Angels Specialist Detachment. FALLEN units in that Detachment gain the FALLEN ANGELS keyword.

STRATAGEMS

If your army includes any Fallen Angels Specialist Detachments, you can use Command Points (CPs) to use the following Stratagems:

WITHOUT A TRACE
1CP

Fallen Stratagem

Having hidden from the Unforgiven for millennia, the Fallen are adept at passing unseen.

Use this Stratagem at the start of the enemy Shooting phase. Pick a FALLEN ANGELS unit from your army that is entirely on or within any terrain feature. Subtract 1 from hit rolls for attacks that target that unit until the end of the phase.

ANCIENT ENMITY
1CP

Fallen Stratagem

Many Fallen have never forgiven their perceived betrayal at the hands of the sons of the Lion.

Use this Stratagem when you pick a FALLEN ANGELS unit from your army to fight with. You can re-roll wound rolls for attacks made by this unit that target DARK ANGELS units until the end of the phase.

If any Chaos Rhinos are included in a Fallen Angels Specialist Detachment, replace their Transport rule with the following rule:

This model can transport 10 FALLEN INFANTRY models. It cannot, however, transport TERMINATORS, CULT OF DESTRUCTION or JUMP PACK models.

If CYPHER is included in a Fallen Angels Specialist Detachment, he gains the following ability:

AGENT OF DISCORD

Cypher's disruptive influence and unpredictable actions are the bane of any sane commander. The effect is amplified by the presence of large numbers of his fellow Fallen.

Enemy units within 12" of CYPHER cannot use any abilities, Warlord Traits or Relics that allow them to gain, return or refund Command Points. The range of this ability is increased to 18" while there are 10 or more other friendly FALLEN ANGELS models within 12" of CYPHER. The range of this ability is instead increased to 24" while there are 20 or more other friendly FALLEN ANGELS models within 12" of CYPHER.

RELICS OF LOST CALIBAN

If your army includes any Fallen Angels Specialist Detachments, you can give the following relic to a FALLEN ANGELS CHARACTER from your army.

CALIBAN STEEL BLADE

This ancient blade was forged on lost Caliban and exemplifies that world's cruelty and beauty in equal measure.

Model with force sword only. The Caliban Steel Blade replaces the bearer's force sword and has the following profile:

WEAPON	RANGE	TYPE	S	AP	D
Caliban Steel Blade	Melee	Melee	User	-3	D3

Abilities: Any attacks with a wound roll of 6+ made with this weapon have a Damage characteristic of D6 instead of D3.

LEGION OF SKULLS

Legions of Skulls are formed in the brazen heart of Khorne's domain. Sent through the roiling tides of the Cicatrix Maledictum to drive a spike of hatred into Mankind's realm, a Legion of Skulls will never rest in its quest to spill blood for the Blood God and claim skulls for the Skull Throne.

SPECIALIST DETACHMENT

If your army is Battle-forged, you can use the Specialist Detachment Stratagem below:

1CP — LEGION OF SKULLS
Specialist Detachment Stratagem

The teeming masses of Khorne's lesser Daemons can shatter worlds when they are gathered in large numbers.

Use this Stratagem when choosing your army. Pick a **KHORNE** Chaos Daemons Detachment (that is, a Chaos Daemons Detachment in which every unit has the **KHORNE** keyword) from your army to be a Legion of Skulls Specialist Detachment. **BLOODLETTER** units in that Detachment gain the **LEGION OF SKULLS** keyword.

WARLORD TRAIT

If a **LEGION OF SKULLS CHARACTER** is your Warlord, you can give them the following Warlord Trait.

BLOODBLESSED

This warlord has bathed in the blood of a thousand champions.

Add 1 to your Warlord's Attacks characteristic. In addition, while there are any enemy **CHARACTERS** within 6" of your Warlord, add another 1 to your Warlord's Attacks characteristic.

RELICS OF KHORNE

If your army includes any Legion of Skulls Specialist Detachments, you can give the following relic to a **LEGION OF SKULLS CHARACTER** from your army.

THE GOREPLATE

These brass plates absorb the arterial sprays from slain foes, invigorating the wearer.

Roll one D6 at the end of the Fight phase if any enemy models were slain by the bearer that phase, adding 2 to the result if any of the slain models was a **CHARACTER**; on a 4+, the bearer regains D3 lost wounds.

STRATAGEMS

If your army includes any Legion of Skulls Specialist Detachments, you can use Command Points (CPs) to use the following Stratagems:

1CP — BRAZEN SKULL
Chaos Daemons Stratagem

Plucking the skull of an enemy from the ground, this servant of Khorne imbues it with his burning rage and hurls it at the foe.

Use this Stratagem in your Shooting phase. Pick a **LEGION OF SKULLS** model from your army. Pick an enemy unit within 8" of this model that is visible to them, and roll a D6; if the result equals or exceeds this model's Ballistic Skill characteristic, that enemy unit suffers D3 mortal wounds.

2CP — RED TIDE
Chaos Daemons Stratagem

When the bloodletting begins, nearby servants of the Blood God are drawn to it with a single-minded focus.

Use this Stratagem in your Charge phase. Pick an enemy unit that was charged by a **LEGION OF SKULLS** unit from your army this phase. You can add 2 to charge rolls for other **LEGION OF SKULLS** units from your army that declare a charge against the same enemy unit (and do not declare charges against any other enemy unit) until the end of the phase.

BLACK LEGION

In this section you'll find rules for Battle-forged armies that include BLACK LEGION Detachments – that is, any Detachment that includes only BLACK LEGION units. These rules include the abilities below and a series of Stratagems that can only be used by the Black Legion. This section also includes the Black Legion's unique Warlord Traits, relics and Tactical Objectives. Together, these rules reflect the character and fighting style of the Black Legion in your games of Warhammer 40,000.

USING A BLACK LEGION ARMY IN WARHAMMER 40,000

The rules presented in this section are intended to be used in addition to those presented in *Codex: Chaos Space Marines* if you have chosen to take any BLACK LEGION Detachments. A BLACK LEGION Detachment is still treated as a Chaos Space Marine Detachment for the purposes of the Stratagems, Artefacts of Chaos and Warlord Traits presented in *Codex: Chaos Space Marines*. The following additional rules apply:

WARLORD TRAITS

If your Warlord is from the BLACK LEGION, you can choose one of the Warlord Traits on page 192 instead of those presented in *Codex: Chaos Space Marines*.

RELICS

If your army is led by a Chaos Space Marine Warlord, you may give one of the Relics of the Legion on page 191 to a BLACK LEGION CHARACTER from your army, instead of those presented in *Codex: Chaos Space Marines*. Named characters such as Abaddon the Despoiler already have one or more artefacts, and cannot be given any of these artefacts.

Note that some weapons replace one of the character's existing weapons. Where this is the case, you must, if you are playing a matched play game or are otherwise using points values, still pay the cost of the weapon that is being replaced. Write down any Relics of the Legion your characters have on your army roster.

STRATAGEMS

If your army is Battle-forged, the Stratagems on page 190 can be used in addition to those presented in *Codex: Chaos Space Marines* to reflect the fighting style of Black Legion warriors. If you choose to use the Relics of the Long War Stratagem presented in this supplement, you cannot also use the Gifts of Chaos Stratagem presented in *Codex: Chaos Space Marines*.

TACTICAL OBJECTIVES

Here we present new Tactical Objectives for use in Maelstrom of War missions to represent the strategies and tactics of the Black Legion on the battlefield.

ABILITIES

BLACK LEGION Detachments gain the following abilities:

THE WARMASTER'S LEGION

The Black Legion still bear the shame of Horus' failure, and their every action is dedicated to expunging that stain by accomplishing what he could not.

If your army is Battle-forged, all Troops units in BLACK LEGION Detachments gain this ability. Such a unit that is within range of an objective marker controls it even if there are more enemy models within range of it. If an enemy unit within range of the objective marker has a similar ability, then it is controlled by the player who has the most models within range as normal.

LEGION TRAIT

If your army is Battle-forged, all Daemon Prince, INFANTRY, BIKERS and HELBRUTE units in BLACK LEGION Detachments gain the Black Crusaders Legion Trait (below).

Mere Mortals

CHAOS CULTIST units do not gain the Black Crusaders Legion Trait.

Black Crusaders

Inexorable and unflinching, the Black Legion exemplify the threat posed by the Heretic Astartes, emerging from the Eye of Terror for the sole purpose of erasing the Imperium from the galaxy.

Add 1 to the Leadership characteristic of models in units with this trait. In addition, if a unit with this trait Advanced, it treats all its Rapid Fire weapons as Assault weapons until the end of the turn (e.g. a Rapid Fire 2 weapon is treated as an Assault 2 weapon).

BLACK LEGION STRATAGEMS

If your army is Battle-forged and includes any BLACK LEGION Detachments (excluding Auxiliary Support Detachments), you have access to the Stratagems shown here, meaning you can spend Command Points to activate them. These help to reflect the unique strategies used by the Black Legion on the battlefield.

LET THE GALAXY BURN
1CP

Black Legion Stratagem
The Black Legion attack with a terrible ferocity.

Use this Stratagem when a BLACK LEGION INFANTRY or BIKER unit from your army is picked to attack in a Shooting or Fight phase. You can re-roll all hit rolls of 1 for that unit for the rest of the phase. If the unit is a CHAOS SPACE MARINES unit, you can re-roll hit rolls for it instead.

MERCILESS FIGHTERS
1CP

Black Legion Stratagem
The Black Legion hunt their foes in packs.

Use this Stratagem at the start of the Fight phase. Pick a BLACK LEGION unit from your army. If that unit has more models than there are enemy models within 3" of it, add 1 to the Attacks characteristic of models in that unit until the end of the phase.

CHOSEN OF THE PANTHEON
1CP

Black Legion Stratagem
The Dark Gods bestow their patronage equally on those of the Black Legion.

Use this Stratagem at the start of your turn. Pick a BLACK LEGION unit from your army with the <MARK OF CHAOS> keyword that you did not dedicate to a specific Dark God. That unit has the KHORNE, TZEENTCH, NURGLE and SLAANESH keywords until the start of your next turn.

TIP OF THE SPEAR
1CP

Black Legion Stratagem
It is a great honour to be the first to slay the foe.

Use this Stratagem at the start of your first Shooting phase. You can re-roll hit rolls for the BLACK LEGION unit from your army that is closest to an enemy unit until the end of the phase. If several units are equidistant, you can pick which one is affected.

WORLD KILLERS
3CP

Black Legion Stratagem
The Black Legion dominate the battlefield.

Use this Stratagem at the start of any battle round. Until the end of that battle round, enemy units cannot use any abilities that allow them to control an objective marker if there are any BLACK LEGION units from your army within 3" of the centre of that objective marker, even if there are more enemy models within range of it.

LEGACY OF HORUS
1CP

Black Legion Stratagem
Horus' sons retain his natural ability to inspire loyalty.

Use this Stratagem at the start of the Morale phase. Until the end of the phase, add 1 to the Leadership characteristic of <LEGION> (except BLACK LEGION) units from your army while they are within 6" of any friendly BLACK LEGION units.

COUNCIL OF TRAITORS
1CP

Black Legion Stratagem
The advisors of the Black Legion are mighty leaders.

RELICS OF THE LONG WAR
1/3CP

Black Legion Stratagem
The Black Legion possess an array of ancient artefacts.

Use this Stratagem before the battle. Your army can have one extra Relic of the Legion for 1 CP, or two extra Relics of the Legion for 3 CPs. All of the Relics of the Legion that you include must be different and be given to different BLACK LEGION CHARACTERS. You can only use this Stratagem once per battle.

Use this Stratagem before the battle if your Warlord is a BLACK LEGION CHAOS LORD, DAEMON PRINCE or ABADDON THE DESPOILER. Pick up to one BLACK LEGION DARK APOSTLE and up to one BLACK LEGION SORCERER from your army. Generate a Warlord Trait for each model you picked (note that these models are only regarded as your Warlord for the purposes of these Warlord Traits). You can only use this Stratagem once per battle. No two characters from your army can have the same Warlord Trait.

RELICS OF THE LEGION

The Black Legion is a vast conglomeration of forces, made up not only of the Sons of Horus, but other traitors who have flocked to the banner and adopted the colours. These forces bring a wide variety of ancient relics, Daemon-tainted weaponry and strange artefacts to the battlefield.

GHORISVEX'S TEETH

When the Daemon Ghorisvex the Red-hand was broken over the knee of Lord Voraddon of the Black Legion, his spirit was bound into Voraddon's chainsword. It resides there still, ripping and tearing at not just the bodies, but also the very souls, of the Black Legion's foes.

Model with chainsword only. Ghorisvex's Teeth replaces the bearer's chainsword and has the following profile:

WEAPON	RANGE	TYPE	S	AP	D
Ghorisvex's Teeth	Melee	Melee	User	-3	2

Abilities: Each time the bearer fights, it can make 2 additional attacks with this weapon. Each time you roll a wound roll of 6+ for an attack made with this weapon, the target of the attack suffers 1 mortal wound in addition to the normal damage.

TROPHIES OF SLAUGHTER

This warrior sports a mighty trophy rack, covered in spoils taken from all over the galaxy, that cements his position and right to lead.

Add 1 to the Leadership characteristic of friendly **BLACK LEGION** units while they are within 6" of the bearer. In addition, subtract 1 from the Leadership characteristic of enemy units while they are within 6" of the bearer.

SIGHTLESS HELM

The lenses of this helm remain forever dark, the wearer unable to perceive the galaxy with their own eyes. Instead, strange warp senses are granted by the helm's machine spirit, illuminating the foe's weaknesses.

Worsen the bearer's Ballistic Skill characteristic by 1 (e.g. BS 2+ becomes BS 3+), but improve the Armour Penetration characteristic of all of the bearer's weapons by 1 (e.g. AP 0 becomes AP -1).

ANGELSBANE

This ornate twin boltgun earned its name at the Siege of Terra, and its Daemon-infused machine spirit delights in slaughtering those faithful to the Emperor.

Model with combi-bolter only. Angelsbane replaces the bearer's combi-bolter and has the following profile:

WEAPON	RANGE	TYPE	S	AP	D
Angelsbane	24"	Rapid Fire 2	5	-2	2

Abilities: This weapon has a Damage characteristic of 3 if the target has the **IMPERIUM** keyword.

CLOAK OF CONQUEST

This patchwork garment is fashioned from scraps of fabric telling of the wearer's many conquests. From the cloaks of Adeptus Astartes heroes to the banners of the Astra Militarum, with each victory the cloak is further adorned.

Each time the bearer slays an enemy **CHARACTER**, add 1 to the bearer's Strength, Attacks and Leadership characteristics until the end of the battle.

SPINESHIVER BLADE

Forged from the spinal column of a mighty Keeper of Secrets, this blade lashes out in mockery of that Daemon's final excessive death throes.

Model with power sword only. The Spineshiver Blade replaces the bearer's power sword and has the following profile:

WEAPON	RANGE	TYPE	S	AP	D
Spineshiver Blade	Melee	Melee	+1	-3	1

Abilities: Each time the bearer fights, it can make D6 additional attacks with this weapon.

BLACK LEGION WARLORD TRAITS

The commanders of the Black Legion are some of the greatest leaders amongst the Heretic Astartes. Many learned their craft from Horus himself, and have consolidated those skills in the millennia that followed his death. Leaving ruin in their wake, these mighty generals command vast hosts dedicated to the Dark Gods.

If a **BLACK LEGION CHARACTER** is your Warlord, he can generate a Warlord Trait from the following table instead of the one in the *Warhammer 40,000* rulebook or *Codex: Chaos Space Marines*. You can either roll on the table below to randomly generate a Warlord Trait, or you can select the one that best suits his preferred style of waging war.

D6 WARLORD TRAIT

1 VETERAN RAIDER

A consummate raider both in the Eye of Terror and on Imperial worlds in realspace, this warlord knows when to strike and when to retreat.

While they are within 6" of your Warlord, friendly **BLACK LEGION** units can declare a charge even if they Fell Back in the same turn.

2 INDOMITABLE

This warlord has done little but fight in the millennia since Horus' defeat, and he grows more resilient with each battle.

All damage suffered by your Warlord is halved, rounding up.

3 BLACK-CLAD BRUTE

This warlord towers over other members of the legion, and is a formidable figure of terrible potency on the battlefield.

Add 1 to your Warlord's Strength characteristic. In addition, after your Warlord makes a charge move, pick an enemy unit within 1" of your Warlord and roll a D6. On a 4+, that unit suffers D3 mortal wounds.

4 SOUL-EATER

This warlord is a peerless fighter, imbibing the very life essence of his defeated foes in a constant quest for greater power.

Each time your Warlord destroys an enemy unit, your Warlord immediately regains D3 lost wounds.

5 TRUSTED WAR-LEADER

This warlord is part of Abaddon's inner circle and a high ranking member of the Black Legion, one of few who are permitted to call Abaddon by name and offer him advice.

While your Warlord is on the battlefield, roll a D6 each time you spend a Command Point to use a Stratagem; on a 5+ that Command Point is immediately refunded.

6 FIRST AMONGST TRAITORS

Black Legion warlords have sworn never to rest in their eternal vendetta against their hated loyalist foes.

The Death to the False Emperor ability triggers an extra attack on rolls of 5+ instead of 6+ for models in friendly **BLACK LEGION** units while they are within 6" of your Warlord.

NAMED CHARACTERS AND WARLORD TRAITS

If Abaddon the Despoiler is your Warlord he must be given the First Amongst Traitors Warlord Trait. If Haarken Worldclaimer is your Warlord he must be given the Lord of Terror Warlord Trait (see *Codex: Chaos Space Marines*).

TACTICAL OBJECTIVES

The Black Legion favour brutal assaults and overwhelming strength to crush their enemies. These strategies are a legacy of their time as the Sons of Horus, and before that amongst the gangs of Cthonia.

If your army is led by a **BLACK LEGION** Warlord, these Tactical Objectives replace the Capture and Control Tactical Objectives (numbers 11-16) in the *Warhammer 40,000* rulebook. If a mission uses Tactical Objectives, players use the normal rules for using Tactical Objectives with the following exception: when a Black Legion player generates a Capture and Control objective (numbers 11-16), they instead generate the corresponding Black Legion Tactical Objective, as shown below. Other Tactical Objectives (numbers 21-66) are generated normally.

D66	TACTICAL OBJECTIVE
11	Death and Destruction
12	Fear the Legion
13	For the Unworthy, Only Death
14	Lead by Example
15	The Long War Continues
16	Conquer the Galaxy

11 — DEATH AND DESTRUCTION

Bring death to any who stand before you. Let them know how hopeless their defiance is, and crush them utterly.

Score 1 victory point if one or more enemy units were destroyed during this turn.

Black Legion

14 — LEAD BY EXAMPLE

The warriors of the Black Legion only accept strong, capable leaders. Prove your worth to those who follow you.

Roll a D6 when this Tactical Objective is generated. Score 1 victory point if your Warlord controls the objective marker whose number corresponds to the result.

Black Legion

12 — FEAR THE LEGION

Stride forth, the might of your legion scattering the foe before you. Reap death, but first sow terror.

Score 1 victory point if one or more enemy units failed a Morale test this turn.

Black Legion

15 — THE LONG WAR CONTINUES

The warriors of the Black Legion have been slaughtering their enemies for millennia.

Score 1 victory point if one or more enemy units were destroyed during this turn. If one or more enemy **IMPERIUM** units were destroyed by any **BLACK LEGION** units from your army, score D3 victory points instead.

Black Legion

13 — FOR THE UNWORTHY, ONLY DEATH

Prove your contempt for the cowards who oppose you by eradicating their leaders where they stand.

Score D3 victory points if the enemy Warlord and all enemy **CHARACTER** models have been slain.

Black Legion

16 — CONQUER THE GALAXY

Take what is yours and let none stand in your way.

Score 1 victory point if you control an objective marker that was controlled by your opponent at the start of this turn. Score D3 victory points instead if you control 2 or more objective markers that were controlled by your opponent at the start of this turn. Score D3+3 victory points instead if you control 2 or more objective markers that were controlled by enemy **IMPERIUM** units at the start of this turn.

Black Legion

RENEGADE CHAPTERS

In this section you'll find rules for Battle-forged armies that include Chaos Space Marine Detachments taken from Renegade Chapters. These rules include the abilities below and a series of Warlord Traits, relics and Stratagems that can only be used by Renegade Chapters. These rules reflect the fighting style of the forces drawn from Renegade Chapters in your games of Warhammer 40,000.

USING A RENEGADE CHAPTERS ARMY IN WARHAMMER 40,000

The rules presented in this section are intended to be used in addition to those presented in *Codex: Chaos Space Marines* if you have chosen to take any Renegade Chapter Detachments. The following rules apply:

WARLORD TRAITS

If your Warlord is from the RED CORSAIRS, CRIMSON SLAUGHTER, PURGE, SCOURGED, BRAZEN BEASTS or FLAWLESS HOST, you can choose one of the Warlord Traits on page 198 instead of those presented in *Codex: Chaos Space Marines*.

RELICS

If your army is led by a Chaos Space Marine Warlord, you may give the appropriate Renegade Artefact from page 200 to a RED CORSAIRS, CRIMSON SLAUGHTER, PURGE, SCOURGED, BRAZEN BEASTS or FLAWLESS HOST CHARACTER from your army, instead of those presented in *Codex: Chaos Space Marines*. Named characters such as Huron Blackheart already have one or more artefacts, and cannot be given any of these artefacts.

Note that some weapons replace one of the character's existing weapons. Where this is the case, you must, if you are playing a matched play game or are otherwise using points values, still pay the cost of the weapon that is being replaced. Write down any Renegade Artefacts your characters have on your army roster.

STRATAGEMS

If your army is Battle-forged, the Stratagems on page 199 can be used in addition to those presented in *Codex: Chaos Space Marines* to reflect the fighting style of Renegade Chapter warriors.

ABILITIES

Renegade Chapter Detachments gain the following abilities:

REAVERS AND DESPOILERS

Renegade Chaos Space Marines are drawn from many places. Whatever their origins, their forces are made up of ranks of bolter-armed warriors, twisted by hatred.

If your army is Battle-forged, all Troops units in Renegade Chapter Detachments gain this ability. Such a unit that is within range of an objective marker controls it even if there are more enemy models within range of it. If an enemy unit within range of the objective marker has a similar ability, then it is controlled by the player who has the most models within range as normal.

RENEGADE TRAITS

If your Chaos Space Marine army is taken from a Renegade Chapter, you can either use the rules presented in *Codex: Chaos Space Marines* (e.g. they can use the Legion Trait ability and gain the Dark Reavers trait), or you can use the rules presented in this supplement. If you choose to use this supplement, and your army is Battle-forged, all Daemon Prince, INFANTRY, BIKER and HELBRUTE units in a Chaos Space Marine Detachment gain a Renegade Trait, so long as every unit in that Detachment is from the same Renegade Chapter. The Renegade Trait gained depends upon which Renegade Chapter they are from, as shown on the right. For example, all such units in a BRAZEN BEASTS Detachment gain the Rend the Foe trait.

If your chosen Renegade Chapter does not have an associated Renegade Trait, you can instead pick the trait that you think best represents your army.

Mere Mortals

CHAOS CULTIST units do not gain a Renegade Trait.

Shadowy Allies

The inclusion of Fabius Bile or FALLEN units in a Detachment does not prevent other units in that Detachment from gaining a Renegade Chapter Trait. However, Fabius Bile and FALLEN units can never themselves benefit from a Renegade Chapter Trait.

RENEGADE TRAITS

RED CORSAIRS: RAIDERS FROM THE MAELSTROM

The Red Corsairs are consummate raiders with vast resources at their disposal. When they emerge from the warp, they strike fast with overwhelming force to achieve their objectives before the enemy can respond.

Units with this trait can Advance and charge in the same turn. In addition, if a Detachment contains three or more units with this trait, that Detachment's Command Benefits are increased by 1 Command Point. That Detachment's Command Benefits are increased by 3 Command Points instead if it contains three or more units of CHAOS SPACE MARINES with this trait.

CRIMSON SLAUGHTER: A MOMENT'S PEACE

For the Crimson Slaughter, the maddening cries of tormented spirits can only be satiated by the spilling of blood.

If a unit with this trait destroys an enemy unit, roll a D6. On a 5+, you gain 1 Command Point. In addition, that unit automatically passes Morale tests until the end of the turn.

THE PURGE: BRINGERS OF OBLIVION

The Purge seek to cleanse the galaxy of everything that lives, not moving on until each of their opponents is completely obliterated.

You can re-roll hit rolls for attacks made by units with this trait that target enemy units that have lost one or more wounds already this turn.

THE SCOURGED: OMNISCIENT

The constant whispering of Daemons ensures that the Scourged know what course of action an enemy will take almost before they themselves do.

You can re-roll one hit roll for an attack made by a model in a unit with this trait each time it shoots or fights. In addition, when a unit with this trait fires Overwatch, they successfully hit on a roll of 5+, instead of only 6, irrespective of the firing model's Ballistic Skill or any modifiers.

BRAZEN BEASTS: REND THE FOE

The Brazen Beasts charge into the enemy with animal fury, tearing them limb from limb.

Each time you make a wound roll of 6+ for an attack made by a model with this trait in the Fight phase during a turn in which it charged, was charged, or performed a Heroic Intervention, that hit is resolved with an AP of -4.

FLAWLESS HOST: DEATH TO THE IMPERFECT

The Flawless Host have an unshakeable faith in their own abilities, their every strike perfectly timed and expertly placed.

Each time you roll a hit roll of 6+ for an attack made by a model with this trait in the Fight phase, it can immediately make an extra attack against the same unit using the same weapon (this is in addition to any extra attacks granted by the Death to the False Emperor ability). These extra attacks cannot themselves generate any further attacks.

RENEGADE WARLORD TRAITS

The charismatic leaders of Renegade Chapters learned much from their time amongst the Adeptus Astartes. Freedom from the strictures of Imperial rule has only expanded their expertise to make these consummate commanders and brutal killers deadly opponents on the battlefield.

If a Chaos Space Marine **CHARACTER** from the **RED CORSAIRS**, **CRIMSON SLAUGHTER**, **PURGE**, **SCOURGED**, **BRAZEN BEASTS** or **FLAWLESS HOST** is your Warlord, he can have the appropriate Warlord Trait from below instead of one in the *Warhammer 40,000* rulebook or *Codex: Chaos Space Marines*.

RED CORSAIRS: REAVER LORD

Over millennia of raiding, this warlord has plundered many items of great power, both from the Imperium and from rival warbands.

Your army can have one extra relic, chosen from the Artefacts of Chaos (see *Codex: Chaos Space Marines*), which must be given to a **RED CORSAIRS CHARACTER** from your army that does not already have a relic. This relic must be different to any relics already included in your army. In addition, each time your Warlord slays an enemy **CHARACTER**, add 1 to your Warlord's Attacks characteristic until the end of the battle.

CRIMSON SLAUGHTER: MAELSTROM OF TORMENT

Terrifying phantasms surround this warlord, sapping the will to fight from nearby foes.

Subtract 1 from the Leadership characteristic of enemy units within 6" of your Warlord. If your Warlord has slain any enemy models, then until the end of the battle, subtract 2 from the Leadership characteristic of enemy units within 9" of your Warlord instead.

THE PURGE: BLESSED MISSION

This warlord is an expert in assuring the utter obliteration of the enemy, leaving none alive.

Re-roll wound rolls of 1 for attacks made by your Warlord. In addition, you can re-roll damage rolls for weapons used by your Warlord.

THE SCOURGED: SHATTERING TRUTH

Voicing just one of the many lies whispered to him, the warlord stops the enemy in their tracks, taking advantage of their hesitation.

At the start of each Fight phase, you can pick an enemy unit within 3" of your Warlord. That unit cannot be picked to fight with in the Fight phase until all other units able to fight have done so. If the target unit has an ability that allows it to fight first in the Fight phase, it instead fights as if it didn't have that ability. If both players have units that cannot fight until all other units have done so, then alternate picking which of those units to fight with, starting with the player whose turn is taking place.

BRAZEN BEASTS: CARVE THE RUNES

This warlord seeks Khorne's bloody blessing by dedicating each worthy kill to his name.

Each time your Warlord slays an enemy **CHARACTER**, add 2 to your Warlord's Strength and Attacks characteristics until the end of the battle.

FLAWLESS HOST: ULTIMATE CONFIDENCE

This warlord is driven by complete arrogance, his faith in his own abilities unshakeable – and he has not been proven wrong yet.

If your Warlord generates extra attacks as a result of their Death to the Imperfect trait, they can immediately make 3 additional attacks, instead of only 1, against the same unit using the same weapon. These extra attacks cannot themselves generate any further attacks.

NAMED CHARACTERS AND WARLORD TRAITS

If Huron Blackheart is your Warlord he must be given the Reaver Lord Warlord Trait.

RENEGADE CHAPTER STRATAGEMS

If your army is Battle-forged and includes any Chaos Space Marine Detachments (excluding Auxiliary Support Detachments) taken from Renegade Chapters, you have access to the Stratagems shown here, meaning you can spend Command Points to activate them. These help to reflect the unique strategies used by these Chapters on the battlefield.

MORE WHERE THEY CAME FROM
3CP

Red Corsairs Stratagem

The Red Corsairs can draw upon vast numbers. When one squad fails, another will take its place.

Use this Stratagem at the end of your Movement phase. Pick a **RED CORSAIRS CHAOS SPACE MARINES** unit from your army that is on the battlefield. Remove that unit from the battlefield and set it up again, wholly within 6" of the edge of the battlefield and more than 9" from any enemy models, at its full starting strength.

ALL LIFE IS WORTHLESS
1CP

Purge Stratagem

When all life must be obliterated, hitting one's own allies is not a concern.

Use this Stratagem in your Shooting phase. Pick a **PURGE** unit from your army that is not within 1" of any enemy models. That unit can target enemy units that are within 1" of friendly units until the end of the phase, but each time you roll an unmodified hit roll of 1 for such an attack, resolve that attack against a friendly unit (your choice) within 1" of the target unit instead.

BURNING DAEMONHEART
1CP

Brazen Beasts Stratagem

The furnace at the heart of all Brazen Beasts' Daemon Engines burns to incandescent levels in its desperation to tear the foe apart.

Use this Stratagem at the end of the Fight phase. Pick an enemy unit that is within 1" of any **BRAZEN BEASTS DAEMON ENGINES** from your army. Roll a D6; on a 2-4 that unit suffers D3 mortal wounds. On a 5-6 it suffers 3 mortal wounds instead.

TERRIFYING PHENOMENA
2CP

Crimson Slaughter Stratagem

Where the Crimson Slaughter walk, the walls run with blood, and the land itself seems haunted.

Use this Stratagem at the start of the enemy Shooting phase. Pick a terrain feature that is within 12" of a **CRIMSON SLAUGHTER** unit from your army. Subtract 1 from hit rolls for attacks made by enemy units within 3" of that terrain feature until the end of the phase.

PRESCIENCE
2CP

Scourged Stratagem

Tzeentch has gifted the Scourged with a measure of foresight, allowing them to read the enemy's signals and know exactly where they will strike.

Use this Stratagem after your opponent sets up a unit that is arriving on the battlefield as reinforcements. Pick a **SCOURGED INFANTRY** unit from your army that is within 12" of that enemy unit. Your unit can immediately shoot at that enemy unit as if it were your Shooting phase.

WE CANNOT FAIL
1CP

Flawless Host Stratagem

The self-belief and desire for perfection that drives the warriors of the Flawless Host is such that their fighting skills far exceed those of less disciplined forces.

Use this Stratagem when you pick a **FLAWLESS HOST INFANTRY** unit from your army to fight with in the Fight phase. Until the end of the phase you can re-roll hit rolls for attacks made by that unit.

RENEGADE CHAPTER ARTEFACTS

From individual squads to entire Chapters, when Renegade Space Marines turn their back on the Imperium, they bring with them a wide array of weapons and equipment, as well as priceless relics. Many of these are imbued with the energies of the warp to make them truly deadly tools of war.

MAELSTROM'S BITE

Fashioned by Huron's army of weaponsmiths, this weapon represents the pinnacle in blending Imperial weaponry with the energies of the immaterium.

RED CORSAIRS model with combi-melta only. Maelstrom's Bite replaces the model's combi-melta and has the following profile:

WEAPON	RANGE	TYPE	S	AP	D
Maelstrom's Bite	When attacking with this weapon, choose one or both of the profiles below. If you choose both, subtract 1 from all hit rolls made for this weapon.				
- Boltgun	24"	Rapid Fire 3	4	-1	2
- Meltagun	12"	Assault 1	9	-4	D6

Abilities: When using the meltagun profile, if the target is within half range of this weapon, roll two dice when inflicting damage with it and discard the lowest result.

BLADE OF THE RELENTLESS

Formerly known as the Imperator Blade, this fabled weapon has long since been renamed after the one that wields it. As it feeds on the lifeblood of its victims, so too does it feed on their souls.

CRIMSON SLAUGHTER model with power sword only. The Blade of the Relentless replaces the model's power sword and has the following profile:

WEAPON	RANGE	TYPE	S	AP	D
Blade of the Relentless	Melee	Melee	+1	-3	1

Abilities: If the bearer slays any enemy models in the Fight phase with this weapon, then from the end of that Fight phase until the end of the battle, wound rolls for attacks made with this weapon are automatically successful (no wound roll is made).

ORB OF UNLIFE

Within this glassy sphere lurks a diluted life-eater virus. Although quick to burn out when the sphere is broken, everything nearby finds itself consumed by the ravaging viral strain.

PURGE model only. Once per battle, in the Shooting phase, the bearer can throw the Orb of Unlife instead of firing any ranged weapons. If they do so, pick a point on the battlefield within 8" of the bearer. Roll a D6 for each unit within D6" of that point, subtracting 2 from the result if the unit is a **VEHICLE**. On a 4+, that unit suffers D3 mortal wounds.

BOOK OF UNTRUTH

The pages of this book are constantly filled and overwritten by Sorcerers of the Scourged, who record every lie they hear. The power of these falsehoods is enough to spell the doom of any who wields knowledge as a weapon.

SCOURGED model only. Each time an enemy **PSYKER** within 18" of the bearer successfully manifests a psychic power, roll a D6. On a 5+, that psyker suffers 1 mortal wound.

DAEMONFLESH PLATE

This dark armour pulses with unnatural life, livid red veins visible in the ceramite, granting the wearer unnatural speed and strength.

BRAZEN BEASTS model only. The bearer has a Save characteristic of 2+. In addition, add 1 to the bearer's Move and Attacks characteristics.

FLAWLESS CLOAK

The fabric of this cloak re-knits when damaged, and never stains or fades with age. The wearer appears as the embodiment of perfection.

FLAWLESS HOST model only. Add 1 to the bearer's Attacks characteristic. In addition, increase the range of the bearer's aura abilities (e.g. Lord of Chaos, Demagogue, etc.) by 3".